A RORSCHACH WORKBOOK FOR THE COMPREHENSIVE SYSTEM®

Fifth Edition

John E. Exner, Jr.

With Contributions By

Susan C. Colligan
Lisa B. Hillman
Andrea S. Metts
Barry A. Ritzler
Karen T. Rogers
Anthony D. Sciara
Donald J. Viglione

Published by
Rorschach Workshops ■ Asheville, North Carolina

Printed December, 2012

Published by Rorschach Workshops
P.O. Box 9010
Asheville, North Carolina 28815-9010

Offset Printing by Daniels Graphics
Asheville, North Carolina

Layout Design and location Illustrations by Andrea S. Metts

Practice Coding Selections by Lisa B. Hillman

Contents

Preface

Anyone using this workbook should do so with two basic objectives in mind. The first is to learn the essential procedures of administering the test. There is no way to exaggerate the importance of proper test administration. It requires skill, sensitivity, and good judgement. Often, people are inclined to feel threatened by the prospect of taking any psychological test, and the Rorschach situation does little to ease that threat.

During the 80 years since the test was first published a rather widespread Rorschach lore has developed, and most people taking the test will have heard something about it. More often than not, their notions about the test are based more on fantasy than fact but, quite frequently, those notions cause a sense of apprehension about the test and the test situation. Even those who have not heard about the Rorschach often feel uneasy about it because it does not seem to make any sense.

Casual or insensitive examiners who fail to prepare the person for the test can easily heighten any apprehensiveness a client may harbor. Some examiners inadvertently reinforce existing sets, or create misleading sets, by the manner in which they introduce the test, or respond to questions raised by the client. These unwanted circumstances can influence the way in which an individual responds to the test and, at times, can blur the picture of the person produced by the test data. In some instances, shoddy administration procedures can lead to a protocol which is not interpretively valid. The bottom line is that *a poorly administered Rorschach is probably worse than no Rorschach at all.*

The second objective for the user of this work is to become familiar with the Rorschach *language* and be able to use it rather easily. The Rorschach language consists of the variety of codes that are used to classify responses and the scores that are generated from those codes to create subsets of data. It is a relatively universal language, common to most all who use the test. For instance, assume that the coding (scoring) of a response is:

W+ FMa.FCo 2 A,Ls 4.5 COP

A person literate in the Rorschach language will readily be aware that the person who gave the response used the entire blot (**W**) but perceived it to be more than one object (+); that the answer involves animal activity (**FMa**) and chromatic colored features of the blot have been used (**FC**); that it is a response involving a common use of form (**o**); that apparently two animals are involved (**2**) and they are reported in some sort of landscape environment (**A,Ls**); that a meaningful relationship has been reported in the answer (**4.5**); and that the activity between the animals is cooperative (**COP**).

It takes time and practice to learn the Rorschach language and most of the material in the workbook focuses on the criteria for the various codes that form the crux of the language. The test cannot be administered properly unless the examiner is familiar with the variety of coding and scoring criteria, and the validity of any interpretation of the data derived from the coding hinges on the accuracy by which it is applied.

As with the learning of any language, practice is the key to proficiency. To that end, a reasonably large number of responses are included in this work for practice. They have been selected to aid the novice in developing coding skills, or to provide the more experienced Rorschacher with a source from which to test out previously developed skills.

The practice responses are subdivided into eight sections, with each containing answers that are somewhat more complex than the answers in the previous section. Any person striving to learn the Rorschach language, that is, how to apply the Rorschach codes (scores) accurately, should be able to gain a respectable level of proficiency by completing *all* of the practice answers, section by section, and reviewing their coding decisions against the keys provided in the Appendix.

Some beginning students of the Rorschach develop the impression that the principles and procedures involved in administering the test and scoring the responses are terribly complex and too time consuming. In reality, that is an illusion that is not shared by the experienced Rorschacher. Nonetheless, the administration and scoring of the first few records can be quite time consuming and often frustrating for the beginner. Hopefully, the material in this work will help to ease the stresses of that initial learning experience.

This work also contains numerous tables. Some are used frequently in conjunction with the coding of responses. Others include data for a variety of reference samples that both the novice and experienced Rorschacher will sometimes find useful when interpreting test results.

The reference tables reflect some of the findings that have accumulated during the more than 30 years since the Rorschach Research Foundation, usually referred to by the nickname *Rorschach Workshops*, was established. It was very early into that period the Comprehensive System was formulated, and it has continued to develop. At frequent intervals during the past 30 years, a relatively substantial number of additions and changes have been made to the System.

The System now appears to stand about as complete as possible, but it is very likely that future research will lead to the development of new approaches to coding some types of responses, or the discovery of new variables or strategies that will enhance the interpretive yield of the test. In other words, it would be foolish to assume that the Comprehensive System has reached the last pinnacle in its development.

Although the test itself continues to pose many mysteries and challenges, in its current state, the System provides the knowledgeable user a formidable array of information regarding the psychological organization and functioning of the person who has taken the test, *if* the test has been administered competently, scored correctly, and interpreted wisely in accordance with the logical data based principles that have been established. Hopefully, this work will be a useful aid to those striving for that level of proficiency.

This work represents the product of more than 1,000 examiners, researchers, assistants, project directors, and associates that have been involved in the work at *Rorschach Workshops* since its inception. They attacked the challenges posed by the test faithfully and conscientiously and, altogether too often, suffered the frustrations of blind alleys and failed hypotheses. The Comprehensive System stands as a tribute to their collective efforts. Although they are too numerous to mention individually here, I hope that they are very aware of my deep appreciation and affection.

JEE
Asheville, NC
January, 2001

PART I

ADMINISTRATION AND SCORING

1 ❖ Procedures of Administration

The administration of the Rorschach is a reasonably straightforward procedure, but it can be made more difficult by examiners who are unprepared or unsure of themselves, or by those who approach it in a casual manner. The procedure requires preparation, thoughtfulness, some clerical skills, and a commitment to listen carefully.

▲ *BE PREPARED.* The proficient examiner thinks ahead, and is concerned with the welfare of the client. Materials are organized, seating is properly arranged, and the test is administered at an appropriate time. These may sound like unnecessary cautions, yet it is not uncommon to encounter the casual examiner who does not have enough paper on hand, or who has Card VIII inverted and sandwiched in between Cards II and III, or who arranged seating so that the client is continuously looking out of a window at a busy playground, or who began the test 15 minutes before the client was scheduled to have lunch. The following are items that should be considered carefully by every examiner before beginning the Rorschach.

▲ *CARDS.* Organize the cards so that they are in the proper order when face down. Place the cards in a convenient location, *out of the reach of the person being tested*, so that when they are handed to the subject the figure will be in the upright position. Be sure the cards are clean and free of pencil marks, grooves caused by fingernails, or spotting.

▲ *OTHER MATERIAL.* Have several pens and pencils readily available. Be prepared with plenty of paper that is set up for writing down easily whatever the subject says. It may not be needed but it is reassuring to know that it is there. Have at least two *Location Sheets* readily available to use during the Inquiry.

▲ *SEATING.* Seating is very critical and *should never* be face-to-face. It is clear that inadvertent nonverbal cues can create misleading sets. Some of those sets can cause answers to be withheld that might otherwise have been given. Other sets can mislead a client into believing that some types of answers are more preferable. Some examiners may chose to sit next to the client at a table. Others may prefer to arrange two comfortable chairs side-by-side and work with a clip board, with materials on a small table next to the examiner, away from the client. Whatever the choice of arrangements, the face-to-face option is unwarranted and probably should not be used for any psychological testing.

▲ *PREPARING THE SUBJECT.* Some examiners have the false impression that it is important to explain the Rorschach in great detail before beginning the test. This is not necessary, and if some lengthy explanation is used it may produce undue anxiety and/or resistance. No special elaboration concerning the nature of the Rorschach should be required *if the client has been properly prepared for the overall assessment process.* In most cases this will be done after a relatively brief interview during which the examiner seeks to insure that the person has a reasonable understanding of the purpose of the assessment.

Many clients are not well prepared by those who have referred them, and examiners often must take some time to make sure that the client is not likely to be haboring negative or erroneous assumptions about the assessment process. Thus, it is very important for the examiner to provide an introductory overview concerning *all of the assessment procedures* to be used, including the Rorschach.

Most people have heard about the Rorschach, or about the inkblot test, and mentioning this is appropriate. During the introductory overview phase the client should be told:

> **"...one of the tests we will be doing is the inkblot test, the Rorschach. Have you ever heard of it, or have you ever taken it?"**

If the person has not heard about the test, a brief explanation should be given such as, *It's just a series of inkblots that I'll show you and I want you to tell me what they look like to you.*

If the person indicates having some awareness about the test, the examiner should take time to find out what they know, or what they think they know. The Rorschach, or facsimiles of it, have appeared in various media, usually cartoons, movies, or television, and the manner in which the figures have been used or discussed often creates erroneous sets about the test. Thus, when a client conveys some awareness about the test, it may be necessary to correct false impressions.

Usually, this is done most easily by a brief, honest explanation about the use of the test as it pertains to the client. For example, *It is a test that gives us some information about personality, and by having that information we can ...* The completion of the statement will depend on the reason that the testing is being done (*plan your treatment easier; understand your problem a bit better; answer some of the questions you have about yourself; make some recommendations that your doctor has requested; get some idea about how your treatment program is progressing, etc.*). The same form of explanation can be used with clients who ask about the use of the test.

Persistent subjects may want to know how the test data are used (*How can you get anything out of this?*). When this occurs it is best to suggest that questions such as these be postponed until all of the testing is completed, with an assurance that all of the client's questions will be answered at that time. Sometimes, clients press the issue with questions such as, "Does each answer mean something?" The appropriate response to such questions is, *No, it doesn't work that way.*

If a client reports having taken the test previously it is important to find out when, where, and for what reason, and to ask what the client remembers about it. Sometimes, examiners tend to contaminate the naivete of a person by excessive questioning during the Inquiry, or by other post testing procedures that may have clinical usefulness but are not part of the Rorschach, such as asking a person to associate to his or her answers. Those elements can be quite influential in determining how a person will respond when tested again.

It is also important that the client not be misled into thinking that imagination is being tested. When that misconception occurs, people tend to generate associations to the figures instead of reporting what they see; *and it is what the person sees and reports that constitutes the Rorschach response.* Similarly, it is important to avoid terms such as "ambiguous" or "unstructured" when describing the Rorschach figures. They are derived from inkblots and should be identified as such and, if necessary, a description of how an inkblot is made can be included.

▲ *YOUNGER CLIENTS.* The procedures described above are applicable to almost all subjects, including young children. Occasionally, some variations in procedure may be required for the overly active youngster. Experience in collecting normative data from 1390 nonpatient children, including 170 five and six year olds, indicates that the standard procedures are appropriate. However, the clinical setting often includes children who are so hyperactive or resistive that they are not managed easily during the assessment routine.

For many such youngsters, the Rorschach may not be an appropriate test, but if Rorschach data are deemed important, it may be necessary to alter the introduction and/or seating. Very young children often prefer to stand or sit on the floor for most testing. Frequently, they have relatively short attention spans and like to proceed as quickly as possible to the task at hand. In such cases the examiner should use good common sense about deviations from the standard procedures and be acutely aware that altered procedures are not common.

A cooperative working relationship with any client is an absolute requirement, and this is especially true when working with children. It is often difficult for young children to endure several hours of testing even if a good relationship has been established. If several tests are required, the testing times should be planned realistically. On occasion, non-testing activity should be interspersed between tests and/or testing should be scheduled across two or even three sessions. *Don't overtest children!*

There is no magic test battery that yields all desired information, and sometimes, a single test that is wisely selected, or an observation period done at a critical time interval during the child's day, can provide all, or most of the information required.

The average adult takes between 40 and 60 minutes to give a complete record. Young children usually take less time, with those under the age of 10 typically averaging between 30 and 45 minutes. Rorschachs of older children usually take about as long to administer as those of adults.

▲ *INSTRUCTIONS.* After the client has been properly prepared for the test, the instructions are relatively simple. When handing the client the first card the examiner says:

> *What might this be?* and nothing else!

These four words are very important and should not be altered or added to in any way. The instruction, *What might this be?* sets off a series of complex cognitive operations that involve scanning, coding, classifying, comparing, discarding and selecting. Numerous decisions occur during the process of responding to each figure. It is important for the examiner to understand the response process. That knowledge is often very useful in gauging how cooperative or at ease the person taking the test may feel in the Rorschach situation. The response process is probably best conceptualized as having three phases such as is shown in Table 1.

TABLE 1. RESPONSE PROCESS PHASES AND OPERATIONS

PHASE 1	PHASE 2	PHASE 3
1. Encoding the Stimulus Field	3. Rescanning the Field to Refine Potential Answers	5. Final Selection From Remaining Potential Answers
2. Classifying the Encoded Image & Its Parts Into Potential Answers	4. Discarding Unuseable Or Unwanted Answers By Paired Comparison Ranking Or Censorship	6. Articulation of the Selected Answer

Almost all people find it easy to form several potential answers to each figure. In fact, Phase 1 of the response process happens very quickly, probably within two to four seconds, depending on the degree to which the stimulus field is solid or broken. Thus, the task is really not finding possible answers, but rather to decide which of those potential answers to select and give as responses. Most of the time consumed during the Response Phase of the test is devoted to this issue. People who are uneasy with the situation often put up forms of resistance by asking questions in an attempt to establish more structure in the situation while others may actually plead incompetence in an attempt to avoid the decision making that is involved.

Occasionally, one hears the novice offer a variation in the instructions such as,

"What could this be?" or, far worse, "What does this remind you of?" The latter is especially risky in that it implies an associative rather than perceptual process, and can easily raise the specter of imagination. If a client appears to have misunderstood the directions and either asks or assumes that the task is to associate to the blot as in, "Well, I suppose the artist is trying to convey..." or "Should I use my imagination?" the examiner should respond with, *Just tell me what you see there, what does it look like to you.*

▲   *ANSWERING QUESTIONS.* If questions occur after the testing begins, the answers of the examiner should be brief, honest, and non-directive. For instance, questions such as, "Can I turn it?" or "Should I use the whole thing," are answered with, *It's up to you.* If, at the beginning of the test, the client asks, "How many should I find?" the examiner should respond, *Almost everyone finds more than one thing.* If the question is, "What do most people see here?" the best response is, *People see all kinds of things.* If a person asks, "How do they make these?" a brief answer regarding the construction of an inkblot is appropriate. Some questions might require lengthy answers as in, "How do you get anything out of these answers?" When this occurs it is best to suggest waiting until the test has been completed before attempting to address them.

▲ *ENCOURAGEMENT.* In some instances a person will give only one response to Card I. When this occurs, the examiner should encourage by saying, *Take your time and look some more. I'm sure you'll find something else too.* If a client has already given two or more answers to Card I and asks, "How many should I find?" the standard response is, *It's up to you.*

▲ *ATTEMPTED REJECTIONS:* Sometimes, a client will report that they cannot see or find anything in the blot. When this sort of attempted rejection occurs to Cards I or II, it is very likely that the examiner failed to create an adequate working relationship with the client, or the client does not have an adequate understanding of the purpose of the testing. In either case, the examiner should stop the test and review either or both of these issues with the client. In most instances this should solve the problem and the test can proceed, *starting again* with Card I.

There are some people who simply do not want to be tested, and no matter how much explanation or encouragement is provided they insist that they cannot find anything in the first card. When this occurs it is probably best to acknowledge that the person obviously does not want to be tested and adhere to those wishes.

Sometimes an individual will give responses to several of the cards, but then attempt a rejection. This occurs most often on Cards VI, VII or IX. If this happens, the examiner should be reasonably firm in not accepting the rejection. Typically, this problem is circumvented by saying, *Take your time. We're in no hurry. Everyone can find something.* In a few instances it may be necessary to wait for a lengthy interval, but most people will deliver a response in less than one minute when confronted with this new instruction.

▲ *BRIEF PROTOCOLS.* The standard procedure for administration provides that, after Card I, the examiner should *not* provide any further encouragement or instruction until after the last answer to Card X has been given. That procedure does not always insure that a subject will give a record of sufficient length (at least 14 answers) to be interpretively valid. For instance, a person may give one answer to Card I and, after encouragement, give a second response, but then proceed to give only one response to the remaining nine figures. The resulting 11 response protocol is probably not reliable and the structural data should not be interpreted.

The problem of brief protocols often poses a dilemma for examiners, especially when it appears that a brief record seems inevitable. Most experienced examiners become aware of the likelihood of a brief record early into the test, and usually can guess, with reasonable accuracy, about the probable cause. There are numerous reasons why brief protocols occur, but either of two causes account for most: (1) resistance/defensiveness, or (2) severe impairment. The first seems to be responsible for the majority.

When resistiveness or defensiveness is the problem, the cues gradually become rather obvious. Many people who are somewhat defensive at the onset of the test will ask questions, either just before the test begins, or shortly after Card I is presented. Some examples and the appropriate responses are: "Does everybody get the same ones?" (*Yes, it's a standard set*), "Do you make these yourself?" (*No, everybody uses the same ones*), "Am I really supposed to find something?" (*Sure, everyone sees things in each one*).

The majority of people who pose questions at the onset of the test are probably not well prepared for the testing, and if examiners encounter this situation often in their practice, they should reflect seriously about the procedures that they use when attempting to create a working relationship with clients.

A large number of people who are defensive at the onset of the test become more at ease by a few interactions with the examiner as the test begins and proceed to give an interpretively valid protocol. However, some retain their resistant or defensive set, and they are the people most likely to give brief protocols. Frequently they attempt to give as a first answer, "It just looks like an inkblot to me," to which an appropriate response could be, *You're right, that's what it is, but what might it be, what else does it look like?*

When the resistance or defensiveness persists, the individual invariably gives one answer to Card I and seeks to return the card. When encouragement is given, there is a considerable time lapse before a second answer is forthcoming. The key issue is whether the resistance or defensiveness will continue through the test and result in a brief protocol. Typically, the answer to that question will be revealed by the manner in which the person responds to the next three cards. The person who is highly resistant or defensive usually will give a second answer to Card I with some reluctance after the encouragement, and proceed to give only one relatively brief answer to each of the next three cards.

Severely impaired people usually do not ask questions at the beginning of the test. Brief records sometimes are given by these individuals because they are threatened by the level of complexity posed by the Rorschach task. Typically, they are inpatients who are neurologically impaired or suffering from long standing psychotic conditions. They often feel that their capacity for control is being challenged by the test and, early into the test, the examiner will be aware of the struggles that the client is experiencing.

Persons such as this tend to follow instructions slowly and concretely and, often, they fail to generalize from any encouragement given during Card I. In fact, when encouragement is given on Card I, the person will often seem irritated or confused. Even when a second answer has been given, following encouragement on Card I, the client quickly slips back into a one response routine on the next three cards. Considerable time usually elapses between the presentation of a card and the response to it, and the responses given tend to involve only a few words, and sometimes, only one word. Sometimes, the person will say "I don't know," or "It doesn't look like anything," and attempt to reject the card (*Take your time, we're in no hurry*).

If, after obtaining only a single response to each of Cards II, III, and IV, an examiner is reasonably convinced that a brief record seems very likely, it is appropriate to consider the option of injecting another form of encouragement, assuming that encouragement also has been provided on Card I. When the client attempts to return Card IV, the examiner should not accept it and instead say:

Wait, don't try to hurry through these. We are in no hurry, take your time.

This form of encouragement is not quite as direct as that used on Card I. It simply prompts the client to take more time. Although this statement does not specifically ask for more answers, as does the encouragement provided on Card I, the implication is there.

This optional form of encouragement should *not* be used routinely, and *definitely not* simply because a person has given only five answers to the first four cards. That occurs often among those who give more than 20 responses in the entire test. This optional prompting is reserved for use *only* when the examiner has detected several clues from which to form the reasonably certain belief that a brief record is inevitable if no intervention occurs. This optional prompting is sometimes useful with young children who simply want to go through the test as quickly as possible, and, in their haste, are likely to produce a short record.

Regardless of whether a Card IV prompting has been employed, any time that a client gives fewer than 14 answers during the Response Phase of the test, the examiner *should not proceed with the Inquiry*. In that situation, the examiner should interrupt the standard routine and explain to the subject:

> **"Now you know how it's done. But there's a problem. You didn't give enough answers for us to get anything out of the test. So we will go through them again and this time I want you to make sure to give me more answers. You *can* include the same ones you've already given if you like but make sure to give me more answers this time."**

Many people will seek direction under this new condition and ask, "How many should I really give?" The response depends mainly on whether the examiner believes that the subject had tried to be cooperative. If the client seemed cooperative it is appropriate to say, *Well, it's really up to you, but you only gave __ answers and I really need more than that to get anything out of the test.* On the other hand, some people obviously are more resistive or guarded, sometimes even ignoring the encouragement to give more than one response to Card I. If a highly resistive subject has given less than 14 responses, the examiner should be more direct if a question is asked about how many answers are required, such as, *Well, it's up to you but I really need several more answers than you gave.*

Although not very time consuming, the procedure of redoing the Response Phase can be frustrating for both the examiner and the client, but it is the only viable alternative if the examiner believes that a usable Rorschach record is critical to the assessment objectives. The only other option is to discontinue the test and employ other assessment methods.

▲ *LENGTHY PROTOCOLS.* Whereas the most common problem in Rorschach administration concerns brief records, there are instances in which people become overly involved with the task and will give endless numbers of responses if permitted to do so. Research concerning lengthy records has shown that the interpretive yield is essentially no different if only the first five answers to each blot are used, as compared to using the entire record. These findings suggest that, *under some circumstances*, it is permissible to limit the number of answers.

Thus, if a person gives five responses to Card I, and retains the card with the obvious intention of giving additional responses, the examiner should intervene by taking the card from the client and saying, *Alright, let's do the next one.* If the person gives five responses to Card II the same procedure should be used.

This tactic should continue to be used for each subsequent card as long as the client *continues to give five answers and still keeps the card*. However, if at any time the client gives fewer than five responses to a card, *the procedure should be discontinued*. No further intervention should occur throughout the remainder of the test *even though* the client may give more than five answers to subsequent blots.

If the procedure of intervening after five responses persists through the entire record, 50 responses will be given. Conversely, if the procedure is discontinued during the test it is possible for the record to be much longer. For instance, intervention might be used for the first three blots but discontinued on Card IV because the person gives only three responses. A total of 18 answers would have been given to that point. However, the individual may then give three answers to Card V, five answers to Card VI, seven responses to Card VII, nine answers each to Cards VIII and IX, and 14 responses to Card X, thereby creating a record of 65 responses.

There are rare occasions, probably less than once in 500 administrations, in which a person may give only two or three answers each to the first few cards, or gives less than five answers to one of the first few cards, but then proceeds to give many responses, sometimes 10 or more, to subsequent cards. Thus, it is possible to obtain a very lengthy record, sometimes exceeding 70 responses. These are rather painful experiences for the examiners. It is like a runaway train. The is no hard fast rule about how best to deal with these situations. If standard procedures are followed, all answers should be included in the final tally of the protocol, but logic and experience argue against the acceptance of extremely long records.

When examiners find themselves in this difficult situation, good judgement should be exercised. For instance, assume that a client gives less than five responses to each of the first three cards but, surprisingly, gives eight or ten answers to Card IV. Logically, no intervention should occur at this point because the unexpected large number of response to Card IV may be a "one time" incident and they may include some answers that, interpretively, are very important. However, if the client proceeds to offer more than five responses to Card V, the examiner probably should remove the card after the sixth or seventh response, and continue with that procedure through the remainder of the test, or until the person give no more than five responses to a card.

There are numerous variations of this model that might be applied, but the decision to use any should be made cautiously and logically. This form of intervention should be used only in those instances in which the judgement of the examiner leads to the conclusion that an inordinately lengthy record will result if it is not employed. The tactic of intervening to prevent very lengthy records has some hazards. It clearly can affect the integrity of the Affective Ratio and/or the

W:D:Dd relationship, and possibly will have an impact on the Egocentricity Index. It is a trade off that attempts to keep administration time within some reasonable parameters and produce a protocol that is interpretively manageable.

RECORDING RESPONSES

Each response *must be recorded verbatim.* This often seems like an impossible task to the novice, but experience indicates that it is not! It does take practice to learn to record rapidly but speed writing *should not* be a primary issue. It is much more important that the responses be recorded legibly so that others also can read them and know exactly what the subject said.

It is critical that the examiner set whatever pace that he or she is comfortable with in administering the test. *Time should not be afforded undue weight when administering the test.* It is far more important that the examiner set a pace that will insure that all of the data have been collected properly in a form that is easily used.

Some clients tend to speak very rapidly, almost as if to challenge the examiner. Although it is not desirable to interrupt a subject, it is necessary in some instances to ask a person to repeat part of an answer, or simply to request that he or she verbalize more slowly. For instance, an examiner might say, *Wait! I'm having trouble keeping up with you. Go a little slower please.*

If it is necessary to ask a person to repeat part of an answer, the examiner should use the last few words that were recorded in forming the question, such as, *I'm sorry, I didn't get all of that. You said two people with hats and...?* This tactic increases the likelihood that the same response will be repeated by the individual, but be sure to repeat the words of the subject exactly as they were said.

Some abbreviations, easily recognized and translated by most people, are very valuable aids when recording the client's words verbatim. There are a substantial number of common abbreviations used by most Rorschachers. Some are phonetic, such as *b* for be and *c* for see. Others are logically derived, such as *ll* for looks like, *st* for something, *ss* for some sort, and *cb* for could be. A third group involves the use of content codes, such as *H* for human, *A* for animal, *Fi* for fire, etc.

Beginners who are uncertain or uncomfortable about their ability to write at the necessary pace when administering the test often find it useful to have others dictate material from a book or newspaper to aid in increasing their writing speed and to become accustomed to using the variety of common abbreviations   A listing of common abbreviations used in recording Rorschach responses is shown in Table 2.

TABLE 2. ABBREVIATIONS COMMONLY USED IN RECORDING RESPONSES

Phonetically Derived		Logically Derived		Derived From Scores	
b	be	abt	about	H	human
c	see	arnd	around	A	animal
g	gee	at	anything	bl	blood
o	oh	bec	because	cg	clothing
r	are	bf	butterfly	cl	cloud
u	you	bk	back	ex	explosion
y	why	cb	could be	fd	food
		dk	don't know	fi	fire
		et	everything	ge	geography
		frt	front	ls	landscape
		j	just	na	nature
		ko	kind of	sc	science
		lik	like	xy	x-ray
		ll	looks like		
		mayb	maybe		
		rite	right		
		scfic	science fiction		
		ss	some sort		
		st	something		
		wm	woman		
		wng	wing		
		-g	-ing		

▲ *QUESTIONS AND COMMENTS.* Any questions asked by the client during the test should be recorded as should the response of the examiner. Similarly, any comments made by the client, such as *"That's an ugly one"* or *"Gee, look at all the colors"* should also be recorded. In most cases they will contribute little to the interpretation, but in some instances they can add significantly to the interpretive yield.

▲ *LAYING OUT THE RECORD.* One of the most important aspects of test administration is the way in which the record is laid out. The responses should be recorded in a manner that makes them easy to use. In other words, not only should each answer be recorded legibly and verbatim, but they should be easy to review.

For instance, it is very important that the response *is aligned* with the material given later in the inquiry concerning that answer. This is important for both scoring and interpretation. Typically, the Inquiry will consist of many more words than the response. Thus, it is necessary to leave considerable space between the responses as they are given, so that space is available to align the Inquiry material later. It is a good practice to record no more than two or three answers on one page and, *defintely*, begin a new page for each card.

Most examiners prefer to use a format for recording responses in which the page is set horizontally, not vertically. A small section to the left is reserved for the card numbers and response numbers. The section next to that, which should not quite extend to the middle of the page is for recording the responses. The next section to the right is the largest. It is used for the Inquiry. Some examiners reserve a column at the right margin to enter the scoring, but this is an option that is less appealing because the coding may include several special scores and require more space than is available in a small area. Thus, most examiners prefer to have the entire right side of the page available for the Inquiry material and usually enter scores beneath the responses in the left section. An illustration of a layout in which scores are entered beneath responses is shown in Figure 1.

As illustrated in Figure 1, responses should be numbered in consecutive order through the entire test. It will also be noted in Figure 1 that carat marks (**v < >**) are used to note the position of the top of the blot when the card is not being held in the upright position. It is also good practice to enter the name or ID number of the subject on each page that is used and on the Location Sheet during the Inquiry.

THE INQUIRY

Unfortunately, the Inquiry has been one of the most misunderstood and abused features of the Rorschach. When done correctly, it completes the richness of the test data. When done incorrectly, it can muddle a protocol terribly and often generates data that may be of clinical interest but which represents something other than true Rorschach data.

▲ *THE OBJECTIVE.* The overall purpose of the Inquiry is to insure that the coding (scoring) of the response is as accurate as possible. The code is designed to represent what the person perceived at the time when the response was delivered. Thus, the immediate objective of the Inquiry is for the examiner to see what the client has seen or, at the very least, to understand where in the blot the person sees something, and what features of the blot cause it to be seen that way.

The Inquiry is the phase of the test when the client shares responses with the examiner. It is not a new test and it is *not* a time when new information is developed. It is simply a time when old information is reviewed and clarified. It is a delicate phase of the test which, if misunderstood by the client or mishandled by the examiner, can lead to many problems in coding responses and/or interpreting the test data.

CARD	RESPONSE & SCORES	INQUIRY

I 1. Ths ll a bat to me, but I'm not sure, yeah I guess a bat, I thot of a bird but I thk a bat is better a bat

E: (Rpts Ss response)

S: Yeah, it has the wgs & the body & I guess thes cb the feelers, I dk if bats have feelers, but I guess thy do, yeah it maks me thk of a bat w the wgs out, flyg

E: Show me where ur seeg it

S: Oh, all of it, c thes r wgs (points) outstrechd lik flying along & ths is the body in the cntr, its all colord lik bats

E: Colord lik bats?

S: Yeah, thyr blk lik ths

Wo FMa.FC'o A P 1.0

(S wants to return card)

E: I thk if u tak ur time & look some more u'll find s.t. else too

2. I guess the centr prt cb a wm stndg ther w her hands up

E: (Rpts Ss response)

S: Yeah, c here (outlines), it's lik the shape of a wm to me, her dress is kinda transparent, at least it ll tht to me

E: Transparent?

S: Well, thes wb her legs & waist, its just curvy, lik a wm, u don't c her head too well, c her hands r up here, lik she's wavyg or s.t., u kind of c her body thru her dress, like it was transparent or mayb thers a light shining behind her

D+ Ma.FVo H,Cg 4.0 GHR

(S: Can I turn it ovr?)

E: Sur, whtevr u lik

<v>

3. No, its bettr ths way, it cb lik a mask, smthg lik for halloween

E: (Rpts Ss resp)

S: Yeah, lik an A mask, the white is for the eyes and mouth & thes thgs stickg out r lik straps tht u tie arnd your head, it sorta ll a cat mask to me

E: Where r u cg ths

S: Its all of it

WSo Fo (Ad) 3.5

Figure 1: Format for recording Rorschach responses

▲ *THE PACE.* It was mentioned earlier that the examiner should set his or her own pace when administering the test. That is even more important during the Inquiry. Whereas the average time for the Response Phase of the test is usually less than 20 minutes, the average time required for the Inquiry is rarely less than 30 minutes.

The actual amount of time involved for the Inquiry will depend largely on how cooperative and/or articulate the client may be. If he or she has been properly prepared for the Inquiry, it will usually proceed quickly and easily. Conversely, when the client is not adequately prepared for the Inquiry, the questions and directions of the examiner can easily provoke anxiety, irritation, and defensiveness.

▲ *INTRODUCING THE INQUIRY.* The importance of introducing the Inquiry correctly cannot be overemphasized. It is critical *that the client understand why the Inquiry is being conducted and what is expected.* As noted earlier, the goal is for the examiner to see what the person has reported, as the person sees it. It follows that if the examiner can see what the client reported, the coding of the response is likely to be done easily and accurately.

The standard explanation to introduce the Inquiry is:

> **"Now we are going to go back through the cards again. It won't take very long. I want to see the things that you said you saw and make sure that I see them like you do. We'll do them one at a time. I'll read what you said and then I want you to show me where it is in the blot and then tell me what there is there that makes it look like that to you, so that I can see it too, just like you did. Is that clear?**

At this point some people ask questions ranging from, "Why do we have to do this?" (*So that I can see the things that you saw*) and "What do you want me to tell you?" (*Just help me to see it. Show me where you saw it and what makes it look like that*) to "Should I find other things too?" (*No, I'm only interested in the things you saw before*). Answers should be direct and honest and always designed to keep the purpose of the Inquiry in focus.

Once the person implies an understanding of the task, the Inquiry can begin *but not before then*. If a client seems unsure about, or resistive to the process, some sort of restatement concerning the task or additional explanation concerning the procedure is wise such as, "*Remember, I need to see it as you do. I need to know where it is and what about the blot makes it look like that.*"

▲ *THE PROCEDURE.* Once the examiner is satisfied that the person is ready to begin, the first card is given to the client with the comment, *O.k., let's try the first one.* Subsequent cards are handed to the client one by one, with the examiner saying, "*Here you said...*" or "*Then you said...*" and finishing with a **verbatim** reading of what was given as the answer. If the person has truly understood the prefatory instructions, he or she will proceed to articulate or point out the area that was involved and identify some of the main features of the object that has been reported.

In some cases a client who appeared to understand the task may flounder at the onset. For example, after hearing the verbatim response read the subject might say, "*Yes, that's right.*" If this happens it becomes necessary to repeat the purpose and procedure as in, "*Remember now why we're doing this. I need to see it too, so you have to help me. Show me where it is and tell me what makes it look like that.*"

Sometimes, especially with younger clients, an individual may point out where the object has been seen with no difficulty but then falter in attempting to articulate features as in, "*I don't know why, it just looks like that to me.*" When this happens the examiner should be supportive yet firm, "*I know it looks like that to you but remember, I need to see it too. So help me. Tell me about some of the things you see there that make it look like ___.*"

In rare instances, it may be appropriate to practice a bit with the young child. If this is to be done, ready access to a well defined, easily identified object is essential (a toy fire truck can serve the purpose quite well). When placing the object before the child, the question is asked, "*What is that?*" After the child replies the examiner says, "*That's right, but how do you know it's a fire truck?*", prompting the child to articulate features that distinguish it such as the ladders, wheels, coloring, etc. After the child has identified some features the examiner provides some reassurance and returns to the task of the Inquiry, "*See, you did that fine, now let's do these.*"

▲ *DECISIONS TO QUESTION.* Each response should be inquired by first reading, *verbatim*, the person's answer. Reasonably cooperative people catch on to the task quickly and usually provide more than enough information for the scoring decision to be made. Under optimal conditions, the examiner will not have to ask any questions during the entire Inquiry. On the other hand, the optimal is not commonplace, and for most records the examiner will have to inject questions to clarify where or why something was seen.

The examiner must be thoroughly familiar with the coding or scoring possibilities. That knowledge forms the basis from which decisions to question or not to question are made. The basics of the response can be divided into three categories; (1) Location (where is it), (2) Determinant(s) (what makes it look like that) and, (3) Content (what is it). If information concerning these three features is given by the subject, the response can be coded (scored) correctly.

The third category (Content) is usually the easiest to define as the response itself almost always tells what the object is. Similarly, for most responses, the first category (Location) is almost always delineated by the subject. When the location is specified the examiner should note this on the *Location Sheet*, either by using the symbol *W* together with the response number, such as *3=W* if the whole blot has been used, or if only an area of the blot has been used by *carefully* outlining that area on the Location Sheet and entering the number of the answer next to the outline. Some experienced examiners often record the area used in a parenthesis in the Inquiry verbiage, such as (*W*), (*D4*), (*Dd21*), etc., and this is a good practice when possible. The overall objective in recording location is for anyone to be able to review the protocol and be able to identify the area used for a response easily.

Whoever scores the protocol must know exactly where the individual's response appears. Without this knowledge it may not be possible to judge the form quality of the response. If the response might be difficult for others to identify easily, or if it includes unusual features, some of the specific characteristics of the object should also be noted on the Location Sheet.

If the person does not specify the location of the answer, or if the location is not clear, a question is posed. It can range from, "*Where is that you see that?*" to "*I don't think I see it correctly, run your finger around it,*" or in extreme instances, "*I'm not sure where it is, put your finger on the...*" (nose, head, wing, wheel, etc.). This is done on the blot *not* the Location Sheet.

Most Inquiry problems focus on the second basic category (Determinants). Whereas the response itself typically reveals the content and most people readily identify location, the issue of why it looks like that can be another matter. Objects look as they do because of shape, color, shading, or in some instances because of apparent movement. It should be assumed that the client is not fully aware of this, and this list of possibilities *is not* provided by the examiner. Thus, the verbal report of the person, free of direction or sets, constitutes the data from which the coding or scoring decisions are generated. Unfortunately, the reports of some people are vague or do not include features suggested by clues contained in the response.

▲ *BASIC INQUIRY QUESTIONS.* Any questions that are posed to the client must be *non-directive* and free of cues that might provoke a set. It is important that the person's response to the question be as accurate as possible but *not* include more than was seen originally, when the response was given. There are several routine questions or prompts that will suffice in the majority of instances, but in many cases the examiner will have to formulate a question from the verbal material the person has given earlier in the response or the Inquiry. The basic prompt is:

"I'm not sure I see it as you do, help me."

This serves as a reminder to the person about the task at hand. Unfortunately, if it is used repeatedly it sounds boring and/or stupid. Thus variations of it such as, **"You'll have to help me, I don't think I'm seeing it yet,"** are often in order.

In some instances, a question that focuses on the determinant issue will be more appropriate:

"I'm not sure what there is there that makes it look like that."

This is probably the best alternative to the reminder prompt because it asks directly for clarification. When the client seems resistively vague, it is appropriate to combine the basic prompt with the more focused question as in:

"I know it looks like that to you, but remember I have to see it too. So help me to understand why it looks like that to you."

▲ *QUESTIONS BASED ON KEY WORDS.* Although the basic prompts and questions usually will suffice for most responses in which the person has not been precise, there is another class of answer for which questioning is necessary even though the individual may have been cooperative. These are the responses in which *key words* were used by the person in the response *or* have been included spontaneously *early* in the Inquiry.

Key words are those that imply the possibility of a determinant that has *not been* articulated by the subject. Some key words are adjectives such as pretty, beautiful, delicate, bumpy, gloomy, fierce, hurt, bright, etc., while others may be nouns or verbs such as circus, party, sad, happy, picnic, fur, blood, etc. The examiner must be alert for any word that implies the presence of a determinant and when one is detected, an appropriate question should be posed. For example:

RESPONSE	INQUIRY
A very pretty flower	**E: (Rpts Ss resp)**
	S: Yes, ths cb the stem & here r the petals

(At this point the subject has confirmed the location and has alluded to the form as the determinant, however, the key word *pretty* implies the possibility that color has been used and must be pursued):

E: U said that it is very pretty?

Had the subject not used the word pretty, the examiner would not pose any question in the Inquiry to this response, *even if the response had been given to a colored area of the blot.*

Sometimes a question must be used to clarify the nature of a determinant that is already established. For instance:

RESPONSE   INQUIRY

It ll 2 peopl doing s.t. at   **E: (Rpts Ss resp)**
night   **S: Yes, c thes r the peopl here (points), c the**
                                      heads & legs & arms

(In this answer the presence of movement has already been established, the people are doing something. But is the movement *active or passive?* And a key word, *night*, also has been used, raising the possibility that the grey-black features of the blot may be involved. The examiner could approach each issue separately but it is best to try one question to address both):

E: U said thy r doing s.t. at night?

(If the client responds to only one of the two issues, a second question must be posed):

S: It ll thy r picking s.t. up
E: And it's at night?

In some responses a key word will not appear until the Inquiry. This raises the issue of whether that feature was present when the response was given. As a general rule of thumb, key words that appear for the first time in the Inquiry should be pursued with questioning *if they occur during the first verbalization of the person or if they appear to have been included spontaneously in the first answer to a question posed by the examiner.*

There are exceptions to this rule! The critical test in deciding whether to pursue a key word is the extent to which the examiner is convinced that the feature existed at the time the response was delivered.

The responses of two people, S1 and S2, that are shown on the next page, may be useful to illustrate this issue:

In the S1 Inquiry, active movement has been included and a key word, *hurt*, has been used. It was questioned because of the possibility that color was being used, which was confirmed by the response.

In the S2 Inquiry the possibility of movement was raised by the word *touching*. It was appropriately questioned, and at the onset of the person's response *passive* movement was confirmed. However, the client then apparently began to consider the color and used the word hurt. It probably should not be pursued further because it seemed to occur as an afterthought ("I *suppose* you could even think of them as *maybe* even being hurt"), provoked by the examiner's

RESPONSE   INQUIRY

S1: That ll 2 bears to me	**E: (Rpts Ss resp)** **S: Yeah, c one here & here, the head & legs, thyr** **standg w their paws togthr lik thyr fiting, at** **least one of them is hurt** **E: U say thyr hurt?** **S: Tht red cb blood, lik thyr hurt**

S2: I'll say a cpl of bears	**E: (Rpts Ss resp)** **S: There's one on each side** **E: I'm not sur wht maks them ll bears** **S: The shape, ths cb the head & legs & here r** **their frnt paws, lik touchg** **E: Touching?** **S: Yeah, lik thy got them togthr, lik thyr standg** **there w their paws togthr, I supp u cld even** **think of them as mayb even being hurt**

second question. Had the client been more definitive and said, "They look like they're hurt," instead of injecting the "possibility" notion (I supp u cld even), the examiner should definitely pursue the issue.

The ultimate challenge is to obtain a description of the object from the individual that represents the perception of the individual when he or she decided to give the response. Often, there are responses in which a key word or phrase occurs late in the Inquiry but is sufficiently compelling to warrant further pursuit.

The following response may serve to exemplify such a situation:

RESPONSE   INQUIRY

Tht ll a cpl of people   **E: (Rpts Ss resp)**
S: Yeah, one on each side
E: I'm not sur what makes them ll peopl
S: Well, their heads & legs & arms, lik thyr bent
    over carryg s.t., like thyr getting ready to cook

(The key phrase, *getting ready to cook*, plus the fact that they are carrying something, clearly warrants further questioning)

                     E: Getting ready to cook?
                     S: Yeah, lik thyr carryg this pot or smthg back to
                       this fire
                     E: Fire?
                     S: Yeah, ths red in the background
                     E: What makes it ll a fire?
                     S: It's red, lik a fire

(The only determinant implied when this response was first delivered was form. Subsequently movement was acknowledged and then dimensionality, and finally color. Although the examiner asked four questions, the flow of the subject's responses offers no hint that the response was reformulated during the Inquiry)

Again, the decision to formulate a question about a key word depends on the spontaneity with which it is given, plus the extent to which the examiner feels reasonably convinced that the feature existed at the time the response was delivered.

The example above is a good illustration of what often happens when people are cautious about taking the test. They tend to be guarded during the Response Phase and their answers are brief and not very elaborate. Later, when operating under the more structured directions of the Inquiry they tend to feel more at ease with the situation and are more willing to elaborate on what they saw earlier.

Those who are learning to administer the Rorschach usually find that decisions about whether to ask a question are frustrating. However, that frustration occurs much less frequently as familiarity with scoring criteria increases. But, regardless of the skill level, the basic rule remains, *do not try to hurry through the Inquiry*. Take time to think carefully about the information that is generated in the Inquiry, and also to review the original answer again. The target is to score the response correctly.

If, after considering the words of the subject, the issue of whether to ask or not to ask a question remains in doubt, *ask the question!* Most Rorschachers find it easier to disregard material inadvertently provoked by an extra Inquiry question than to contend with the irritation created later by deciding that an important question was not asked.

▲ *INAPPROPRIATE QUESTIONS:* There are some classes of question that should *never* be asked during the Inquiry. These are direct or leading questions, or those formulated to develop material that is not directly related to the issue of coding or scoring. Direct questions such as, "Did the color help?" or "Are they doing anything?" or "Did you see that in perspective?" only serve to create unwanted sets for the subject and, in turn, can contaminate much of the protocol. Likewise, leading questions such as, "Which side of the skin is up?" or, "Would it look like that if it were a different color?" or, "Is there anything else you can tell me about it?" create the same sorts of unwanted sets that can ruin a potentially valid record.

Questions such as these usually occur because an examiner has become tempted by an "almost certain" feeling that a determinant remains concealed. Nonetheless, *these types of questions should never be asked*, and the only solace for examiners who are frustrated because they could not pursue a hunch is the fact that the presence or absence of one single determinant will not alter the interpretation of a protocol so much as to be overwhelmingly important.

The other class of question that should never be asked pertains to material that is *not* relevant to the coding (scoring) even though it may be clinically intriguing. It might be interesting to know if a human figure that has been reported is male or female, or why a cat described as "sad" feels that way. Such information may seem clinically intriguing, *but it is not Rorschach*. If it is elicited, an entirely new set about the test is created, and as a consequence the empirically based principles of interpretation must be cast to the wind, as they are no longer applicable.

▲ *RESISTANCE DURING THE INQUIRY:* Some people, especially those who look on the test as a burden or imposition, become irritated by the Inquiry. In all fairness, they were not told at the beginning of the test that more explanations would be required, and learning this after having struggled to select responses to the 10 figures can be very provoking to their defensiveness. Some may attempt to deny that a response was given (*I did not say that*). Others may attempt to reject a response (*I don't know, I can't see it now*).

Most resistive subjects use a more subtle form of evasive non-cooperation during the Inquiry (*I don't know, it just looks like that to me*). Whatever form the resistence takes, the examiner must be firm, but tactful. For example, for the person who claims an answer was not given, the examiner might say, "*Come on now. Look, I wrote it down. You can find it, take your time.*" Or, to the individual who claims to be unable to find an answer, the examiner might say, "*Take your time. We're in no hurry. You found it once. I'm sure you can find it again.*" Examiners are sometimes challenged by silence during the Inquiry. This should not provoke a poorly thought through question or a premature abandonment of the Inquiry.

▲ *INQUIRYING YOUNGER CLIENTS:* Those who deal frequently with the very young child know that it is sometimes difficult to keep their attention on a single task. Some have suggested that, because of this, it may be best to complete the Inquiry after each card rather than wait until responses have been given to all 10 cards. This technique has some obvious advantages for working with the difficult youngster, but it also has some serious liabilities. The experience of examiners who have tested large numbers of patient and nonpatient children in conjunction with research for the Rorschach Research Foundation, suggests that in more than 95% of the cases the standard procedure worked quite well.

Conversely, it was noted that a small group of children, mainly hyperactive youngsters between the ages of six and nine, gave the obvious impression that they could not stay "on target" very long, and certainly not the 30 to 40 minutes that might be required for the Rorschach. In most situations, the logical decision would be to defer the Rorschach or not use it. However, if the Rorschach data are deemed essential, the procedure of inquirying after each card may be used.

To do this, the original instructions are altered. Instead of saying, "What might this be?", the examiner says:

"I want you to look at this and tell me what it might be, and show it to me so that I can see it just like you do."

In this procedure the Inquiry questions are sharply limited. Ordinarily the prompts of, *I don't think I see it like you do, help me*, or, *I'm not sure why it looks like that, help me to see it too*, constitute the limit of questioning. Key words given in the basic response are pursued appropriately, but cautiously. Key words given in the Inquiry, after a prompt, are not pursued. This modified procedure is less than satisfactory and should be used only as a last resort in those instances when Rorschach findings seem essential.

▲ *TESTING LIMITS:* Sometimes it may be important to determine if a person can easily see objects that are commonly reported by most people but have not been reported by the client. Usually, this becomes an issue when a person has failed to give any *Popular* answers, or has given only one or two. This is most common among severely disturbed psychiatric subjects, but it can also be the case when a person tries to be overly creative in selecting answers, and therefore rejects the commonplace answer. The tactic of Limits Testing is quite simple.

After the Inquiry has been completed, the examiner selects two or three blots (typically VIII, III, and possibly V) to which the person has not given the Popular response. The examiner says, "We are just about finished, but here (hands the subject the card), look at this one again. Sometimes people see (state the Popular answer) in this one. Do you see anything that looks like that there?" The location area of the Popular is not identified for the client. Typically, the person who has been overly creative in selecting answers will quickly note the Popular answer, whereas the severely disturbed psychiatric subject may express amazement that people might see something such as that. In deciding to test limits, the examiner should be sure that the information is really important, as the procedure can have some influence on any retest that might be done in the future.

▲ *SUMMARY:* It should be clear that a competently administered Rorschach will be properly introduced, faithfully recorded verbatim, and thoughtfully inquired. The latter obviously depends on the awareness of the examiner of coding (scoring) possibilities for a given response. Once the coding (scoring) is a quick and easy process for the examiner, the Inquiry can be accomplished easily, consuming relatively little time, and yet dealing effectively with the issues.

2 ❖ Location and Developmental Quality

The first, and probably least complex, of the coding decisions concerns the location of the response, that is, to which part of the blot did the response occur. The open-endedness of the test permits either of two approaches in formulating responses. The person may decide to use the entire blot, or may select only a portion of it.

When the entire blot is used, it is a *Whole* response and the coding is simple and straightforward, using the symbol *W*. All other answers are *Detail* responses, and the symbol used in coding the location will depend on whether the area selected is one that is commonly used. If it is, the symbol *D* will be employed to note this. Conversely, if the area selected is not among those used frequently by subjects, the symbol *Dd* is assigned. Whenever the client includes use of the white space in the answer, the symbol *S* is added to the location code.

In some instances, the information necessary for deciding on the location code will be given in the response such as, *Well the whole thing looks like ...,* or *If I use only this upper part it could be...* When this occurs, only a brief verification concerning location area is required in the Inquiry. However, in many responses the person does not specify the area of the blot being used during the response, and this matter becomes an important target during the Inquiry.

Ordinarily, information about location is easily derived, especially when the person taking the test has been prepared properly for the Inquiry. Nonetheless, some people remain vague about location and when that occurs, the examiner must persist by using instructions such as, *Run your finger around it carefully*, or *Point to some of the features so that I can see it too.* The four symbols used in coding location and the criterion for each are shown in Table 3.

TABLE 3: SYMBOLS USED FOR CODING THE LOCATION OF RESPONSES

Symbol	Definition	Criterion
W	Whole Response	Where the entire blot is used in the response. All portions must be used.
D	Common Detail Response	A frequently identified area of the blot.
Dd	Unusual Detail Response	An infrequently identified area of the blot.
S	Space Response	A white space area is used in the response (scored only with another location symbol, as in WS, DS, or DdS).

As noted in the preceding chapter, the *Location Sheet* provides the permanent record from which the coding for location is generated. Thus, it is critically important that the area specified by the subject is clearly delineated on the Location Sheet, and notes regarding some of the specific features of the object, such as eyes, hat, feet, etc., especially unusual features, be recorded.

Anyone should be able to look at the Location Sheet and easily reconstruct the response. The astute examiner will often delineate a location area by simply entering the location number together with the response number such as, "1 = D4." However, if the response location is in an area that is not numbered, the area used should be carefully outlined on the Location Sheet. Outlining that is vague or sloppy is not sufficient for accurate location coding.

W The criterion for coding *W* is an either-or issue. Either the subject uses the entire blot, or less than the entire blot. Only the former is coded *W*. It is quite important that the examiner verify that the entire blot has been used in a response. Occasionally, a person will report a response that is like those commonly given to the whole but, in fact, has not used the entire blot in forming the answer. For example, the response, "bat," is among the most frequently given answer to both Cards I and V. About 97% of subjects who give either of these responses use the entire blot, but a few people exclude some portions of the blot in order to be more precise about the answer. Those kinds of responses are *not* coded as *W*, even though only a few small segments are omitted.

D If the response is not a *W*, then it must be coded either as *D* or *Dd*. All *D* areas have been identified on the basis of frequency of use by large numbers of subjects. The format for the Comprehensive System includes 82 areas that have been designated as *D*. Many include large blot areas, but this is not always the case. Several involve only small portions of the total figure. These areas are shown by number, for each of the 10 cards, in the figures included in Table A of this workbook. When a response is not *W*, the examiner should look at the appropriate figure in Table A to determine if the area involved should be coded as *D*.

Dd Any response that is not *W* or *D* is automatically coded as *Dd*. Size is not a factor in coding *Dd*, as some *Dd* areas are very small and others quite large. Some *Dd* areas are identified by number in the figures in Table A. These are areas to which a sufficient number of answers have been recorded to be included in the statistical frequency data recorded at the Rorschach Research Foundation, and for which some information concerning appropriate form use has evolved. If an area is used by a subject that *is not* included in Table A, the coding will always be *Dd* and the correct location number is *Dd99*.

$\boxed{S}$ The symbol S is included in the location coding whenever a white space area is used in the response. White space can be used in an answer in either of two ways. The person may integrate the white space with other blot areas, or may elect to deliver a response that includes only a white space area. Regardless of which form of white space use occurs, the S is never used alone as a location code. Instead, it is always used with another location symbol, as in *WS, DS,* or *DdS*.

▲ *LOCATION CODING FOR MULTIPLE D AREAS.* Some responses will involve the use of two or more D areas. In some of these responses, the appropriate coding will be D, whereas in other instances the coding of *Dd* is correct. Some D areas are, in fact, a combination of other D areas. For example, the D1 area on Card III is actually the composite of the two D9 areas plus D7. Similarly, the composite of D1 and D3 on Card IX equals the D12 area. Naturally, a response to any area listed as D will be coded as D.

Nonetheless, there are instances when people combine D areas to form a new area that is not commonplace. If the combination involves *only one object*, the answer will be coded *Dd*. Conversely, if the individual is using each of the combined D areas as *separate objects*, the appropriate location code will still be D, even though more than one common detail area is involved. These are synthesized responses and will be noted as such by the coding for Developmental Quality.

For example, on Card III an individual might report a person (D9) working on some pottery (D7). In this answer, the integrity of each D area is maintained by reporting separate objects, one being used for the person and one for the pottery. On the other hand, the same two areas might be integrated more uniquely if the response were a person (D9) with a grotesque hand (D7). Here, the subject is reporting the composite of the two D areas as a single area, a very uncommon event, and requiring the coding of *Dd*.

DEVELOPMENTAL QUALITY

The full interpretive value of the data concerning location selection is increased substantially by the addition of a second code to differentiate the characteristic or quality of processing that has been involved in forming the answer. All responses are not formulated in the same manner.

Some answers are concrete and not well organized. They require no specification of features, as in clouds, dirt, blood, etc. These undifferentiated responses reflect a somewhat nonchalant use of the stimulus field, identifying it in a manner that avoids the need to be specific. These answers involve objects that can take any of a variety of forms *and for which the person fails to include any form demand.*

At a higher, but still somewhat simple and economical level, the blot area is identified as a single object that does require specificity, such as a bat, a person, a vase, a chair, etc. In these answers, the cognitive activity includes organizing some of the stimulus features in a meaningful way.

A much higher level of cognitive action is required for combinatory responses, that is, those in which two or more objects are specified in a meaningful relationship. For example, two people picking something up; a tree casting a shadow across the water in the moonlight; or a person wearing a hat.

The location codes *W, D,* and *Dd* do not provide information that differentiates the variations in the quality and specificity of answers. Thus, a second coding is required to note this. There are four Developmental Quality (*DQ*) codes. The symbols used, and the criterion for each are shown in Table 4.

TABLE 4: SYMBOLS AND CRITERIA USED FOR DEVELOPMENTAL QUALITY

Symbol	Definition	Criterion
+	Synthesized Response	Two or more objects are described as separate but related. *At least one* of the objects involved must have a specific form demand, or be described in a manner that creates a specific form demand (ex. a dog walking among some bushes, a man with a funny hat on, an airplane flying through some clouds, the head of a little girl, she has a hair ribbon).
o	Ordinary Response	An area of the blot is identified as a single object which has features that create a natural form demand or the *description of the object is such as to create* a specific form demand (ex. a fir tree, a cat, a totem pole, a maple leaf, a bat, a flag, a man's head).
v/+	Synthesized Response	Two or more objects are described as separate but related. *None of the objects* involved have a specific form demand and **the articulation does not introduce a form demand for any of the objects** (ex. clouds coming together, some sort of bay with the vegetation around the shore, a rock and some dirt around it).
v	Vague	An object is reported which has no specific form demand, *and the articulation does not introduce* a specific form demand for the object (ex. a cloud, the sky, the colors of sunset, some ice).

▲ *THE SYNTHESIS RESPONSES.* For each of the two types of synthesis (+ and v/+) responses the criterion statement includes, "...separate but related." More than one object must be involved *and* they must be reported in a meaningful relationship to each other. For example, *two birds sitting on a fence,* would be coded + because there are three objects in the response and all are interrelated. The two birds are sitting on the same fence. If the response had been, "two birds," alluding to the symmetry of the blot, the DQ code would be **o** (ordinary) as there is no meaningful relationship between them.

A response such as *two clouds coming together,* would be scored **v/+** as the words "coming together" creates the required relationship, but neither objects (clouds) includes a specific form requirement. Conversely, *two clouds are building up, like expanding, and coming together,* would be coded + because the person has injected a form requirement with the words, "building up, like expanding."

If the separate objects involve clothing on a figure, the clothing must be specified in a way that *alters the natural contour of the figure,* or be a discrete blot area itself for the synthesis coding of + to be assigned. For example, people often report one or two human figures on Card III. Occasionally, the figure is described as wearing a tuxedo, which is defined because the figure is dark in coloring. This is coded **o** rather than + because the same blot area is being used for both the figure and the clothing, and the clothing does not change the natural contour of the figure.

On the other hand, if the figure (*D9*) were described as wearing a jacket and the lapel (*Dd27*, which is part of *D9*) is sticking out, or a person (*D9*) wearing mittens (*Dd31*), a + would be appropriate. In the first example the lapel has altered the natural contour of the person. In the second two discrete blot areas have been used. Similarly, if the figure (*D9*) is described as wearing shoes (*Dd33*, which is part of *D9*), the coding of + is appropriate.

▲ *THE ISSUE OF FORM DEMAND.* The criteria for the *DQ* codings of + and o include the requirement of *specific form demand.* This means that the object being reported generally has a consistent form, that is, when the noun identifying the object is used, some specific shapes are implied. For example, the words man, bird, butterfly, spider, lion, chair, ship, house, etc., each identify a class of objects that have some specific form characteristics *even though some variations may exist within each class.* Men may be short or tall, thin or fat, etc. Similarly, chairs can come in a very wide variety of shapes, yet they all have some common features or form requirements.

Any object that *does have* a specific form requirement must be coded as **o** (ordinary), or + (synthesis) if it is in a meaningful relationship with another object *even if the second object does not have a form demand.*

Other words such as cloud, lake, island, foliage, paint, abstract art, etc., represent classes of objects that can take almost any of a wide variety of shapes. The objects in each class do not have a specific form requirement or demand. When objects that have no specific form demand are reported, the *DQ* coding will be **v** (vague), or **v/+** (synthesis) if it is meaningfully combined with another object that also has no form demand.

However, at times, a person will report an object that has no specific form requirement, but in elaborating on the object *the individual may inject a form demand*. For example, the response, "cloud" will usually be coded **v**, however, a person might elaborate, "building up like a cumulus cloud." This injects a form demand, requiring the coding of **o** rather than **v**. Similarly, *a leaf* or *a bush*, or blood will usually be coded **v**, but some sort of form demand can be injected into any of those. For example, *a leaf that has these three pointed parts* or, *a leaf, here's the stem and the pointed top*, are both answers in which a form demand has been included by the client, and the *DQ* coding would be **o**. Likewise, blood that is *running down* includes form demand, as does a *bush with all the branches sticking up*. Both would have a *DQ* coding of **o**.

▲ *SUMMARY.* The location component of each response will always include two symbols. One is for the area used (*W, D,* or *Dd* with *S* as a possible second code). The second for the *DQ* (+, **o**, **v/+**, or **v**), and the examiner should always be alert for instances in which the person injects form demand for objects that otherwise would be coded **v**.

3 ❖ Determinants

Determinant coding often seems to be the most complex feature of scoring to the beginning Rorschacher. This impression is probably created because the examiner must consider all of the possibilities that contribute to *why* an object that is reported, actually looks like that to the person. The world is complex, and when we identify things in it, we usually are influenced by multiple stimulus elements, such as shape, color, shading, apparent movement, etc. So too is it with the Rorschach figures which, in a microcosmic way, contain many of the visual stimuli that we find in the environment.

Although the stimulus field is nothing more than a series of arbitrary forms and colors, it does have many salient stimulus features or distal bits that are similar to, but not exactly the same as, objects known or imagined by the person taking the test. This similarity, which may be based on any of the stimulus features, shape, color, etc., permits the necessary process of classification(s) to occur. As noted earlier, the process of classifying the blot actually creates many more potential answers than are required. Thus, some must be discarded.

After several possible answers are discarded, usually there are still more than enough to meet the demands of the task, and another selection process occurs. This final selection is influenced very markedly by the habits, or personality features of the person, plus the psychological state of the individual at the time of taking the test. The needs, attitudes, sets, conflicts, response styles, etc. all can become influential in the final selection of the answers that are delivered.

Unfortunately, there is no way to measure this complex intrapsychic process accurately as it occurs during the several seconds between the presentation of the card and the delivery of the first answer. However, the product of the process, *the response itself*, usually will contain elements that reflect some of the features that have been involved in the process. When those elements are coded correctly, the codes represent something about the psychological operations of the person.

The coding for a single response provides little, if any, useful information about the psychological characteristics of the person, but frequency data for each of the various codes, particularly for the determinants, can be used to generate a broad array of information about the psychology of an individual.

The words of the client are the data from which coding decisions evolve. Unfortunately, individuals vary in their vocabularies and manners of expression. Thus, while information concerning location usually is obtained easily, information about the determinant(s) can be revealed in many ways.

In the most favorable circumstance, the person gives the critical data directly, as in *It has that general shape* or, *It's colored like they are* or *The different shades here give that impression.* This is not uncommon among cooperative people who understand and appreciate the task of the Inquiry but, sometimes, even the cooperative person does not express the critical information that precisely.

Instead, the verbiage is less direct and only contains clues to the possible existence of a determinant. These clues generally occur in the form of key words or phrases, such as those described in Chapter I, and they must be pursued diligently, but non-directly by the examiner during the Inquiry, focusing on the issue, *what makes it look like that?*

The examiner who is thoroughly familiar with the variety of possible determinants should have little trouble detecting these clues and forming prompts or questions that will pursue them appropriately. Experience suggests that this kind of familiarity develops only through practice, and it is for this reason that a substantial number of varied responses have been included in the *Appendix* for practice coding.

▲ *DETERMINANT CATEGORIES.* There are 7 broad categories of determinants, each of which represents a way in which the stimulus field may be translated by the person. In that context, each reflects some aspect of cognitive activity that has been involved in formulating the answer. Some have sub-categories to note different ways in which an element has been used in the answer. Many responses will involve more than one category and any category may coexist with any of the others, or with one exception, may occur independently. The 7 categories are:

1. **Form.** This determinant is common to almost all responses, either as the only determinant, or combined with other determinants.
2. **Movement.** This category has three sub-categories, (1) Human Movement (2) Animal Movement, and (3) Inanimate Movement. All movement answers are also coded as Active or Passive.
3. **Chromatic Color.** Includes 3 symbols, the choice of which depends on the extent to which form is involved in the answer.
4. **Achromatic Color.** Includes 3 symbols, the choice of which depends on the extent of form involvement in the answer.
5. **Shading.** This category has three sub-categories, each with 3 symbols, to account for different uses of shading, (1) Texture, (2) Depth or dimensionality, and (3) Diffuse.
6. **Form Dimension.** One symbol is used for responses in which the impression of dimensionality is based on size or contour.
7. **Pairs and Reflection.** Will always involve some use of form and are based on the symmetry of the blots.

The 7 categories include 24 symbols for coding determinants. They are shown, with the criteria for application, in Table 5.

TABLE 5: SYMBOLS AND CRITERIA FOR DETERMINANT CODING

Category	Symbol	Criterion
Form	F	*Form answers.* Used for responses based exclusively on the form features of the blot.
Movement	M	*Human movement response.* Used for responses involving the kinesthetic activity of a human, or of an animal or fictitional character in human-like activity.
	FM	*Animal movement response.* Used for responses involving a kinesthetic activity of an animal. The movement perceived must be congruent to the species identified in the content. Animals reported in movement not common to their species should be coded as *M*.
	m	*Inanimate movement response.* Used for responses involving the movement of inanimate, inorganic, or insensate objects.
Chromatic Color	C	*Pure color response.* Used for answers based exclusively on the chromatic color features of the blot. *No* form is involved.
	CF	*Color-form response.* Used for answers that are formulated *primarily* because of the chromatic color features of the blot. Form features are used, but are of secondary importance.
	FC	*Form-color response.* Used for answers that are created mainly because of form features. Chromatic color is used, but is of secondary importance.
	Cn	*Color naming response.* Used when the colors of the blot are identified *by name*, and with the intention of giving a response.
Achromatic Color	C'	*Pure achromatic color response.* Used when the response is based exclusively on the grey, black, or white features of the blot, when they are clearly used as color. *No* form is involved.
	C'F	*Achromatic color-form response.* Used for responses that are created *mainly* because of the black, white, or grey features, clearly used as color. Form features are used, but are of secondary importance.
	FC'	*Form-achromatic color response.* Used for answers that are based *mainly* on the form features. The achromatic features, clearly used as color, are also included, but are of secondary importance.
Shading-Texture	T	*Pure texture response.* Used for answers in which the shading components of the blot are translated to represent a tactual phenomenon, with no consideration to the form features.
	TF	*Texture-form response.* To be used for responses in which the shading features of the blot are interpreted as tactual, and form is used secondarily, for purposes of elaboration and/or clarification.

TABLE 5 (Continued):

Category	Symbol	Criterion
	FT	*Form-texture response.* Used for responses that are based *mainly* on the form features. Shading features of the blot are translated as tactual, but are of secondary importance.
Shading-Dimension	V	*Pure vista response.* Used for answers in which the shading features are interpreted as depth or dimensionality. *No* form is involved.
	VF	*Vista-form response.* Used for responses in which the shading features are interpreted as depth or dimensionality. Form features are included, but are of secondary importance.
	FV	*Form-vista response.* Used for answers that are based mainly on the form features of the blot. Shading features are also interpreted to note depth and/or dimensionality, but are of secondary importance to the formulation of the answer.
Shading-Diffuse	Y	*Pure shading response.* Used for responses that are based exclusively on the light-dark features of the blot that are completely formless and do not involve reference to either texture or dimension.
	YF	*Shading form response.* Used for responses based primarily on the light-dark features of the blot, not involving texture or dimension. Form features are included, but are of secondary importance.
	FY	*Form-shading response.* Used for responses that are based mainly on the form features of the blot. The light-dark features of the figure, not used to articulate texture or dimension, are included as elaboration and/or clarification and are secondary to the use of form.
Form Dimension	FD	*Form based dimensional response.* Used for answers in which the impression of depth, distance, or dimensionality is created by using the elements of size and/or shape of contours. *No* use of shading is involved in creating this impression.
Pairs & Reflections	(2)	*The pair response.* Used for answers in which two identical objects are reported, based on the symmetry of the blot. The objects must be equivalent in all respects, but must *not* be identified as being reflected or as mirror images.
	rF	*Reflection-form response.* Used for answers in which the blot or blot area is reported as a reflection or mirror image, because of the symmetry of the blot. The object or content reported has no specific form requirement, as in clouds, landscape, shadows, etc.
	Fr	*Form-reflection response.* Used for answers in which the blot or blot area is identified as reflected or a mirror image, based on the symmetry of the blot. The substance of the response is based on form features, and the object reported has a specific form demand.

CLARIFICATION

▲ *FORM.* There are many ways in which a subject may specify the use of form.
| F | Probably the least frequent is the use of the word *form*. Instead, people often use the word *shape*, or more commonly, they simply allude to different form features of the object reported.

The examiner should not be concerned if the words, "form," or "shape" are not used, provided that the form characteristics to which the individual refers are *obvious*, as in, *These are the wings, and the body, and the tail*, or, *This is the head and here are the legs, and this is the tree trunk.*

The absence of a *specific form demand* for an object does not necessarily mean the absence of form. For instance, the response *a rain cloud* might not include any specific form use as in, *it's just all black like a rain cloud*, which would be coded *C'*. Conversely, the subject might have said, *It's all irregular and more narrow at the the top like rain clouds*, which would be coded *F*.

The symbol *F* will always be included with the coding for other determinants when form features are used, *except* if the codes *M*, or *m* are the only ones assigned to an answer. *Form is subsumed* in the codes *M* and *m*.

The decision to code *F* is straightforward when no other determinant is included in the response. However, examiners sometimes struggle with the issue of whether form is primary or secondary in an answer when another determinant is involved. This probably occurs most often when chromatic color is the other determinant.

Take, for example, the response, *A very pretty flower*. The first explanation of the client in the Inquiry is, *Well, it's red like a rose and this would be the petals and the stem is here*. There is no question that chromatic color has been used, but the issue lingers about whether it is primary or secondary in forming the answer. The combination of words given in the response plus the first Inquiry explanation could be used as a basis from which to argue in favor of either a *CF* or *FC* coding.

The examiner should attempt to resolve the issue by a prompt, such as, *I'm not sure I see it as you do, help me*. If the person responds to the prompt by saying, *It just looks like a rose, see the petals and the stem*, the coding of *FC* is most appropriate as the new information focuses on the form. Conversely, if the response to the prompt is, *It's just so pretty, like a bright red rose, here are the petals*, the coding of *CF* is correct because the individual has re-emphasized the coloring and not the form.

Unfortunately, some people will respond to an Inquiry prompt by simply rephrasing the things that have been stated earlier, such as, *Well, it's like a rose, it's red and has the petals and stem.* When that occurs, the decision about whether the form use is primary or secondary becomes a judgement call made by the examiner.

In the example above, some examiners might decide to code *CF*, assuming that form use is secondary because the word *pretty* was included in the original response and the word *red* occurred first when the person identified the features of the object. However, it can also be argued that form use is primary in this answer because the word *pretty* was not used again in the Inquiry, and the Inquiry did not include any special emphasis on the color. This position, supporting the coding of *FC*, is more conservative and, in this instance, is probably the more appropriate. Nonetheless, the decision does remain a close judgement call.

The problem of differentiating primary versus secondary use of form will be addressed again in several sections of this chapter.

▲ *MOVEMENT.* The three codes for movement are quite discrete, and usually

$\boxed{\text{M}}$ $\boxed{\text{FM}}$ $\boxed{\text{m}}$ easy to discriminate.

♦ *M:* Human Movement is scored for all types of human activity which can range from very active movement such as *fighting, jumping, lifting, sawing*, etc. to very passive activity such as *thinking, sleeping, pondering, leaning, looking*, etc.

M is not only coded for the movement of human figures, but also for human like figures or *animals or inanimate objects in human activity*. For example, "Two bears *playing poker*," or "Two insects *arguing*," or "A very *happy* tree" are all scored *M*.

M is also scored when the response involves a sensory experience, even though it may be presented as an abstract, such as, "That just reminds me of *gloom*," "It looks like *love* to me," or "When I look at this *I hear a loud sound*."

The alert student of the Rorschach will recognize that some, or all of these responses might be *formless*, and represent those rare instances in which *M* is assigned, but no code for form quality is entered.

♦ *FM:* Animal movement is scored for all types of animal activity. However, the type of movement *must be* common to the species. Animals that are reported in activity *that is not common to their species*, such as "bears playing poker," "two insects pushing a wheelbarrow," "a fish standing next to a tree," or a "a frog that is flying" are scored *M*.

♦ *m:* Inanimate movement answers also span a very broad range. They are probably identified most easily when only the inanimate object is included in the response such as, "A cloud *rising*," "A *waterfall*," "A flag *flying* in the breeze," "A bullet *smashing* through something," or "Flames *leaping* up."

In some instances the inanimate movement is *static*. For example, "A coat *hanging* on a post," or "A skin *stretched out* to dry" are both scored *m* because there is *an unnatural tension state*. If the unnatural tension state does not exist, as in "A rug laying on the floor," *m* would *not* be scored. For instance, "A hanged man, *dangling* from a rope" is coded *m*, whereas "A dead person, lying there" is *not* coded *m*. On the other hand, *A dead person lying there, his head is tilted upward*, would be coded as an *m* response. The determination that an unnatural tension state exists when scoring static objects as *m* is very important and if the verbiage does not support that determination, *m* should not be scored.

♦ *Active-Passive Superscripts.* A second coding that must be assigned to *all* movement responses is a superscript that notes whether the movement is active or passive (*a* for active, *p* for passive).

One of the more frustrating issues associated with the development of the Comprehensive System has involved attempts to establish precise criteria for the application of the *a* and *p* superscripts. That objective has never been achieved. Nevertheless, most people do seem able to agree on the meaning of the terms active and passive when applied to movement answers.

The agreement is especially high when a "benchmark," or comparative reference point is used by everyone. The verb *talking* is probably the best benchmark. It should *always* be coded as *passive*. It can serve as a good reference in addressing questionable responses. For example, verbs such as whispering, looking, standing, slouching, bending, sighing, etc. are easily defined as *passive*, when judged against the benchmark, while verbs such as arguing, yelling, glaring, reaching, lifting, etc. are easily identified as *active* in the same context.

Some movement responses are always coded *passive*. They are the answers in which the movement reported is *static*. The static feature of the response is created by a qualification to the answer, in which the object, or scene reported is described as an abstract, a caricature, a painting, or a picture. These are all coded as *p* regardless of the description of the movement reported, such as, "An abstract of fireworks," "A painting of two dogs fighting," or "A picture of two men lifting something up."

Naturally, it is very important to make sure that the person has truly qualified a response rather than simply used a qualifying word as a manner of articulation. For instance, children will often use the words "picture" or "painting" in their responses, referring to the blot rather than to the response itself. Occasionally, an examiner may not be sure if an individual is qualifying a response or is using an articulation style. Typically, the latter will occur repeatedly in several responses, (It looks like a picture of a bat), but when in doubt, a clarifying question should be asked in the Inquiry.

◆ *Active and Passive in the Same Response.* There are some answers in which the *a* and *p* superscripts are both assigned to the same movement determinant. These are responses in which *two or more objects* are described in movement but at least one is active while the other(s) are passive.

For example, "*Two people dancing* (**active**) *around a person standing* (**passive**) *in the middle*," is scored $M^{a\text{-}p}$. The determinant is entered only once and counted only once in the frequency tally for M, but both superscripts are counted when tallying the number of active and passive movement answers.

The assignment of both superscripts to a single movement determinant is done *only* when more than one object is involved in the movement. Some answers will be given in which the same object is involved in both active and passive movement, such as, "*A dog sitting there* (**passive**) *howling at the moon* (**active**)." When this occurs *only* the active movement is coded, FM^{a}.

▲ *CHROMATIC COLOR.* As noted earlier, the most common dilemma encoun-
$\boxed{\text{FC}}\ \boxed{\text{CF}}\ \boxed{\text{C}}\ \boxed{\text{Cn}}$ tered in coding chromatic color responses involves the distinction between *FC* and *CF*, or in the differentiation between *C* and *CF*. The key to these issues probably rests most with the accurate identification of the *CF* answer.

◆ *CF:* There is no absolute rule of thumb that can be applied easily to identify *CF* answers. Most *CF* responses are readily distinguished because the emphasis on color is clearly evident, and the form features are clearly secondary. But that emphasis spans a considerable range. For example:

RESPONSE	INQUIRY
A pretty flower	S: It's a beautiful orange w green leaves & ths is the stem
It's a forest of some sort	S: It's all different colored plants and trees
A very exotic butterfly	S: It's a beautiful red, unusual in its color, the wgs r out
Eggs fried in butter	S: They'r yellow, lik fried in butter, c the yoke in the cntr

Each of these responses should be scored *CF* because in each the color is dominant and only modest form use has occurred. But in each one the color was not mentioned until in the Inquiry. In fact, any or all could have developed into *FC* responses or even into *Pure F* answers as illustrated below.

RESPONSE	INQUIRY
A pretty flower	S: Here is the stem, these r the leaves, this is the flower, its in a pot. E: U said it is pretty? S: Yes, it has an orange flower
It's a forest of some sort	S: U can c the shapes of some trees & bushes and this might be a road running down the middle
A very exotic butterfly	S: It has very unusual wings, I think tht u find wgs shaped lik tht on rare butterflies, some r red too lik ths is
Eggs fried in butter	S: Well, it has an irregular shape to it, like an egg does after u break it & this is the yoke E: U said fried in butter S: Well, thyr yellow so I thot thy might be fried in butter

Three of these answers (flower, butterfly, eggs) would be scored *FC* because color has been used, but the main emphasis is on form. The fourth (forest) is scored as *F* because nothing but form has been included and there is no key word or phrase that might cause the examiner to inject a question.

Other responses may appear to be *Pure C* answers at first glance, but the coding of *CF* is necessary because a modest form requirement is injected by the subject. For example, the italicized wording in "that red looks like blood *running down*," or "Wow, look at all the colors, like fireworks exploding *outward*," or "the pink reminds me of strawberry ice cream, *two scoops*," makes each of these *CF* responses even though form use is minimal.

Quite often, objects that have no specific form demand will be *CF*, but this *is not* a hard-fast rule. For example, a person might say, *This green is colored like leaves, like leaves you might see on a bush.* If no further form elaboration occurs, the answer should be coded *CF*. However, the response could be elaborated, as in *This green, it's colored like a leaf, a leaf from a bush, like a berry bush, see the way that it comes to a point like, what are they, raspberries I think, they're shaped like that.* The more precise form elaboration would require a coding of *FC*.

◆ *FC:* The main characteristic of the *FC* answer is the form emphasis. Often the color use is almost as a passing comment as in, *There are two people leaning toward each other, whispering maybe, they have red hats on.* In other instances the color is used more distinctly but remains secondary to the form. For instance, *These are two little pink mice, they are pink when they are first born, see their little legs and the head and a tail.*

FC can also be the correct scoring for objects that usually are formless. Consider the following three answers:

RESPONSE	INQUIRY
The orange there cb fire	S: It's the way that you see the orange flames when you look at a fire
Tht orange re me of fire	S: The orange looks like flames, sort of darting upward
The orange ll flames	S: Thyr darting upward, like you might see from a camp fire in which all the logs burn evenly creating a symmetrical impression, like the burning on one side is almost exactly the same as the burning on the other

The first of the three answers would be scored *C* as there is no use of form. The second should be scored *CF* because the words *darting up* have injected a form requirement. The third is clearly an *FC* response. In spite of the fact that the color was mentioned first in the answer, the overall emphasis in the response is on form.

The majority of difficulties in discriminating the *CF* from *FC* are created by the hurried examiner who does not take the time to inquire the issue with one more question. The question selected should deliberately be vague, as in, *I don't think I'm seeing it like you are, can you help me?* or, *I think I see it alright, but I'm not really sure what there is that makes it look like that.* These added questions should not be used routinely, and they should not be expected to solve all of the *CF* versus *FC* dilemmas that will arise. But used wisely, they can resolve many issues that can become problems when the record is reviewed.

◆ *The Step-Down Principle.* The distinction between *C* and *CF* is usually less of a dilemma. The *C* answers are often blatant, *This red, it's like blood, all red like that,* or *It's blue so it could be water,* or *Just a lot of different colored paint, that's all,* or *It's blue, like ice gets blue sometimes.* These illustrations are the obvious *C* responses, but sometimes an object that ordinarily would be scored as *C* must be coded as *CF* because it is *touching* a formed object.

For instance, *The red must be blood, it's on these bears that are probably fighting with each other.* Whereas red blood would typically be coded C, the coding is stepped down one interval to *CF* because of the direct proximity to a form dominated object. If the response had been, *Two bears that are fighting, maybe they are hurt because this red back here in the background is like blood,* the coding would remain C because the blood is not on the bears, even though it is associated with them.

◆ *Confirming Color Use.* Either of two circumstances can occur that lead to a quandary about whether color has been used. First, many people will articulate color to denote the location of an object, such as, *This red looks like a butterfly,* or, *This blue is like a spider.* Neither of these statements warrants a decision to code for color as both are simply location definitions. Either or both might ultimately contain color, but if that is true, the presence of color as a determinant would be confirmed by other wording.

The second circumstance usually is more frustrating for the examiner. It occurs because an individual has reported an object in a colored area of the blot, and it seems almost certain that color has influenced the formation of the answer. But the person *has not reported* the color, either directly or through implication.

A good illustration of this was noted earlier, *This looks like a very beautiful flower.* In the Inquiry, the examiner bases the question on the key word, *You mentioned it is beautiful?* to which the person responds, *Yes, it looks very thin and very delicate.* Color is not coded for this response, even though the entire area used might be colored. The coding *must* reflect the verbalization of the client.

♦ *Direct Unequivocal Color Use.* There are some responses in which the way that a person articulates a color makes it clear that the color is being used as a determinant. These are instances in which the color and content converge directly. For example:

> *That red sure looks like blood to me*

> *That orange looks like a forest fire*

> *The blue is the water*

> *The green is the leaf*

In these answers the use of color seems unequivocal and should be scored. However, most color use is not so obvious, even in many responses in which the color and content appear to converge. For example:

> *That red could be blood*

> *The orange might be a fire or something*

> *This blue part might be water*

> *The green part is probably a forest*

In these responses, the person has not been definite. Instead, there is equivocation (*could be, might be, is probably*). Thus, the examiner should inquire further to test the color use by asking, *I'm not sure what makes it look like _____?* or *What is there about it that makes it look like _____?*

▲ *ACHROMATIC COLOR.* The issues concerning differentiation of the chromatic color symbols are also applicable for the coding of achromatic $\boxed{C'}$ $\boxed{C'F}$ $\boxed{FC'}$ color. Achromatic color responses occur with a much lower frequency than chromatic color answers, and the majority are *FC'* answers.

The criterion indicates that the use of the achromatic features of the blot, as color, *must be clear and unequivocal.* Fortunately, most achromatic color responses will include the words, "black," "white," or "grey," used in a manner that settles the issue quickly. For instance, This bat is *black*, like most bats, or It's *white* like snow, or It must be a shadow because it's all *grey*. In each of these answers the use of achromatic color is quite clear.

Two other key words are often used to convey the use of achromatic color, *light* and *dark*. Either may be used to denote color, but unfortunately, either may also be used to indicate the use of shading.

For example, "It's all *dark* like at night," indicates the use of the grey-black features as color, but, "It's all *dark*, like it is deeper here," indicates the use of the shading to produce the impression of depth, which is coded as **vista**, and "It's *lighter* up here like at the top of a cloud," indicates the use of **diffuse shading**.

Smoke and x-ray responses almost always involve either the use of achromatic color or diffuse shading features. It is possible that either might be coded as *F* because the person fails to articulate grey-black features even though the examiner has posed a well thought through question, but the vast majority of smoke and x-ray answers will have a *C'* or *Y* component in the scoring. Most people articulate either smoke or x-ray responses using words such as, *It's dark like that.* These answers should be coded for achromatic color.

Occasionally, a person will say, *The way the colors are,* and this may, or may not, signal achromatic color. In these instances, the examiner must pursue the issue further with another question, such as repeating the person's words, or struggle with the indecision about whether the response should be scored as diffuse shading or achromatic color.

If the intent is not clear in responses that contain the words *light* or *dark*, or the phrase, *the way the colors are*, the coding for diffuse shading should be entered.

Caution must also be used about the key words that convey achromatic color, black, white, grey, light, or dark, because, sometimes, they simply denote location selection, as in, *This white part looks like...* or *This dark area could be ...* Thus, as in the case of chromatic color answers, the decision to code for achromatic color hinges on the rule that the intent of the subject is clear and unequivocal.

▲ *SHADING - TEXTURE.* The decision to code shading appears to be easier for
| T | TF | FT | the novice than the decision about which kind of shading has
occurred. The differentiation is really not complex, and can
be based on a process of elimination.

The texture symbols are used to code responses in which the shading features
are employed to create a *tactile* impression, as in, soft, rough, smooth, furry, wet,
etc. The critical issue is that the person *must* convey the use of shading features
in some way.

Most people do not use the word *shading*. It is much more common to hear the
word *color* employed, as in, *The way the colors are here*, or, *The different coloring
is like that*. In other instances, a person may indicate, *It's the way the lines go in
there*, which can sound like contour use but really is a reference to different levels
of saturation. Some people, especially children, often rub the card to convey the
tactile impression, and *this is sufficient for the coding of texture* provided that the
rubbing occurs at a time when the verbiage used conveys some sort of tactual
feature for the object.

Under ideal conditions, an individual will indicate the tactile impression directly,
It looks like it *feels* soft, or, It looks like it would *feel* hot if you touched it.
However, it is very important to avoid the assumption that a response should be
coded as texture simply because the content implies that, as in, *A piece of fur*, or
because a key word has been used that *might* imply a tactile impression, such as
rough or cold.

A piece of fur can be described as looking like that because, *It is all irregular
around the edges*, which is simply *F*. Similarly, an area can be described as rough
because, *The lines make it look like there are indentations there, like bumpy*, which
denotes the use of shading to convey the impression of dimensionality. In the
same context, an area might be described as looking cold because, *There are
different shades of blue, like ice gets when it's really cold*. Shading is used, but in
this case it is diffuse shading and no tactile impression has been included.
Conversely, texture would be coded if the response was, *These different shades of
blue give the impression of ice that feels really cold*, or if the person had rubbed the
card when saying, *like ice gets when it's really cold*.

The subtle differences between texture and diffuse shading, or texture and vista,
can often be perplexing and underscore the importance of a good Inquiry.

▲ *SHADING - VISTA.* The vista symbols are assigned when the shading features
| V | VF | FV | have been used to create the impression of depth or dimen-
sionality as in, It's *down in*, It's *behind*, It's *rounded* at the
edges, It's *higher* than, It's *folded over*, It's an *aerial* view of... etc.

Usually, the presence of the depth or dimension impression is obvious, and the task of the examiner is to determine *if it is based on the shading or if the impression is simply created because of the size or the contour features of the blot*. When the latter occurs, the coding is *FD* and not vista.

The most troublesome differentiations concerning vista are those involving the possibility of texture. For instance, it is relatively easy to discriminate the mountain range (**vista**) from rough sandpaper (**texture**), but sometimes words like *bumpy, indented,* or *rough* can imply either vista or texture.

For example, This looks like the brain, see the way the lines are there gives the impression of the convolutions, it looks *very bumpy*. This is a *vista* answer because the shading is used (*the way the lines are*) and there is no implication of tactile impression (it *looks* very bumpy). If the response had been, ...it looks like it would *feel* very bumpy if you touch it, texture would be coded instead of vista.

At times, the dimensional quality of a response is subtle and examiners should be alert to the necessity of asking a relevant Inquiry question. For instance, a response to Card IV might be, *A monster with his head between his legs*. This might convey dimensionality, either based on form or based on shading. In either event, the examiner must pursue the issue with a question such as, *You said his head is between his legs?*

▲ *SHADING - DIFFUSE.* Any shading response that is not texture or vista is $\boxed{Y}$ $\boxed{YF}$ $\boxed{FY}$ coded as diffuse shading. Most of these decisions are relatively straightforward, although in some cases, as noted earlier, a person may use words such as *light, dark, blackness,* etc., in an equivocal manner, implying either achromatic color or diffuse shading. In those instances, the rule concerning achromatic color forces the decision. Namely, unless the examiner is convinced that the light or dark features are being used as achromatic color, the coding for diffuse shading should be assigned.

Sometimes people convey diffuse shading by mentioning a contrast in *colors*, as in, *The different pinks makes it look rotten*, or *It has different greys in it, like during a storm*, or *The way the coloring comes together gives the impression of dried blood*, or *The colors are mixed here, like in a finger painting*.

▲ *FORM DIMENSION.* *FD* is coded for answers that involve impressions of depth, $\boxed{FD}$ distance, or dimension that are *not* based on shading features. Usually, size differentiation is the contributing element, such as, The feet *are so much bigger* than the head, he must be lying down, or It's *so small*, it must be way off in the distance, or It looks like it's *in perspective*, like I'm looking up at him.

Sometimes, the absence of some features of an object are translated by the individual to mean that depth or dimensionality exists, as in, I can only see the leg and part of the arm, so it *must be behind* this... These answers are also scored *FD*.

Some *FD* answers can be much more subtle and examiners often will have to work hard to determine if they really should be scored for dimension. For example, a response might be, *A person standing with a hood on.* The issue which must be inquired concerns whether the hood covers anything, such as the face or part of it, and if so, what gives that impression. In some instances, the hood will be a two dimensional feature, but in other responses a person will report that, *You can only see part of the face.* This is an *FD* answer.

▲ *PAIRS AND REFLECTIONS.* Each of these represents a response in which the person has used the symmetry of the blot to specify two identical objects.

$\boxed{(2)}$ Pairs are often reported as, *There are two...,"* but in many instances the word *two* is not included. Instead, a plural of the object may be used as in, *bears, dogs, people,* or a synonym for two may be employed, such as, *A couple of...* Sometimes, a person will allude to only one object in the response, *This looks like a dog,* and then note that, *There is one on each side,* in the Inquiry. When this occurs, the pair should be coded.

In rare instances, an individual may report that a pair exists, *This looks like two people,* but later in the response, or in the Inquiry will differentiate the two, *It looks like a man and a woman.* If the objects are differentiated in *any* way (this one is bigger, this one is fatter, this one is darker, etc.), the pair *is not coded.*

The coding for a pair (2) is placed well to the right of other determinants, and after the coding for form quality. This makes them easier to identify during the frequency tabulation.

$\boxed{\textbf{Fr}}$ $\boxed{\textbf{rF}}$ The coding of the reflection includes the same requirements as the coding for the pair, that is, symmetry must be involved and the objects identical, but the person also reports the object as being reflected, or as a mirror image. For example, *Someone looking in the mirror, An animal seeing his reflection in a lake,* or *This is all being reflected in the water.*

In each instance, the reflection must be based on symmetry and the objects, by word or implication, are identical. Whereas the coding for a pair is recorded separately, to the right of the determinant coding, the reflection codes, *Fr* and *rF* are included in the determinant segment of the coding. *A pair is not recorded when the reflection determinant is scored.*

MULTIPLE DETERMINANTS - THE BLEND

Most records will contain at least one response in which more than one determinant exists. This is the *Blend*. Each determinant is shown in the coding, separated from each other by a dot (.) or *Blend sign*. For instance, $M^p.FC.Fr$ notes that the response contains passive human movement, a form dominated color feature, and a reflection.

Theoretically, there is no limit to the number of determinant combinations that might occur. Most blends will include two determinants, although many will have three. More than three determinants is very unusual, and as a general rule, responses with more than three determinants recorded should be reviewed again to insure coding accuracy. Nonetheless, some answers are very complex and this complexity will be represented in the blend, such as, $M^a.m^p.CF.FT.FD$, which signifies that the response contains active human movement, passive inanimate movement, a chromatic color form related answer, texture, and form dimension.

Blends should be coded *in the order that the determinants have appeared in the response*. For example, if the subject reports, "There is a fire (later clarified to be based on chromatic color), and there is a butterfly flying over it," the blend would be $C.FM^a$. On the other hand, if the response has been, "There is a butterfly flying over a fire," the blend would be $FM^a.C$.

It is extremely unusual, but not impossible, for F to be included separately in a blend. Assuming that such a response is coded correctly, it signals some sort of very concrete cognitive functioning, because this coding indicates that more than one object has been reported in the answer, but *no relationship has been specified*.

For example, *There are two people, and a butterfly, and they are picking something up*. This response almost sounds like two responses, one concerning two people and the second the butterfly. The examiner must exercise caution to insure that this is not the case. The Inquiry to this answer may provide the best illustration:

E: (Rpts Ss response)
S: Yes, here are the people, see their heads and legs
E: You mentioned that there is a butterfly there
S: Yes, right in the middle
E: You mentioned that the people are picking something up
S: Yeah, this here, maybe it's a pot
E: I'm not sure I'm seeing the butterfly like you are
S: It's right there, see it has wings

The procedure for the Inquiry has been to take each component in the order that they were given in the response. The butterfly has been queried twice. The person has reaffirmed the people, something that they are picking up, and the butterfly. But there is no integration of the butterfly with the people or the pot. Consequently, the appropriate coding is $M^a.F$.

Had the butterfly been mentioned *last* in the original response, *These are two people picking something up, and there is a butterfly there*, the examiner should ask, at the beginning of the Inquiry, *after* repeating the response verbatim, *Did you mean those as separate answers?* However, when the unrelated object has been injected in the midst of an answer, that question is not appropriate. Instead, the examiner must attempt to address the issue less directly, as in the illustration, by asking something specific about each of the components in the response. This tactic will usually cause the person to indicate, *I didn't mean them together*, but when that does not occur, the entry of *F*, alone in a blend, is correct.

It is also unusual, but not impossible for a blend to contain more than one kind of shading determinant, such as FV.FT, or FT.FY., but a word of caution is required. *The same words or phrase cannot be coded twice.* For example, *These dark wavy lines make it look furry*, offers the temptation to consider diffuse shading (dark wavy lines) as well as texture (furry), but it is the dark wavy lines that create the tactile impression.

A blend that *is impossible* is one containing two or more scores for the same determinant such as FC.CF, FY.YF, or FC'.C'. These are erroneous scores! It is true that some answers might contain multiple objects that could qualify for different categories of the same determinant. However, any time a response contains elements that qualify for different categories of the same determinant, the code that involves the *least* form emphasis should be used.

An example is the response, *Two bears with red hats on, they are fighting and the red down here is blood on them*. Ordinarily the *red hats* would be scored *FC* but that is superceded by the *CF* component, *the red down here is blood on them*. Thus, the answer would be scored $FM^a.CF$.

▲ *SUMMARY.* It should be obvious that mastery of the criteria for determinants is crucial to an adequate administration of the test. That knowledge forms the basis for a competent Inquiry which, in turn, leads to correct coding, and correct determinant coding ultimately provides some of the richest interpretive data that is gleaned from the test.

4 ❖ Form Quality

The entry for form quality *(FQ)* is a very important feature in the coding (scoring) of a Rorschach response. It provides information about the "fit" of the response, that is, does the area of the blot being used really conform to the form requirements of the object specified?

This is an important issue because one of the common problems of people who encounter severe stress or pathology concerns the ability to maintain a good grasp on reality. This is not to suggest that well adjusted people never bend or distort reality, but the issue can be reduced to one of *how much* perceptual uniqueness or inaccuracy can occur without significantly disrupting one's adjustment or, *how extensive* can inaccuracies be before one's efficiency is markedly limited.

The format for scoring form quality uses four codes to differentiate levels of form adequacy. Three represent answers in which form is used appropriately. Two are commonly given answers, while the third represents answers that have a content reported by a low frequency of people. The fourth represents those answers in which the form use has been inappropriate and/or distorted. These categories, and the criterion for each are shown in Table 6.

TABLE 6: SYMBOLS AND CRITERIA FOR CODING FORM QUALITY

Symbol	Definition	Criterion
+	Ordinary–Elaborated	The unusually detailed articulation of *form* in responses that otherwise would be scored ordinary. It is done in a manner that tends to enrich the quality of the response without sacrificing the appropriateness of the form use. The + answer is not necessarily original or creative but, rather, it stands out by the manner in which form details are used and specified. Examples are shown in Chapter 10, Table B.
o	Ordinary	The common response in which general form features are easily articulated to identify an object. These are easy to see answers that have been reported by at least 2% of persons in the Form Quality data pool for *W* and *D* areas, or by at least 50 persons in the pool who responded to *Dd* areas. There is no unusual enrichment of the answer by elaboration of the form features.
u	Unusual	A low frequency response in which the basic contours involved are appropriate for the response. These are uncommon answers that are seen quickly and easily by the observer.
–	Minus	The distorted, arbitrary, unrealistic use of form in creating a response. The answer is imposed on the blot structure with total, or near total disregard for the contours of the area used. Often substantial arbitrary lines or contours will be created where none exist.

The appropriate symbol for form quality is entered at the end of the determinant coding. Responses based exclusively on form will be coded as *F+, Fo, Fu, or F–*. Likewise, when determinants other than pure Form are present in the answer, or when multiple determinants create a *blend*, the placement of the form quality coding remains the same, as in, $M^a o$, *TFu, FC.FD–*, or $FM^p.FC.FC'+$.

The decision concerning which symbol to employ will begin with an examination of Table A, which is one of the working tables included in Chapter 10 in Part II. It provides a listing of responses, card by card, and by location areas.

Table A has been revised several times. The most recent version was created using 9,500 protocols that include 205,701 responses. These include the records of nonpatient adults (51,183 responses), nonschizophrenic outpatients (92,951 responses), and nonschizophrenic inpatients (61,567 responses).

The result is a listing of 5,018 items, or classes of items, each of which is identified as *ordinary* (o), *unusual* (u), or *minus* (–).

If the item, or class of items, is designated in Table A as *ordinary* (o), and involves a *W* or *D* area, this signifies that the object was reported in at least 2% (190 or more) of the 9,500 records, and that it involves blot contours that do exist and are reasonably consistent with the form of the reported object. There are 865 items or item classes designated as o for *W* or *D* locations.

If the item listed as o involves a *Dd* location, this signifies that the area was used by at least 50 people, that the object was reported by no fewer than two–thirds of those using the area, and involves blot contours that do exist. Table A includes 146 items classified as o for the *Dd* locations.

▲ *DIFFERENTIATING ORDINARY AND PLUS RESPONSES.* If the object reported in a response matches an item or item class that is listed as *ordinary* in Table A, the coding for form quality must always be either o or +. Most of these responses will be coded o as the frequency of + responses is quite low in all groups. Nonetheless, examiners should not be casual and neglect possible + answers. Responses that should be coded + are usually easy to distinguish. This is because the person describes more *form* details when describing the object(s) than do most people who give a similar answer. The + answers usually stand out because of the attention to form characteristics.

For example, when most people give a human figure response, they note the head, body, and legs. The *elaborated* description will also include three or four other features, such as noting some facial characteristics, mentioning the arms, waistline, and often describing the feet or shoes. Similarly, when most people describe an animal, they include mention of the head and body, and sometimes the legs. The elaborated description includes two or three additional features, such as the nose, ears, tail, feet, etc.

The decision to code + versus o does include some subjective judgement of the coder, but this usually develops easily with experience. Most protocols given by well educated persons will contain one or two + answers, but + answers also appear in the records of less well educated persons, and examiners should always be alert for this possibility.

Examiners/coders should not confuse lengthy and/or creative answers with the legitimate + answer. *Plus* responses simply contain *more* form articulation than is customary. They may also be lengthy and/or creative, but those features are not essential. Examples of + responses are shown in Table B in Chapter 10.

▲ *CODING UNUSUAL RESPONSES.* The requirement concerning appropriate form use is no different for *unusual* responses than for those coded as *ordinary*. The differentiation is based simply on whether the response has occurred in at least 2% of the 9,500 records from which Table A was created. If an item in Table A is designated as unusual (**u**), and involves a *W* or *D* area, this indicates that it appeared in fewer than the 2% criterion used to designate o answers but, in the unanimous opinion of at least three judges working independently of each other, the object is seen *quickly and easily* and is appropriate to the contours that are used. Table A includes 1,611 such items.

If an item is designated as **u** in Table A for a *Dd* area, this signifies that it was reported by fewer than 50 people but, in the unanimous opinion of at least three judges working independently of each other, it is seen *quickly and easily* and is appropriate to the contours that are involved. Table A includes 565 items designated as **u** for *Dd* locations.

▲ *FQ CODING BY EXTRAPOLATION.* Although Table A includes a large number of items identified as *ordinary* or *unusual*, it does not include all possible responses in those categories. In many instances, if a response does not appear in Table A it will probably be coded as *unusual* or *minus*. However, the examiner should make an effort at *conservative extrapolation* from items existing in Table A before reaching a decision about Form Quality because, for some answers, extrapolation will lead to the coding of **o** for an object not listed in Table A. Extrapolation simply involves a careful search of the listing of answers given in the table for those that are very similar to one reported.

For instance, a *gyroscope* is not listed for the *DS5* area of Card II, but a review of that listing indicates that a *top* is listed as **o**. A top is very similar to a gyroscope. Therefore, it is not unrealistic to also code a gyroscope as **o**. Similarly, there is no location number for Card V if the external *D10* areas are excluded, but sometimes people will exclude those areas when giving the bat, butterfly, or bird responses. In such instances it is appropriate to extrapolate from the listing for *W* responses and assign the coding of **o** because the excluded area is very minor.

Extrapolation involves a search for like shapes. If the object in a response is as bad as some of the minus answers listed in Table A, obviously it should be scored as a *minus*. Similarly, if the object in a response is similar to some of the answers listed in Table A as *unusual* it should be scored as **u**.

But a word of caution! Extrapolations are judgement calls, and it is important to avoid overgeneralization. *Be logically conservative!* At times, reported objects will have only a remote similarity to items listed in Table A. When that is the case it is best to abandon the notion of extrapolation and apply the rules for **u** versus *minus* in making the form quality decision. Some additional illustrations of extrapolation procedures are provided in the beginning section of Chapter 10.

▲ *CODING MINUS RESPONSES.* The listing of *minus* answers in Table A is limited. It includes 1,395 − items for *W* and *D* areas, and 436 − items for *Dd* locations. Those listed as *minus* have been included because they have occurred at least four times among the 9,500 protocols in the sample. A huge number of *minus* answers have not been included in Table A to avoid making the Table unwieldy.

As noted above, when an item is not included in Table A, a judgement call is required, and the majority of these answers will be coded as either *unusual* or *minus*, depending on whether the blot contours have been used appropriately. When attempts at extrapolation are not successful, the criterion for distinguishing *unusual* from *minus* answers should be applied carefully and faithfully. In other words, if the response can be seen *quickly and easily*, and does not violate the blot contours significantly, it should be coded *unusual*. Otherwise, it should be coded *minus*.

It is important to note that the blot areas used for the majority of *minus* answers *do have* some contours that are congruent with the object reported. However, the overall "fit" of the object(s) tends to violate the contours considerably. Typically, these are not responses that can be seen "quickly and easily." Many *minus* responses require the person to *create* contours that do not exist. Whenever those *nonexistent* contours are critical in defining the object, the response will always be coded as *minus*.

Also, as a rule of thumb, it is best to code questionable responses as *minus*, following the principle that one or two *minus* responses will not contribute significantly to the overall interpretation of the record. Some examiners are loathe to code a response *minus*, apparently influenced by the faulty impression that a *minus* answer will have great interpretive significance. This is not true! The majority of people, from all groups, give one or more *minus* responses. *Minus* answers become interpretively important when the frequency is high, or in some cases, when they all involve a single content.

It is also important to note that items that are listed as *minus* in Table A are not necessarily low frequency answers for all groups. For instance, the response of a face, using all of Card X inverted, is relatively commonplace among some groups of adolescents, both patients and nonpatients. It is a curious phenomenon that is not well understood, but which apparently occurs because those subjects tend to perceptually close the broken figure. Nonetheless, it is properly coded as *minus* because the person must create contours that do not exist in the blot.

▲ *MULTIPLE OBJECT RESPONSES.* Some responses will contain multiple objects that do not all have the same form quality. As a rule, the "less favorable" form quality is assigned for the entire response, **o** being more favorable than **u,** and **u** more favorable than *minus*; however, *this rule is applied only to objects that are clearly important to the overall response.*

For example, on Card III a person reports, *Two people (D9) bending over pulling on some lungs (D7) down here.* D9 as a human figure is listed as **o** in Table A and, in fact, is also a Popular response. However, *D7*, as lungs, which are important in this answer because they create a special score and are the focal point of the activity, is listed in Table A as *minus*. Thus, the form quality for the response is *minus*.

On the other hand, if one object that is not very important to the overall response has a listed form quality that is less favorable than the other objects in the answer, the more favorable form quality is assigned. For instance, a response to Card III might be, *Two people (D9) dancing around this thing in the center (D7), something like a drum.* Again, the people are listed as **o** in Table A but *D7*, as a drum, is listed as *unusual*. In this response the important objects are the two people and the drum is added somewhat casually, *maybe a drum*. Thus, the form quality scoring of *ordinary* seems to be the more appropriate. This illustrates why the Table A listing for the *D1* area of Card III lists "Humans, 2, with *D7* as a separate object" as *ordinary*, that is, the vast majority of responses to *D1* involving two people will include *D7* in a casual way and not grossly distort the use of the form characteristics of that area.

Obviously, the coder must use good judgement about the separate object(s). If the object described does not violate the contours of *D7* significantly, such as a drum or a table which would be scored as **u** if reported separately, the scoring of **o** will be appropriate. Conversely, if the *D7* is identified as an object that is clearly important to the total answer, and involves significant form distortion, such as pulling on lungs, tearing a head apart, or fighting over a submarine, the response will be scored as *minus*.

Another example could involve a response to Card II, *Two dogs (D1) in a circus doing an act, the red gives a circus atmosphere and they seem to be balancing something on their noses (D4), probably a ball.* *D*1 as dogs is Popular, however, *D*4 as a ball is not listed in Table A, and it really doesn't look much like a ball. Should the response be coded as **o**, **u**, or even *minus*? The logic conveyed by the person in giving the response may help with the final decision. The most important elements seem to be the dogs and the circus atmosphere. To this point the scoring is **o**. How important now is the ball? Probably not very much. The person has said that they are doing an act...balancing something. It is logical that the "something" might be a ball. Thus, even though *D*4 doesn't look much like a ball, the logic is consistent and the form distortion is not very serious. Therefore, the coding of **o** is probably more appropriate than a coding of either **u** or *minus*.

This issue occurs most frequently on Card X when a subject, describing several insects or underwater creatures, most of which are listed as *ordinary*, includes one that may be listed as *unusual* or even *minus*. Assuming the one listed as *unusual* or *minus* is not critical to the overall answer, the correct coding should be *ordinary*.

▲ *SUMMARY.* The importance of being as accurate as possible in form quality coding cannot be given too much emphasis. Some Rorschachers tend to be overly concrete or overly casual about scoring form quality. Both approaches do an injustice to the client. Martin Mayman, a very distinguished Rorschacher, has pointed out that form quality represents, in a microcosm, the attitude with which the person maintains a hold on the object world. In other words, form quality relates to reality testing operations and in that context should never be taken lightly.

5 ❖ Contents and Populars

The codes for contents and Populars are the least complex of all the features in the response coding. Content coding is very straightforward, consisting of abbreviations for the category in which a reported object belongs. The symbols and criteria for coding content are shown in Table 7.

TABLE 7: SYMBOLS AND CRITERIA USED FOR CODING CONTENT

Category	Symbol	Criterion
Whole Human	*H*	For responses involving a whole human form. If the response involves a *real* historical figure, such as Napoleon, Joan of Arc, etc., the content code *Ay* should be added as a secondary code.
Whole Human, Fictional or Mythological	(*H*)	For responses involving a whole human form that is fictional or mythological, such as clowns, fairies, giants, witches, fairy tale characters, angels, dwarfs, devils, ghosts, science fiction creatures that are humanoid, human-like monsters, silhouettes of human figures.
Human Detail	*Hd*	For responses involving an incomplete human form, such as an arm, head, leg, fingers, feet, the lower part of a person, a person without a head.
Human Detail, Fictional or Mythological	(*Hd*)	For responses involving an incomplete human form that is fictional or mythological such as, the head of the devil, the arm of a witch, the eyes of an angel, parts of humanoid science fiction creatures, jack-o-lantern, and all masks *except* animal masks.
Human Experience	*Hx*	Usually coded as a secondary content for answers that clearly involve the attribution of a human emotion or sensory experience to the object(s) in the response, such as *Two people who are in love looking at each other*; *A cat that is very sad*; *People who are angry at each other*; *A woman smelling something nasty*; *A very happy person*; *A man who is very excited*; *A person in great pain*. The attribution of the emotion or sensory experience must be clear and unequivocal. Answers such as, *People at a party, An angry looking face, A mean looking person*; *Two people who look tired*, are not coded *Hx* as the attribution is equivocal. *Hx* is scored as a primary content for formless *M* responses that involve the emotion or sensory experience such as love, hate, depression, happiness, sound, smell, fear, etc. These answers will also include the use of AB as a special score.
Whole Animal	*A*	For responses involving a whole animal form.
Whole Animal, Fictional or Mythological	(*A*)	For responses involving a whole animal that is fictional or mythological, such as a unicorn, dragon, magic frog, flying horse, Black Beauty, Jonathan Livingston Seagull.

TABLE 7: Continued

Category	Symbol	Criterion
Animal Detail	*Ad*	For responses involving an incomplete animal form, such as the hoof of a horse, claw of a lobster, head of a dog, animal skin.
Animal Detail, Fictional or Mythological	*(Ad)*	For responses involving an incomplete animal form that is fictional or mythological such as, the wing of Pegasus, the head of Peter Rabbit, the legs of Pooh Bear, and all animal masks.
Anatomy	*An*	For responses in which the content is skeletal, muscular, or of internal anatomy such as bone structure, skull, rib cage, heart, lungs, stomach, liver, muscle fiber, vertebrae, brain. If the response involves a tissue slide, the content *Art* should be added as secondary.
Art	*Art*	For responses of paintings, drawings, or illustrations, either abstract or definitive, art objects, such as statues, jewelry, chandelier, candelabra, crests, badges, seals, and decorations. A feather seen worn as a decoration, often seen on Card VII, also should be coded as Art. In many responses coded for Art a second content will also be coded, such as a painting of two dogs would be Art, A, a sculpture of two witches would be Art, (H), a caricature of two people bending over would be Art, H.
Anthropology	*Ay*	For responses that have a specific cultural or historical connotation such as totem, Roman helmet, Magna Carta, Santa Maria, Napoleon's hat, Cleopatra's crown, arrowhead, prehistoric axe, an Indian war bonnet.
Blood	*Bl*	For responses of blood, either human or animal.
Botany	*Bt*	For responses involving any plant life such as bushes, flowers, seaweed, trees, or parts of plant life, such as leaves, petals, tree trunk, root, bird's nest.
Clothing	*Cg*	For responses involving any article of clothing such as hat, boots, belt, dress, necktie, jacket, trousers, scarf.
Clouds	*Cl*	Used specifically for the content cloud. Variations of this category, such as fog or mist are coded *Na*.
Explosion	*Ex*	For responses involving a blast or explosion, including fireworks.
Fire	*Fi*	For responses of fire or smoke.
Food	*Fd*	Used for any edible common for humans, such as fried chicken, ice cream, fried shrimp, vegetables, cotton candy, chewing gum, steak, a filet of fish, or for animals eating a food that is natural for their species, such as a bird eating a worm or insect.

TABLE 7: Continued

Category	Symbol	Criterion
Geography	*Ge*	Used for the response of a map, specified or unspecified.
Household	*Hh*	Used for responses that include household items, such as bed, carving knife, chair, cooking utensil, cup, garden hose, glass, lamp, lawnchair, plate, rug (*animal skin rug should be coded Ad and Hh entered as a secondary content*), silverware. Some items coded *Hh* will also be coded as *Art*, such as candelabra, chandelier, or artistic pieces such as a centerpiece bowl.
Landscape	*Ls*	For responses that involve landscape, such as mountain, mountain range, hill, island, cave, rocks, desert, swamp, or seascapes, such as coral reef or underwater scene.
Nature	*Na*	Used for a broad variety of contents from the natural environment that are not coded as *Bt* or *Ls*, such as sun, moon, planet, sky, water, ocean, lake, river, ice, snow, rain, fog, mist, rainbow, storm, tornado, night, raindrop.
Science	*Sc*	For responses that are associated with, or are the direct or indirect products of science or science fiction, such as airplanes, buildings, bridges, cars, light bulb, microscope, motorcycles, motors, musical instrument, radar station, road, rocket ships, ships, space ships, trains, telescope, TV aerial, weapons, etc..
Sex	*Sx*	For responses involving sex organs or activity of a sexual nature, such as penis, vagina, buttocks, breasts (except when used to identify the sex of a human figure), testes, menstruation, abortion, intercourse. *Sx* is usually scored as a secondary content. Primary contents are typically *H*, *Hd*, or *An*.
X-ray	*Xy*	Used specifically for the content of x-ray and may include either skeletal or organs. When *xy* is coded, *An* is *not* included as a secondary code.

CODING MULTIPLE CONTENTS

Many responses will contain more than one content. *All* should be included in the coding *with two exceptions* that concern the categories Nature (*Na*), Botany (*Bt*), and Landscape (*Ls*). *Na always* takes priority over *Bt* or *Ls*. In other words, if a response includes *Na* and *Bt* and/or *Ls*, *only Na* is scored. For example, *This is an animal stepping on some stones that are in the water, he's trying to get to this bush*. This answer contains four contents, animal (*A*), stones (*Ls*), water (*Na*), and bush (*Bt*), but the correct content coding is *A,Na*.

If a response does not include *Na* but contains both *Bt* and *Ls*, only one of the two is scored. Thus, if the response were, *An animal stepping over some stones next to this bush*, the correct content coding would be *A,Bt* or *A,Ls*.

The reason for the rule concerning Nature, Botany, and Landscape is that all are included in the calculation of the *Isolation Index*, and the rule is designed to insure that no single answer will contribute excessively to that calculation.

When multiple contents are entered, they are separated by a comma, with the first representing the content that is *most* central to the response. Usually, but not always, the main content will be the first item mentioned in the response.

For instance, the response, *A painting of a person with a large hat on, standing next to a tree*, would be *Art, H, Cg, Bt*. Here, the painting is the main content, and the substance of the painting forms the additional contents. If the response had been, *Let's see, this could be a tree I suppose, and there is a person standing there, next to the tree, she's got a big hat on*, the central feature is the person even though the tree was mentioned first. Thus, the coding would be *H, Bt, Cg*.

It is quite important to include all of the contents from an answer in the coding. Some of the interpretive ratios are based on the total number of contents, and omissions in content coding can create misleading data.

▲ *UNUSUAL CONTENTS.* Some responses will include contents that do not seem to fit into one of the standard content categories. When that occurs, the unique content should be written out and entered under idiographic contents (*Id*) on the Structural Summary Blank. However, it is important to make sure that the item does not fit into one of the standard content categories before deciding to enter it idiographically.

For example, a *test tube* is a very unusual response, and at first glance, it may seem appropriate to list it idiographically because of its rarity. Nonetheless, it does fit neatly into the *Sc* category, and should be coded as such. Similarly, a *carousel* is also a fairly unusual content. Technically, it could be scored as *Sc*, using the premise that it can be considered as a product of science, but it might be more appropriate to score it as *Art* and include *Sc* as an additional content.

Similarly, it can be argued that a *boomerang* should be coded *Sc* as it is a weapon. Some might also argue that, at least, it should have an additional content code of *Art* because it is a carving. Both codes, and especially *Sc,* are appropriate, and preferable to merely recording it as *Id*.

POPULAR RESPONSES

There are 13 responses that occur with an unusually high frequency among the protocols of most groups of people. They are identified as *Popular* answers, defined using a criterion that requires the answer to appear *at least* once in every three protocols.

The presence of a Popular response is identified by the coding of *P*. When a Popular response occurs, the coding is entered in a separate column, after the coding for the content of the response.

The decision to assign the coding of *P* is an *either-or* proposition. The response is Popular, or it is not. In some instances, a response will be very similar to, but not exactly like the true Popular. The content may be altered slightly, or the location used may not coincide exactly with the requirements. These *are not* coded *P*.

The most common of these "near" Popular answers occurs on Card V, when the person identifies the figure as a *bat* or *butterfly*, but then proceeds to eliminate the external *D10* areas when identifying the location. These answers are not coded *P*.

Caution should also be exercised concerning the blot position when deciding whether a response is to be coded as *P*. The blot need not be in the upright position for the coding of *P* to be assigned but, in the case of several of the Popular answers, the head of the human or animal reported must be identified as being in the same position *as if* the blot were upright. This rule is applicable to the *P* responses for Cards I, II, III, IV, V, VII, VIII, and IX.

For example, *P* should be scored for the *bat* and *butterfly* responses to Cards I and V, if the answer is a *W* when the card is inverted, *provided* that the head area identified is the same as would be the case if the card were upright. The *Popular* animal response to the *D1* area of Card VIII is often reported with the card inverted, but the head is always reported in the same area as if the card were in the upright position.

The listing of Popular responses used in the Comprehensive System is shown in Table 8, with the location requirement and criterion for each.

TABLE 8: POPULAR RESPONSES USED IN THE COMPREHENSIVE SYSTEM

Card	Location	Criterion
I	*W*	Bat, with the true apex of the blot being identified as the top portion of the bat, and *always* involving the whole blot.
I	*W*	Butterfly, with the true apex of the blot being identified as the top portion of the butterfly, and *always* involving the whole blot.
II	*D1*	Animal, specifically identified as bear, dog, elephant, or lamb. The response is usually the head or upper body, however, responses involving the whole animal are also coded *P*.
III	*D9*	Human figure or representations thereof such as dolls, caricatures, etc. If *D1* is used as two human figures, *D7* or *Dd*31 should *not* be reported as part of the human figure if the coding *P* is to be applied.
IV	*W or D7*	Human or human-like figure such as giant, monster, science fiction creature, etc. Animal figures are not coded as *P*.
V	*W*	Bat, with the true apex of the blot being identified as the top portion of the bat, and *always* involving the whole blot.
V	*W*	Butterfly, with the true apex of the blot being identified as the top portion of the butterfly, and *always* involving the whole blot.
VI	*W or D1*	Animal skin, hide, rug, or pelt. Often, the skin, hide, or pelt will be included in the description of a whole animal, such as a cat or fox, either in natural or unnatural form. The decision about whether to code *P* in these responses is based on whether the skin or hide is actually mentioned, or clearly implied in the description given by the client.
VII	*D9*	Human head or face, specifically identified as female, child, or Indian, or with gender not identified. This Popular is usually embedded in answers given to the larger areas *D1*, *D2*, or *Dd*23. If *D1* is used, the upper segment (*D5*) is usually identified as hair, feather, etc. If the response includes the entire *D2* or *Dd*23 areas, *P* is coded only if the head or face is restricted to the *D9* area.
VIII	*D1*	Whole animal figure, usually of the canine, feline, or rodent varieties, with the head of the animal adjacent to the *D4* area.
IX	*D3*	Human or human-like figure such as witch, giant, monster, science fiction creature, etc.
X	*D1*	Crab, with all appendages restricted to the *D1* area.
X	*D1*	Spider, with all appendages restricted to the *D1* area.

6 ❖ Organizational Activity

Organizational activity is another feature that *may* occur in the response. Answers in which organization occurs are assigned a numerical value, called a Z score. Individual Z scores have no interpretive value but, the frequency with which they occur (*Zf*) and the sum of the values (*ZSum*), provides important information concerning the extent to which the person tends to organize new stimulus fields, and whether the effort usually is efficient.

When organizing activity occurs, relationships are established between elements of the stimulus field. In most of the Rorschach figures, it is easier to create a response to a common detail area of the blot than to deliver a *W* answer. This is because most of the common detail areas are readily identifiable as one or more possible objects. Thus, when the person chooses to give a *W* answer, some more extensive organization of the field is required.

The economical person may choose to report objects, singularly, or as a pair using the symmetry. These types of answers do not require that a relationship be created between the object(s), or with other parts of the blot. That occurs only when the person organizes the material in the field in a way that creates a meaningful relationship. For instance, the *D*1 area of Card VIII is frequently identified as an animal. It is a Popular response. Some simply report an animal to the *D*1 area while others report an animal on each side of the blot. Both are simple answers. Conversely, many people report that the animal(s) are climbing a tree or mountain, or turn the card and report that the animal is walking across some rocks. These represent higher levels of cognitive activity that organize the stimulus field at a more sophisticated level, and are denoted by a *Z* score.

A Z score is assigned to any response that *includes form,* and meets at least one of the following criteria:

1. **ZW**. Is a Whole response that has a *DQ* coding of **+**, **o**, or **v/+** (answers that have a *DQ* coding of **v** are never assigned a Z score).

2. **ZA**. Is a response in which two or more separate objects, identified in adjacent detail areas of the blot (*areas that touch*), are reported in a meaningful relation.

3. **ZD**. Is a response in which two or more separate objects, identified in non-adjacent (*distant*) detail areas of the blot (*areas that do not touch*), are reported in a meaningful relationship.

4. **ZS**. Is a response in which white space is integrated with other areas of the blot in forming a response. Responses using *only* white space are not assigned a Z score.

It will be noted that two of the criteria, (1) *ZW* and (4) *ZS*, pertain to how the blot has been used. Any *W* response that is not *Wv*, and any response in which white space is used as part, *but not all*, of the answer qualify as *Z*.

The other criteria, (2) *ZA*, involving blot areas that are adjacent and (3) *ZD*, involving blot areas that are not adjacent, require that *separate or discrete* objects be reported in a *meaningful* relationship. If either of these criteria are met, the *DQ* coding will be + or **v/+**, to reflect the synthesizing activity that has occurred, such as, *Two people looking at each other*; *An animal walking across a creek*; *Fire coming out of a rocket*; *A monster sitting on a stump*, etc.

Form must always be used in responses coded *Z*. Thus, *some paint splotches*, as a *DQv* response, that has a determinant coding of *C*, is not afforded a *Z score*. Likewise, *Some smoke, it's all grey like smoke*, that has a determinant coding of *C'*, is not assigned a *Z* score. *Wv* responses are not assigned *Z* scores because they do not have specific form requirements.

If white space use qualifies for a *Z* score, other areas of the blot *must also* be used. For instance, the white areas of Card I are often reported as eyes and/or mouth in answers such as, *The whole thing looks like a mask of some sort, like a halloween mask, these are the eyes*. Similarly, the *DS5* area of Card II is often reported as a space ship, with the red *D3* area identified as an exhaust. Both of these answers meet the criteria for *Z*. On the other hand, if *DS5* is simply reported as a rocket, but no other blot area is used, the criterion for *Z* is not met.

Caution should be exercised about assuming an integration of white space with other blot areas. When defining the location of an object, a person may outline a blot area that includes white space *but fail to specify that the white space is being used as part of the response*. When this happens *ZS* should *not* be scored.

The erroneous scoring of *ZS* occurs most often on Cards III and X in which the blot areas are more broken. Sometimes parts of the blot are collectively identified as a face, and *D* or *Dd* areas are identified as eyes, nose, mouth, ears, beard, etc. When the person specifies the area being used, arbitrary lines are created which include the various parts and also encompass much of the white ground, leading to the logical conclusion that the white is also being integrated. *But this is not true*. In most of these answers the person is simply manifesting the Gestalt principle of closure and *ignoring* the white background. Thus *ZS* is not scored.

There are some face responses to Cards III and X in which the white space is integrated. These are answers that contain specific use of the white area as in,

"It's the face of a clown, these are the eyes and the nose and he has *white* paint on." Naturally, *ZS* is scored for this type of answer.

Once it is apparent that at least one of the four criteria for *Z* exists in a response, the next step is to select the appropriate value to assign. The values differ, card by card, and by which of the criteria are applicable. The values, shown in Table 9, increase in relation to the complexity and/or effort required.

TABLE 9: ORGANIZATIONAL (Z) VALUES FOR EACH OF THE 10 CARDS

CARD	Type of Organizational Activity			
	W (DQ: +, v/+, o)	Adjacent Detail	Distant Detail	White Space Integration
I	1.0	4.0	6.0	3.5
II	4.5	3.0	5.5	4.5
III	5.5	3.0	4.0	4.5
IV	2.0	4.0	3.5	5.0
V	1.0	2.5	5.0	4.0
VI	2.5	2.5	6.0	6.5
VII	2.5	1.0	3.0	4.0
VIII	4.5	3.0	3.0	4.0
IX	5.5	2.5	4.5	5.0
X	5.5	4.0	4.5	6.0

If more than one of the criteria for *Z* exists in a response, *the higher value is assigned.* For instance, if a response to the whole Card I is, *A person in the middle (D4), and two people dancing around her (D2)*, the criteria for *ZW* (Whole) and *ZA* (Adjacent Detail) are both positive. The Card I value for *ZW* is 1.0 versus 4.0 for *ZA*. Thus, the higher value of 4.0 is assigned to the response.

The *Z* values are entered after the codes for content and Popular such as is shown below for a whole response to Card VIII.

$$W + FM^a.FCo\ (2)\ A,\ Ls\ P\ 4.5$$

7 ❖ Special Scores

The final task in coding the Rorschach response is to determine if the answer has any of the features that require the addition of one or more *Special Scores*. Like most other components in the Rorschach lexicon used to identify features of a response, Special Scores are really codes, rather than numerical scores. They are used to signify the presence of an unusual characteristic in the response.

The use of Special Scores permits quantification of many features of responses that have been interpreted more qualitatively in the past. Currently, there are fifteen Special Scores in the Comprehensive System. Six, identify unusual verbalizations, one is used for perseverations, four pertain to special features of content, two are used to differentiate answers containing human representations, one is for personalized answers, and one identifies a special color phenomenon.

UNUSUAL VERBALIZATIONS

Unusual verbalizations are an important element in the study of cognitive activity, especially issues of dysfunction. When some form of cognitive slippage occurs, whether momentary or for a longer interval, it will often manifest verbally. Evidence of cognitive slippage appears in the verbiage of most adults from time to time, and even more often among children. Few people express themselves clearly and precisely *all* of the time, and most everyone can identify instances in which their logic or judgement faltered temporarily.

Similar slips in cognitive activity sometimes occur when a person is taking the Rorschach, and the appropriate identification of them can provide useful information when evaluating the thinking of the person. These cognitive mishaps are evidenced in Rorschach responses in any of three ways: (1) *Deviant Verbalizations*, (2) *Inappropriate Combinations*, or (3) *Inappropriate Logic*.

Six Special Scores are used to note the presence of some sort of cognitive disarray in Rorschach answers. Two are for the Deviant Verbalizations (*DV* and *DR*), three for the Inappropriate Combinations (*INCOM, FABCOM, CONTAM*), and one for Inappropriate Logic (*ALOG*).

Four of the six Special Scores are also differentiated for bizarreness, and designated as either *Level 1* or *Level 2*. The four include the two used for Deviant Verbalizations (*DV* and *DR*), and two of the three scores used to identify Inappropriate Combinations (*INCOM* and *FABCOM*). This differentiation is necessary because a considerable range of dysfunction exists within each category.

▲   *LEVEL 1 - LEVEL 2 DIFFERENTIATION.* The Level 1 versus Level 2 differentation is designed to identify those responses that represent mild or modest forms of cognitive mismanagement as contrasted with those that reflect more serious forms of cognitive disarray. Although there is some subjectivity in making these differentiations, they are usually accomplished quite reliably by using the criteria of bizarreness versus naive inappropriateness.

When making these discriminations, the scorer should attempt to gauge the extent to which the person disregards reality when giving the answer. In other words, does the cognitive disarray reflected in the answer represent a casual form of ideational negligence, or is it more the result of strained, disrupted, inappropriate thinking that departs rather noticeably from reality.

♦ *Level 1 Responses.* A value of 1 is assigned to those answers in which a mild or relatively modest instance of illogical, fluid, peculiar, or circumstantial thinking is present. Although the Level 1 responses meet the criterion for the assigned Special Score, usually they are not markedly different from the cognitive slips that often occur when people do not pay close attention to how they are expressing themselves, or to the judgements that they are making.

In other words, although the Level 1 Scores do reflect inapplicable word use, detachment from the task, or faulty judgement, their quality is *not* really bizarre. Instead, they typically sound like the products of careless word selection, immaturity, limited education, or judgements that simply are not well thought through.

♦ *Level 2 Responses.* A value of 2 is assigned to those answers which reflect more severe instances of dissociated, illogical, fluid, or circumstantial thinking. Level 2 responses deviate markedly in the flawed judgement that is conveyed, the very unusual detachment from the task, or mode of expression that is used.

Level 2 responses stand out because they are manifestly inappropriate or bizarre. They seldom leave doubt concerning their scoring. When a scorer has doubts about whether a response meets the Level 2 criterion, a conservative decision should be adopted, and the Level 1 score assigned to the answer.

Extraneous elements such as age, educational level, or cultural background *should not be considered* in making the distinction between Level 1 and Level 2. These elements are considered when the Special Scores *are interpreted.* They should never be used as some artificial guideline from which decisions about coding are made.

▲ *DEVIANT VERBALIZATIONS.* There are two Special Scores for Deviant Verbalizations (*DV* and *DR*). One is used to identify instances in which cognitive mishaps have led to inappropriate word selection. The second identifies segments of a response which have a strange quality. Both are characterized by modes of expression that tend to impede the person's ability to communicate clearly.

♦ *1. Deviant Verbalization (DV).* *DV* is assigned to those answers in which an inapplicable word or words have been used. *DV*'s appear in either of two forms, *neologisms* or *redundancies*, both of which create the impression of oddity in the answer. *DV* responses are almost always easy to detect because the word(s) that is inappropriate stands out in the answer.

a. *Neologism.* Involving the use of an inapplicable word, or neologism, in place of an appropriate word that falls well within the person's verbal capacity. Some examples, differentiated by Level 1 and Level 2 are:

Response	Score
Spiders trying to *squish* each other	DV1
A woman with a *disrethal* air about her	DV2
Some bacteria you might see under a *telescope*	DV2
The *public* arch of somebody	DV2
A fly *plopping*	DV1
A *misappropriated* person, like from Russia	DV1
These flowers have a *butterscotchy* center	DV1
This blood is all *smushy*	DV1
These are snakes in the Bible, from the garden of *evil*	DV2
These people are *cahooping* on this rock	DV2

At times, a person may use the wrong word when identifying parts of an object, such as the word *tentacles* instead of *antennae* when describing a butterfly. These *are not* coded *DV*. They are *INCOM*'s.

b. *Redundancy*. Involving the odd use of language in which the person identifies *twice* the nature of the objects(s) reported. Some examples, differentiated by Level 1 and Level 2 are:

Response	Score
The *two twin* lips of a vagina	DV2
A *tiny little* bird (**Note:** The wording *little tiny* would not be a *DV*)	DV1
The *dead corpse* of a person	DV1
A *trio of three* people	DV2
A *matched brace* of lungs	DV2
It's empty, like a *hollow void*	DV1
Like the *double two* balls on a pawnbroker's sign	DV2

♦ *2. Deviant Response (DR)*. DR is assigned for answers that have a strange or peculiar quality because the person has injected wording that reflects a tendency to detach from, or to distort, the task at hand. Some *DR*'s are coded when the person injects a phrase that is not relevant to the task. Other *DR*'s reflect answers in which the person tends to ramble inappropriately. Deviant Responses are not necessarily bizarre, but the verbiage clearly is inappropriate to the task at hand. Some *DR* responses will also contain a *DV*. When this occurs, *only* the *DR* is coded. *DR* answers will manifest in either of two ways.

a. *Inappropriate Phrases*. These are answers that include phrases that are inappropriate, or completely irrelevant, to the response or the task at hand. It is important to distinguish short, parenthetical statements, such as, "These are really hard to figure out," or "Oh, we're getting color for a change," or "I guess I could find a lot of things here if I try," from the true *DR* answer.

The *DR* coding for inappropriate phrases is limited to phrases embedded in the response itself, and offered in relation to the response. They represent comments that make the answer more unusual than should be the case. They are extraneous to the task, but for some reason, the person has inserted them in the verbiage concerning the response.

Most *DR*'s will be benign, but those coded as *DR2* tend to reflect problems in maintaining adequate ideational control. Some illustrations, differentiated by Level 1 and Level 2 are shown below:

Response	Score
It could be oysters *but I guess they're out of season*	DR1
It might be a cat, *my father always hated cats*	DR1
It's some kind of bug that *no one has ever seen*	DR2
It looks like the face of Clinton *if you're a Democrat*	DR2
A bird, *but I wanted to see a butterfly*	DR2
A vagina, *whoever made these was preoccupied*	DR1

b. *Circumstantial Responses*. Involving answers that are fluid or rambling in which the person becomes inappropriately elaborative in ways that seem to ignore the task. Most examiners find the circumstantial *DR* easy to detect because so much of the verbiage has little relevance to the response. It represents a form of ideational distraction from the task, and illustrates the marked difficulty that the person has in achieving a definition of the object or bringing closure to the response.

Circumstantial *DR*'s are not necessarily long explications, and caution should be exercised to avoid confusing the circumstantial *DR* response with answers that are "stilted," but on target, or answers that are very detailed, but appropriate to the task.

Some people struggle to explain themselves, and their wording often seems stilted. For instance, a person might say, *Over here, no wait. O.k., over here it seems like a head, maybe. Yes a head, like the head of ah, ah, I'll guess a dog. No wait, not a dog, a fox is better.* It is a strained response, but it is not circumstantial. The person works to stay on target. It *is not* coded *DR*.

In a similar context, some people elaborate in considerable detail when giving a response, or when describing it in the Inquiry. These are appropriate answers, provided the person stays on target and simply provides considerable detail as he or she verbalizes the organization of the response.

In the circumstantial *DR*, the individual tends to wander off target and, in some instances, may actually never return to the response object. Some examples, differentiated by Level 1 and Level 2 are shown below:

Response	Score
I'm not sure what this could be, something like an animal nose, maybe equine or bovine, *like in that play that was so filled with passions and psychological drama. I saw it twice.* Yes, the nose of a horse.	DR2
It's like chicken, like you get from Colonel Sanders, *but my mother makes it better, I think I must be getting hungry.*	DR1
It's like a map of Ireland, maybe not Ireland, maybe someplace else, but it could be Ireland. *I don't know much about Ireland but I know about Mexico.*	DR2
Maybe two snakes, *I always hated snakes, my brother used to tease me about it something awful.*	DR1
It looks like some trees way off on a hill, it looks so peaceful, *like a place that you'd want to go to get away from everything.*	DR1
It looks like oil on water and garbage too, just a lot of pollution with all the foul impurities that filthy people have thrown into the environment. *People really are filthy, they ought to make laws to eliminate them or force them to wallow in their own filth.*	DR2

♦ *INAPPROPRIATE COMBINATIONS.* There are three Special Scores (*INCOM, FABCOM,* and *CONTAM*) used to identify responses in which unreal features are reported concerning an object, implausible relationships are reported or inferred between objects, implausible activities are attributed to objects, or an inappropriate condensation of impressions occurs in a manner that violates reality. Two of the three types of inappropriate combinatory responses, (*INCOM* and *FABCOM*) are also differentiated as Level 1 or Level 2.

1. Incongruous Combinations (<u>INCOM</u>). The *INCOM* code is used to identify responses in which one or more highly implausible, or impossible, features or activities are attributed to a *single* object. If the object is portrayed as in a cartoon, the *INCOM* is not assigned as cartoon characters can take any form, or engage in activities that are otherwise implausible.

As with the *DV* and *DR* answers, Level 1 and Level 2 distinctions are made in terms of bizarreness. Level 1 *INCOM* responses tend to be casual and/or benign, whereas the Level 2 *INCOM* is strange and unrealistic. Some examples, differentiated as Level 1 and Level 2 are:

Response	Score
A frog with *four testicles*	INCOM2
A bat, here are the wings, body and these are his *hands*	INCOM1
A woman with the *head of a chicken*	INCOM2
Red bears	INCOM1
A marvelous penis *with wings*	INCOM2
A man with *yellow* eyes	INCOM1
A dog there, he's *laughing out loud*	INCOM2
A person with *two heads*	INCOM2
A spider with a lot of *antlers* sticking out	INCOM1
A cat's face, it looks like he's *smiling*	INCOM1

2. Fabulized Combination (<u>FABCOM</u>). The *FABCOM* code is used to identify answers in which an implausible, or impossible, relationship is posited to exist between two or more objects. *FABCOM* is also scored for implausible transparencies. Except for transparencies, *FABCOM* answers *always* include two or more objects.

FABCOM responses are differentiated as Level 1 and Level 2 using the criterion of bizzareness as a basic guideline. Level 1 *FABCOM's* often include answers which, if identified as a cartoon, would not have a Special Score. The Level 2 *FABCOM's* are much more striking or bizarre in the manner by which they violate reality. Implausible transparencies are *always* coded as Level 2. Some examples, differentiated as Level 1 and Level 2 are:

Response	Score
Two chickens holding *basketballs*	FABCOM1
Two woman attacking a *submarine*	FABCOM2
Two ants *dancing*	FABCOM1
There is a big man sitting there and you *can see his heart pumping*	FABCOM2
Some mice on a *merry-go-round*	FABCOM1
The head of a rabbit with *smoke coming out of his eyes*	FABCOM2
Two dogs there, they are doing a *high five*	FABCOM1
It looks like a lot of insects *having a party*	FABCOM1
Two beavers *trimming* a Christmas tree	FABCOM1

♦ *3. Contamination (CONTAM).* This is the most bizarre of the inappropriate combinations. The *CONTAM* represents two or more impressions that have been fused into a single response in a manner that clearly violates reality. The process of fusion causes impairment to the adequacy of either impression in contrast to the situation where they might be reported separately.

Whereas the *INCOM* combines impressions from discrete blot areas into a single implausible object, the *CONTAM* response involves the use of a single discrete area. In effect, one response has been psychologically overlaid another, as in a photographic double exposure.

Contaminations often, but not always, include the use of a neologism or other peculiar verbalizations to describe the object. A classic illustration of the neologistic *CONTAM* is the condensation of the front view of a bug and the front view of an ox into, *The face of a bug-ox.* Another involves viewing Card III upright, and then inverted, and then concluding that the center red *D3* is, *No doubt a butterflower*, apparently fusing the impressions of a flower and a butterfly.

In other instances, the strained logic that characterizes the *CONTAM* is more directly manifest as in, *It looks like blood, and an island, it must be a bloody island* or *It looks like fire and it looks like a mountain so it must be some sort of a fire mountain.*

Some Contaminations are less obvious or dramatic in the basic response and only become apparent in the Inquiry. A response to the whole Card I serves as a good illustration:

Response	Inquiry
It's a butterfly	E: (Rpts Ss resp) S: These are his wings (*D2*) and his body (*D4*) and here are his eyes (*DdS26*) and mouth (*DdS29*) and ears (*Dd28*)

In this answer the subject has fused the *Popular* butterfly response with a face response. The form quality for both is *ordinary* and thus the coding for the entire response is:

WSo Fo A P 3.5 CONTAM

If a response is coded *CONTAM*, none of the other Special Scores for unusual verbalizations (*DV, DR, INCOM, FABCOM, ALOG*) should be included in the scoring *even though some of the wording* of the response meets the criteria for them.

▲ *INAPPROPRIATE LOGIC (ALOG).* The *ALOG* coding is assigned whenever the person, *without prompting*, uses strained, unconventional reasoning to justify the answer. It represents a loose and simplistic form of thinking that breeds very flawed judgement.

Often, the *ALOG* is readily identifiable by a concrete "because" factor that is articulated by the person to justify a conclusion. Usually, this manifests as an emphasis on features such as size, spatial elements, coloring, or some features of the object, in a very illogical manner, to justify the stated characteristic of the object. Some examples are:

> This must be the north pole because it is at the top of the card
>
> He must be a coal miner because he's all black
>
> It must be lettuce because it's next to this rabbit
>
> It has to be a giant bird because it takes up all of it [the card]

The *ALOG* is coded *only* when the strained logic is offered spontaneously, and without any prompting by the examiner. Frequently, *ALOG* answers are evident in the basic response but, sometimes, they may occur at the onset of the Inquiry to a response, or in response to a question asked by the examiner regarding a key word *that was given in the basic response*. Some examples are below with the wording that confirms the *ALOG* shown in italics.

Response	Inquiry
That must be a giant	E:(Rpts Ss resp) S:Here's his head & arms, it must be a giant *cuz he's got those big feet*
That ll an evil person	E: (Rpts Ss resp) S: Here's his head & hat & legs E: U said he is an evil person S: *He must be, he's wearing a black hat*
That ll a cat	E: (Rpts Ss resp) S: There's his head & legs, *he must be dead because you can't see his eyes.*
That ll the face of a sad man	E: (Rpts Ss resp) S: Here r the eyes and nose and mouth and he has a mustache E: U said it's a sad man? S: *It has to be, his mustache droops*
Two dragons eating a woman	E: (Rpts Ss resp) S: She's in the middl & thyr on each side E: I'm not sur I c it lik u are S: Well her head is already gone, these thgs *r so big, thy must be dragons, thy r the only one tht eat women*

In two of the examples above (evil person and sad man), a key word mentioned in the response was inquired and an *ALOG* answer resulted. In neither instance was the *ALOG* provoked. In two of the other three examples, the *ALOG* was offered spontaneously in the Inquiry, following the repeat of the response. In the third, the *ALOG* followed a generalized request for clarification.

At times, flawed logic manifests during the Inquiry in response to specific questions from the examiner that *are not* related to a key word in the response proper. Even though the flawed logic exists, *ALOG* should *not* be scored because it may have been provoked by the question or by the general nature of the Inquiry task as the person works to explain a response. For instance:

Response	Inquiry
It ll two people doing smthg, mayb dancing	E: (Rpts Ss resp)
	S: Yes, there are two of them, one here and one here, c the heads & legs, they r bent over lik in a dance, probably African people
	E: African people?
	S: Well thyr dark colored, black, I guess that other thing (points to *D7*) *must b a drum cuz that's what they dance around, they do that all the time*

The flawed logic (*must be a drum, that's what they dance around*) is quite obvious, but the issue is whether it was provoked. The examiner's question (*African people*) may or may not have provoked it, but it does seem certain that it would not have occurred if the examiner had not asked the question. Thus, it should not be coded as *ALOG*. In this instance, it is appropriate to include a *DR* in the coding to reflect the strained reasoning and the concreteness that is added, (*they do that all the time*).

PERSEVERATION

The Special Score (*PSV*) is used to indicate the presence of any of three kinds of answers. One is when two or more almost identical responses are given to the same card. A second reflect instances in which a previously given response is alluded to again when the person is responding to a different card. The third is the situation in which the person redundantly gives the same answer across several cards. These sorts of responses reflect forms of perseveration that may be caused by cognitive inflexibility, cognitive dysfunction, or a marked psychological preoccupation.

Although it is clear that at least three types of perseveration may occur, all are assigned the same Special Score, *PSV*. Only one form of coding is used because there are no validation data from which to argue that each type of perseveration should be identified separately, even though logic suggests that the sorts of cognitive dysfunction and/or psychological preoccupation that they reflect are probably quite different.

♦ *1. Within Card Perseveration.* The Within Card *PSV* responses are consecutive answers in which the *same location, DQ, determinant(s), FQ, content, and same Z score*, if one has been assigned, appear in both answers. The specific content may change slightly, but the content category remains the same. Special Scores do not have to be the same in both answers.

The most common instance of the Within Card *PSV* occurs to Card V, to which the person first gives the response "bat," (*Wo Fo A P 1.0*) and then gives the response "bird," (*Wo Fo A 1.0*) which is coded identically except it is not *Popular.* Replication of the *P* coding is *not* essential to code a Within Card PSV, but all other codes, except special scores, must be identical and the responses must occur consecutively.

♦ *2. Content Perseveration.* Whereas the Within Card *PSV* is only for consecutive responses within a single card, Content *PSV* usually does not occur within the same card. These are answers in which the person identifies the object as *the same one* seen previously. The coding of the second answer need not be the same as the first, and often the codings will differ quite significantly.

For instance, an individual may report two people fighting on one card, and then indicate, *Oh, there are those people again, but they are not fighting now.* The critical issue in coding Content perseveration is that the person identifies the new object as being the same as one reported in an earlier response.

♦ *3. Mechanical Perseveration.* A third type of perseveration response is found most frequently among people who are intellectually and/or neurologically impaired. Usually, this type of perseveration occurs in brief and simplistic records. The person *mechanistically reports* the same object over and over. Card I is a bat, Card II is a bat, Card III is another bat, etc.

People who perseverate mechanistically are likely to give records of less than 14 answers, that is, invalid records. If this occurs, the examiner should weigh carefully the merits of attempting to retest the individual.

SPECIAL CONTENT CHARACTERISTICS

Some studies have focused on the special issues of content, and especially those features of responses that tend to reflect specific cognitive features or projected characteristics of the self. These are response characteristics that go beyond simple levels of coding for content. As such, they require some form of special scoring to denote the presence of these characteristics. Four Special Scores have been devised for this purpose. Each relates to some characteristics of thinking and/or issues of self image and interpersonal relations.

▲ *ABSTRACT CONTENT (AB).* The *AB* Special Score is used for two classes of answers, each of which incorporate a clear and specific symbolic representation. The first class of *AB* answers are those for which the only content code is *Human Experience (Hx)*, used to note human emotion or sensory experience. These are *DQv* answers that contain a formless *M* determinant, such as, *This whole thing represents depression, it's all black and gloomy looking* (Wv Mp.C' Hx AB); *It's all anger, the intense colors are blended together* (Wv Ma.C.Y Hx AB); or, *It's a mess, it's like a tremendously loud sound* (Wv Ma Hx AB).

The second class of *AB* answers are those in which *form is used*, and the person also articulates a *clear and specific symbolic representation* in the response. In some instances, a symbolic meaning is attributed directly to an object as in, "This statue *represents the love of life*" (Do Fu Art AB). In other responses, *a separate* blot feature is used to denote the symbolic representation that is attributed to the formed object(s) such as, "These are two people in love, longing for each other. *The middle red part shows their love and longing*" (D+ Ma.Co 2 H,Hx P 4.0 AB)

Abstract paintings *are not* scored AB unless a specific representation is included. Some examples of this class of *AB* answers are:

> A statue representing communist tyranny
>
> A state flag with the forests and rivers represented
>
> Some people in a modern dance representing the beauty of women
>
> A heart, it's a symbol for Valentine's day
>
> Two animals with blood on them and the person who drew this put this red down here to symbolize their pain
>
> A mask that represents evil
>
> An abstract painting that depicts the agony of life
>
> A Blake painting of man's struggle for purity
>
> Two statues that illustrate how children get along
>
> Two people holding hands, they're blue to symbolize their serenity

▲ *AGGRESSIVE MOVEMENT (AG).* The AG coding is used for any movement response (*M, FM, or m*) in which the action is clearly aggressive, such as fighting, breaking, arguing, looking very angry, etc. The aggression *must* be occurring. Caution should be exercised to avoid coding *AG* for responses in which the object has been subjected to aggression, such as, "A bear that has been shot," or "A ship that has been bombed." These *are not* AG responses. Similarly, an explosion *per se* is not *AG*, but something *being* destroyed by an explosion is *AG*. Some examples are:

The face of a man, he's furious about something
It looks like a bullet smashing through something
It looks like a piece of denim that's being torn
Two people arguing about something
Two insects are trying to knock down this post
It looks like a man glaring right at you

▲ *COOPERATIVE MOVEMENT (COP).* The *COP* coding is assigned to any movement response (*M, FM, or m*) involving two or more objects in which the interaction is *clearly* positive or cooperative. The positive or cooperative characteristic of the interaction must be *unequivocal*. Thus, two people looking at something, or two people talking are *not* scored *COP*. Dancing will be *always* be coded as *COP*, provided two or more objects are involved. Some responses will be coded for both *AG* and *COP* when humans or animals are cooperating in the aggressive act. Some examples are:

Two men lifting something up
Two insects trying to knock down this post
Two people leaning toward each other, sharing a secret
Three people doing a dance together
A bird feeding her young
Two children playing on a see-saw
Two wolves attacking some other animal

▲ *MORBID CONTENT (MOR).* The MOR coding is used for any response in which an object is identified by either of two classes of characteristics:

1. Identification of the object as dead, destroyed, ruined, spoiled, damaged, injured, or broken.

    Some examples are: a *broken* mirror, a *dead* dog, a *worn out* pair of boots, a bear that is *hurt*, a *wound*, a *torn* coat, a *decaying* leaf, a lab *slide* of an amoeba, some roots that have been *torn out* of the ground, a *bleeding* face, a *broken down* house, a *battered* butterfly, etc.

2. Attribution to an object of a clearly dysphoric feeling or characteristic. Examples are, a *gloomy* house, a *sad* tree, an *unhappy* person, a person *crying*, *depression*, etc.

HUMAN REPRESENTATIONAL RESPONSES

Most all protocols will contain some answers in which there is a form of human representation. These responses relate, in some ways, to the manner in which people perceive and/or interact with others. Human representational answers are identified by the other codings that have been assigned to the response, and then differentiated, using two Special Scores, as "good" (*GHR*) or "poor" (*PHR*).

Typically, human representational answers will be easily identified because they include one or more of the codings for human content, *H*, (*H*), *Hd*, (*Hd*), or *Hx*. However, in some responses, human-like features will be manifest in other ways. For instance, *A rabbit dancing a ballet*, would have a determinant coding of *M* because of the human-like activity. In a similar vein, *Two dogs playing*, would be assigned the Special Score *COP* because of the attribution of a positive interaction.

In this context, Human Representational Responses are defined as those answers which meet any of the following three criteria:

1. Responses that contain any Human Content Coding [*H*, (*H*), *Hd*, (*Hd*), *Hx*].
2. Responses which contain the determinant *M*.
3. FM responses that have *COP* or *AG* special scores.

In the course of entering codes pertaining to other response features, each answer should also be reviewed to determine if any of the coding criteria for defining human representational answers is met. If so, the scorer then determines which of the two Special Scores, *GHR* or *PHR*, is appropriate by using the sequence of steps that is shown in Table 10.

TABLE 10. STEPS USED TO ASSIGN GOOD (*GHR*) OR POOR (*PHR*) DESIGNATIONS TO HUMAN REPRESENTATIONAL RESPONSES

1. Score *GHR* for answers containing a Pure *H* coding that also *have all* of the following:
   (a) Form Quality of *FQ+*, *FQo* or *FQu*
   (b) No cognitive special scores except *DV*
   (c) No special scores of *AG* or *MOR*

2. Score *PHR* for answers that have either:
   (a) *FQ* minus or *FQ*none (No Form), or
   (b) *FQ+*, *FQo* or *FQu* and have an *ALOG*, *CONTAM*, or *any* Level 2 cognitive special score

3. Score *GHR* for any remaining human representational answers that have the special score *COP*, *but do not* have the special score *AG*

4. Score *PHR* for any remaining human representational answers that have either:
   (a) The special scores *FABCOM* or *MOR*
   (b) The content score *An*

5. Score *GHR* for any remaining human representational answers to Cards III, IV, VII, and IX that are coded Popular

6. Score *PHR* for any remaining human represential answers that have any of the following:
   (a) The special scores *AG*, *INCOM*, or *DR*
   (b) An *Hd* coding [not (*Hd*) coding]

7. Score *GHR* for all remaining human representational answers

These steps are followed *in order* until a coding decision is made. Assume, for instance, that an answer is coded *Do Fo H*. It meets the criteria listed in Step 1 for *GHR*. It is a Pure *H* response, with o form quality, and has no Special Scores. Conversely, if the coding were *Do Fo Hd*, the decision would not be made at Step 1 because the content is *Hd*, rather than Pure *H*. The answer would finally be classified as *PHR* at Step 6 because of the *Hd* content coding. Other illustrations, showing the step at which the coding decision is made, are shown below:

Card	Response Coding	GHR/PHR Decision
III	*D+ Ma.FYo 2 H,Cg P 3.0 FABCOM*	Coded *PHR* at Step 4
IX	*DSo FC'o (Hd)*	Coded *GHR* at Step 7
VIII	*W+ FMa.FCo 2 A,Bt 4.5 COP, ALOG*	Coded *PHR* at Step 2
VII	*D+ Ma.mpo 2 Hd, Art P 3.0 DV*	Coded *GHR* at Step 5

PERSONALIZED ANSWERS

Many responses contain personal pronouns such as I, me, my, or we. Most are used naturally in the course of articulating a response such as, "It looks like a bat to me," or "I think that it looks like two people." However, there are instances in which these forms of self reference are used as part of the justification for an answer. When that occurs a Special Score is required as it signals a form of defensiveness.

▲ *PERSONAL (PER)*. The *PER* code is assigned to any response in which the person refers to personal knowledge or experience as part of the basis for justifying and/or clarifying a response. Ordinarily, *PER* responses include the use of a personal pronoun, I, me, my or we, but in some instances the personal knowledge or experience is conveyed without a personal pronoun being employed. In these cases, the examiner should *be convinced* that the individual is injecting personal knowledge or experience to *justify* the response rather than simply offering commentary. For instance, comments such as, *They used them a long time ago*, or *I've never seen one but I think they are like that* or *I don't like them* are not *PER*. Some examples of *PER* are:

We had one like that once

I see them all the time in the yard

I used to make them like this

They make you wear ones like it in the army

My father showed me some once

If you ever took biology you know they look like that

I bought one like it for my daughter

My grandfather used to collect them

I've seen one's like that on TV

You know, like they have hanging over the door

People use them for decorations a lot

SPECIAL COLOR PHENOMENA

In most instances people identifying chromatic colors will do so correctly, that is, red as red, green as green, and so on. In rare instances, some people misidentify chromatic colors. If this occurs, the examiner should pursue the issue cautiously in the Inquiry to determine if a verbal lapse may have occurred. If the person makes an appropriate correction, the response should be coded *DV* to indicate the verbal slip. Conversely, if no correction is made, an appropriate examination for color vision probably should be conducted. If it can be assumed that color vision is intact, the response is a *DV*.

There is another special phenomenon involving color for which a Special Score is assigned.

▲ *COLOR PROJECTION (CP)*. The *CP* coding is assigned to any response in which a person identifies an achromatic blot or blot area as being chromatically colored. These are rare responses, occurring most frequently to Cards IV or V. In most, the chromatic coloring is hinted at, but not specified in the original response, such as, *Oh, what a beautiful butterfly*. Obviously, the key word, "beautiful" should be pursued in the Inquiry, and some people do report that the blot has *a pleasant purple coloring*, or *different yellows and blues* and the like.

There are no data to suggest that responses such as these are related to deficiencies in color vision and research indicates that they do have a special interpretive significance.

CP is coded only when the person identifies the presence of chromatic coloring in the achromatic blot area. Most people who give *CP* answers tend to delineate the chromatic colors by using the shading features of the blot, thus requiring a determinant coding for diffuse shading (*FY, YF, or Y*). Obviously, the determinants for chromatic color (*FC, CF, or C*) are never included in the scoring for these answers because there is no chromatic coloring in the blot.

MULTIPLE SPECIAL SCORES

It is not uncommon for a response to meet the criteria for more than one Special Score and, usually, when that occurs all of the Special Scores that apply should be included in the coding. However, there are exceptions to this rule. Nine of the 15 Special Scores (*PSV, AB, AG, COP, MOR, GHR, PHR, PER, and*

CP) are independent of each other and should always be included in the coding when they occur. The remaining six, often referred to as the *Six Critical Special Scores*, may/do have some inter-relationships and caution is required about coding more than one of them for a single answer. Some of these cautions have been mentioned earlier.

None of the other five "critical" Special Scores (*DV, DR, INCOM, FABCOM, or ALOG*) will be included if a *CONTAM* has been scored. The *CONTAM* reflects a very serious form of cognitive disarray and even though they often include a *DV* or *DR* and always, implicitly or explicitly, meet the criterion for *ALOG*, the addition of a second critical Special Score can confuse interpretation.

The issue of whether more than one of the remaining five critical Special Scores should be coded for a response is less precise. The decision is based on whether they occur discretely. If the verbiage meeting the criterion for one critical score is completely independent of the verbiage meeting the criterion for a second critical score, both should be scored. However, if the criteria overlap, only the score with the higher weighted value (*WSum6*) should be assigned.

For example, *Two bears slapping their hands together* contains both an *INCOM* (hands) and a *FABCOM* (slapping their hands together). However, only the *FABCOM* should be coded because the *INCOM* is embedded in the wording that identifies the *FABCOM*. The same wording, or the same instance of cognitive confusion, should *never* be used as a source from which to code more than one of the critical Special Scores. As noted earlier, a *DV* may appear in the context of a *DR*, and when this happens, the *DV* should not be scored.

On the other hand, if an answer includes discrete verbiage meeting the criteria for more than one critical score and no overlap exists, both critical Special Scores should be entered. For example, *Two pink bears climbing the sides of an ice cream sundae* contains both an *INCOM1* (pink bears) and a *FABCOM2* (climbing the sides of an ice cream sundae). These are discrete instances, the wording does not overlap. The fact that the bears are pink has nothing to do with the fact that they are climbing the sides of a sundae. Thus both Special Scores should be entered for the answer.

8 ❖ A Strategy for Scoring

Some Rorschachers use a procedure for scoring responses that might best be described as a *component approach*. It focuses on each major component of the score separately. The Response and the Inquiry are reviewed first for Location data, then for Determinant(s), then for Content, and so on. This procedure is probably encouraged because of the way the recording form for the *Sequence of Scores* is laid out, with each component of the score set off in its own column.

This component approach may be adequate for the very cautious scorer, but it also has some hazzards because it is redundant. The same wording is reviewed several times, and there is no need to *think* in terms of the total integrated score. This can breed errors, both of omission and commission.

▲ *A CONTINUOUS APPROACH.* A more preferred strategy involves a single reading of the answer, pausing at logical points when decisions, or tentative decisions concerning any of the components of the score seem feasible. This procedure tends to insure that each bit of critical wording in the Response and in the Inquiry is heeded and used appropriately.

♦ *The Nine Questions.* The objective of the scoring is to obtain a coded representation of some of the psychological activities or influences that contributed to the person's decision to give the response in the manner that it was articulated. The challenge to the scorer is to make sure that all possibilities are considered. Thus, he or she must be mentally attuned to nine questions. Some beginners often prefer to write these on a cue card, just to make sure that each are considered.

---

1. What is the location?

2. What is the developmental quality?

3. What are the determinants?

4. What is the form quality?

5. Is there a pair?

6. What are the contents?

7. Is it Popular?

8. Should there be a *Z* score?

9. Are there any Special Scores?

♦ *Noting Key Words.* Many scorers find it useful to note words that relate to coding by underlining or crossing through them. As noted earlier, the recording form for the *Sequence of Scores* is laid out with each major component of the total score set off in its own column. Thus, the notation of the key word or words can serve as a stimulus to record codes as they occur in the answer.

♦ *Beginning with the Basic Response.* The first verbiage to be reviewed is the basic response, with the goal of coding as much of the answer as possible. Sometimes little more than content can be scored by using the basic response but, fortunately, many people will give answers in which *all or most all* of the relevant scoring information is readily available in the basic response. For these answers the Inquiry is almost extraneous, simply serving to confirm what is already known. The following is an illustration of what can be gleaned from the basic response, before the Inquiry is reviewed:

Card	Response	Inquiry
III	The dark area ll **2 men** **pickg s.t. up**	

The first key word that will be readily identified in the vast majority of answers will pertain to either the location or content. In this instance, it is the content (men) *H*, and a second content (something) that has not yet been defined. There is also information concerning one determinant, the men are *picking something up*. This is M^a. It also signals the need for a Special Score. The men are engaged in cooperative movement (*COP*).

The issue of location is not clear. The person has said, *the dark area* and, because Card III also contains chromatic areas, it can be assumed that the answer is *not W*, but the specific location is unknown. On the other hand, the developmental quality decision is definite. There are multiple objects (2 men and something) that are *separate but related*, and at least one (men) has common form features. Thus, the DQ coding is +.

There is probably a pair (two men), but that will not be confirmed until the location is clarified. Similarly, the decision concerning form quality and checking for whether the answer is Popular must wait until location is defined. A *Z* score will be required, but it is not certain whether it will be for Adjacent or Distant detail because the location is not known.

Thus, by using the wording of the basic response, information concerning five of the nine crucial questions has been generated and the total score has several entries already:

Loc	DQ	Determinants	FQ	Pair	Contents	Pop	Z	Special Scores
?	+	M^a	?	2?	H, ?	?	Z?	COP

Now the review proceeds to the verbiage of the Inquiry and the task of completing the total score.

Card	Response	Inquiry
III	The dark area ll 2 men pickg s.t. up	E: (Rpts Ss resp) S: Yes, one here & here (*outlines D9*) see their heads, arms, legs & thyr pickg up ths thg (*D7*), *I dk what it is*

The information in the Inquiry has clarified the location. It is the entire *D1* area, with *D9* as the men and *D7* as the *something*. Now the location code can be entered, **D**. A pair has been confirmed (each *D9* is one man). A review of Table A indicates that the form quality is *ordinary* and there is no unusual elaboration of form (only head, arms and legs have been specified). Table A also reveals that the response is *Popular*. The second content remains elusive as the person has said, *I don't know what it is*. Consequently an *Id* will be added. The location figure for Card III in Table A indicates that the *D1* area is all connected. Therefore the *Z* score will be for Adjacent Detail, 3.0. Now the question marks that existed earlier can be replaced with codes, and all nine issues have been addressed. The final coding is:

Loc	DQ	Determinants	FQ	Pair	Contents	Pop	Z	Special Scores
D	+	M^a	o	(2)	H, Id	P	3.0	COP

As noted earlier, there are unusual instances in which the entire coding for a response can be generated from the basic response. For example:

Card	Response	Inquiry
I	The **whole** thg ll a flying **bat**, it's **black**. The wings r out lik **it's flying**, here (points), & here's the body	

In this answer both the location, *W* and the content, *A* are identified at the onset, and two determinants, *FC'* (it's black) and *FMa* (it's flying) have been included. A *Z* score is required because it is a whole response involving form use. A review of Table A reveals that the form quality for a "bat" response given to the whole blot is *ordinary* and that the answer is also *Popular*. Thus, the scoring to this point is:

Loc DQ	Determinants	FQ	Pair	Contents	Pop	Z	Special Scores
W o	FC'.FM^a	o		A	P	1.0	

It is always possible that the Inquiry will add coding information, and that possibility should never be neglected simply because it appears as if the total score has been completed from the basic response. For instance, the person giving the response shown above might have added:

Card	Response	Inquiry
I	The whole thg ll a flyg bat, it's blk. The wgs r out lik it's flyg, here & here's the body	E: (Rpts Ss resp) S: Yeah, all of it, it's all black lik a bat, c the wgs & body & these r the **antennae** lik bats hav

Most of the Inquiry reaffirms what was given in the basic response, but an incongruous feature has been added spontaneously (*antennae*). This requires that the total score be modified to include the *INCOM*.

Unfortunately, there are some answers in which most of the key words that lead to coding decisions occur in the Inquiry and very little is available in the basic response. For example:

Card	Response	Inquiry
VI	It's pretty gruesome, a **bullet** I guess	

This answer contains nothing but content, *Sc* (bullet). The word *gruesome* hints at more to come and possibly a Special Score *MOR*, but at this point the only firm scoring decision that can be made is for content.

Loc	DQ	Determinants	FQ	Pair	Contents	Pop	Z	Special Scores
					Sc			

The Inquiry now becomes the source for all other scoring decisions.

Card	Response	Inquiry
VI	It's pretty gruesome, a bullet I guess	E: (Rpts Ss resp) S: Yeah, right **here** (Points to *D6*) E: I'm not sur wht maks it ll tht S: It just ll one, lik it's **tearing thru an A** E: I dnt thk I'm seeg it lik u r, help me S: Look, it's up here, c the point & it's lik just tore thru ths cat dwn **here** (*D1*), c thes **lines** (Dd22) repres the impact E: U said it's a cat? S: Yeah, prob a tabby cat, it has all **thos dark lines** lik on a tabby cat, the legs are out here, I guess the **head got blown away cuz I don't c it**

In this instance the Inquiry is made complex because the person is not very articulate, and three questions by the examiner were required. Nonetheless, the response is ultimately scorable.

The location, which at first seemed to be *D*, turns out to be *W*. The person has used *D6* as the bullet, *D1* as the animal and the remainder of the blot, *Dd22* as the impact. After the first question, a determinant, *m*^a (*tearing through*) is articulated, as is a second content, *A*, which later becomes *Ad* (*the head got blown away cuz I don't see it*). At this point, the criteria for two Special Scores, *AG* and *MOR* have also been met.

The second question simply reaffirms the determinant but the third question unveils a second determinant, *FY* (*those dark lines*). It might be argued that *YF* might be more appropriate than *FY* because so little form articulation has occurred regarding the cat. But that is probably not correct because the emphasis throughout the Inquiry has been on form, and the shading is included only in the last comment.

Separate objects are involved in a relationship and both have form. Thus, the developmental quality will be + and a *Z* score is required. The response meets the criteria for *Z*, as both a *Whole* and for *Adjacent Detail*. For this card, the values for both are the same, 2.5.

Finally, Table A does not list this specific answer for *W*, but *D6* is listed as *ordinary* for a bullet and *D1* is listed as *ordinary* for an animal hide or skin. Therefore, it is appropriate to assign a form quality coding of **o** for the response. An animal skin is also *Popular*. Thus, the complete score is:

Loc	DQ	Determinants	FQ	Pair	Contents	Pop	Z	Special Scores
W	+	m^a.FY	o		Sc,Ad	P	2.5	AG,MOR

In most answers, the basic response and Inquiry will both contribute significantly to the coding decisions. For instance:

Card	Response	Inquiry
II	That ll 2 **witches huddled together**, they have **black cloaks** and **red hats**	

There is considerable information given in the basic response that might account for almost all of the scoring. The location is not clear but two contents have appeared, (*H*) (*witches*), and *Cg* (*cloaks, hats*). Passive movement, M^p, has been articulated (*huddled together*) and two other determinants, *FC'* (*black cloaks*) and *FC* (*red hats*), have also been given. The developmental quality will be +, and a *Z* score will be necessary. A pair is possible, but no decision concerning that, or about form quality can be made until the location has been clarified. To this point the coding is:

Loc	DQ	Determinants	FQ	Pair	Contents	Pop	Z	Special Scores
?	+	M^p.FC'.FC	?	?	(H),Cg		?	

It can be expected that the Inquiry will add the missing information necessary to complete the entire coding, and provide some clarification for information that has already been given. That proves to be the case and, in fact, the coding for the answer becomes somewhat more complex than was anticipated.

Card	Response	Inquiry
II	Tht ll 2 witches huddled togthr, thy hav blk cloaks & red hats	E: (Rpts Ss resp) S: It's like thyr sitting or kneeling **behind** a **fire**, sort of leaning toward each other, like thy r **whispering** to e.o., c the hats up here (*D2*) & here's their bodies (*D1*) E: U say thyr behind a fire? S: Yes, ths **red** dwn here (*D3*) ll **flames darting up** lik a small fire & thyr behind it, keepg warm E: I'm not sur wht makes it ll thyr behnd it S: It's just in frnt of them, it **covers where their feet wld b**

Two more determinants have been injected, *FD* (*behind, covers where their feet would be*), and *mᵃ* (*flames darting up*), and a determinant coded earlier must be changed. *FC* had been scored for *red* hats but, *red flames darting up* is scored *CF* and replaces the earlier score. The nature of the interaction requires a Special Score of *COP* (*whispering*) and a third content, *Fi*, has also been added. The presence of a pair has been confirmed. The location has been clarified as being *W*. It is a synthesized response and so the *DQ* code will be +, and the response meets two criteria for *Z*. It is a *Whole* (4.5) and *Adjacent Detail* (3.0). Therefore, the higher 4.5 value will be assigned. According to Table A, two human-like figures is *ordinary*. Thus, the complete score is:

Loc	DQ	Determinants	FQ	Pair	Contents	Pop	Z	Special Scores
W	+	$M^p.FC'.CF.m^a.FD$	o	(2)	(H), Cg, Fi		4.5	COP

Obviously, the continuous approach to scoring requires practice. A large number of responses have been included in Part III and should be useful for that purpose.

9 ❖ The Structural Summary

The ultimate objective of coding each response accurately is to be able to complete the *Structural Summary*. The Summary represents the composite of code frequencies plus many ratios, percentages and numerical derivations. They are the data from which many interpretive postulates concerning psychological characteristics and functioning are generated.

A *Structural Summary Blank* has been created for use with the System to facilitate the summarization of the protocol. The first page is used to record demographic data. The second page, the *Sequence of Scores,* is designed for recording of the scoring for each response. The third page is the actual *Structural Summary*. The fourth is a worksheet for tallying six important constellations and indices. The fifth contains a Table of Z scores and Estimated Z scores, plus age adjustment data for three variables, and the last page is the Rorschach *Location Sheet* for use to identify various location selections when administering the test .

There are three procedures involved in creating the *Structural Summary:* (1) listing the Sequence of codes or scores, (2) recording frequencies for each variable, and (3) performing various calculations required to obtain the ratios, percentages, and derived scores. These procedures are probably illustrated best by using the data from an actual protocol.

▲ *SEQUENCE OF SCORES.* The first step is the listing of the codes for each response in the order that they occurred. This is done card by card, and with the responses numbered consecutively. This may have been done at the time the responses were scored, but most examiners prefer to record the scoring on the protocol itself, beneath each response, and then copy those scores on to the recording form for the *Sequence of Scores.*

The consolidation of the codes makes it easier to do the frequency tallies that are required, and the *Sequence* itself is often an additional source of important interpretive data. The *Sequence of Scores* page of the *Structural Summary Blank* includes columns for card number, response number, and each of the major categories of coding used. It also has a column after the Location section, headed *Loc.No.*, that can be used to record the location number of the area used in the response, such as *D3, DdS26,* etc. If a *Dd* area used is not numbered in Table A, the number 99 is entered. The listing of location numbers in the *Sequence of Scores* will sometimes contribute to the interpretation of individual records, and they are extremely useful for research purposes.

The scoring for the protocol of a 19 year old female is shown on the next page and will be used in illustrating the preparation of the *Structural Summary*.

SEQUENCE OF SCORES

Card	Resp. No.	Location and DQ	Loc. No.	Determinant(s) and Form Quality	(2)	Content(s)	Pop	Z-Score	Special Scores
I	1	Wo	1	Fo		A	P	1.0	
	2	D+	4	Mao	2	H, Id		4.0	GHR
	3	WSo	1	Mau		(Hd)		3.5	GHR
II	4	WSo	1	Mp.CF−		Hd		4.5	MOR, AB, PHR
III	5	D+	1	Mao	2	H, Hh	P	3.0	COP, GHR
	6	WSo	1	F−		Hd		5.5	PHR
IV	7	Wo	1	FDo		(A)		2.0	
V	8	Wo	1	Fo		A	P	1.0	
	9	Do	7	Fu		(A)			
VI	10	Wo	1	Fo		(A)		2.5	MOR, DV
VII	11	D+	9	Ma.FYo	2	Hd	P	3.0	AG, GHR
VIII	12	W+	1	FMa.Fr.FCo		A, Na	P	4.5	INC
	13	D/	4	FC.FVo		Ls		3.0	
	14	DdSo	99	FC−		Ad		4.0	PER
IX	15	Wv	1	Ma.C		Hx			AB, PHR
X	16	W+	1	Mpu		(H), Art		5.5	GHR
	17	DdS+	22	F−		Hd, Id		4.0	PHR

STRUCTURAL SUMMARY

LOCATION FEATURES

Zf	=	15
ZSum	=	51.0
ZEst	=	49.0
W	=	10
D	=	5
W+D	=	15
Dd	=	2
S	=	5

DQ

+	=	6
o	=	9
v/+	=	1
v	=	1

FORM QUALITY

	FQx	MQual	W+D
+	=	=	=
o	= 9	= 3	= 9
u	= 3	= 2	= 3
-	= 4	= 1	= 2
none	= 1	= 1	= 1

DETERMINANTS

BLENDS

M.CF
M.FY
FM.Fr.FC
FC.FV
M.C

SINGLE

M	=	4
FM	=	
m	=	
FC	=	1
CF	=	
C	=	
Cn	=	
FC'	=	
C'F	=	
C'	=	
FT	=	
TF	=	
T	=	
FV	=	
VF	=	
V	=	
FY	=	
YF	=	
Y	=	
Fr	=	
rF	=	
FD	=	1
F	=	6
(2)	=	3

CONTENTS

H	=	2
(H)	=	1
Hd	=	4
(Hd)	=	1
Hx	=	1
A	=	3
(A)	=	3
Ad	=	1
(Ad)	=	
An	=	
Art	=	1
Ay	=	
Bl	=	
Bt	=	
Cg	=	
Cl	=	
Ex	=	
Fd	=	
Fi	=	
Ge	=	
Hh	=	1
Ls	=	1
Na	=	1
Sc	=	
Sx	=	
Xy	=	
Id	=	2

APPROACH

I	W.D.WS
II	WS
III	D.WS
IV	W
V	W.D
VI	W
VII	D
VIII	W.D.DdS
IX	W
X	W.DdS

SPECIAL SCORES

		Lv1	Lv2
DV	=	1x1	x2
INC	=	1x2	x4
DR	=	x3	x6
FAB	=	x4	x7
ALOG	=	x5	
CON	=	x7	
Raw Sum6	= 2		
Wgtd Sum6	= 3		

AB	= 2		GHR	= 5
AG	= 1		PHR	= 4
COP	= 1		MOR	= 2
CP	=		PER	= 1
			PSV	=

RATIOS, PERCENTAGES, AND DERIVATIONS

R = 17	L = 0.55

EB	= 7: 4.0	EA	= 11.0	EBPer=	1.8
eb	= 1: 2	es	= 3	D	= +3
		Adj es=	3	Adj D	= +3

FM	= 1	SumC' = 0	SumT = 0
m	= 0	SumV = 1	SumY = 1

FC:CF+C	= 3: 2
Pure C	= 1
SumC':WSumC	= 0: 4.0
Afr	= 0.55
S	= 5
Blends:R	= 5: 17
CP	= 0

COP = 1	AG = 1
GHR:PHR	= 5: 4
a:p	= 6: 2
Food	= 0
SumT	= 0
Human Cont	= 8
Pure H	= 2
PER	= 1
Isol Indx	= 0.18

a:p	= 6: 2	Sum6	= 2
Ma:Mp	= 5: 2	Lv2	= 0
2AB+Art+Ay = 5	WSum6	= 3
MOR	= 2	M-	= 1
		Mnone	= 1

XA%	= 0.71
WDA%	= 0.80
X-%	= 0.24
S-	= 4
P	= 5
X+%	= 0.53
Xu%	= 0.18

Zf	= 15
W:D:Dd	= 10: 5: 2
W:M	= 10: 7
Zd	= +2.0
PSV	= 0
DQ+	= 6
DQv	= 1

3r+(2)/R	= 0.35
Fr+rF	= 1
SumV	= 1
FD	= 1
An+Xy	= 0
MOR	= 2
H:(H)+Hd+(Hd)	= 2: 6

PTI = 0	DEPI = 5	CDI = 1	S-CON = 3	HVI = YES	OBS = No

THE STRUCTURAL SUMMARY - UPPER SECTION

The second step in preparing the *Structural Summary* is the entry of frequency tallies for each of the codes in the upper section of the *Structural Summary Blank*, as shown on the preceding page for the sample protocol.

▲ *1. LOCATION FEATURES.* There are three elements regarding location for which entries are required, (1) Organizational Activity, (2) Location Codes, and (3) Developmental Quality.

♦ *a. Organizational Activity.* Three entries are required at the top of the *Summary* for organizational activity. The first, *Zf* (Z frequency) is the number of times a Z response has occurred in the record. The second, *ZSum*, is for the summation of the weighted Z scores that have been assigned. The third is the estimated weighted *Z Sum (Zest)* which is derived from a Table of Estimates shown below as Table 11. The *Zest* value is the one that corresponds to the *Zf* for the protocol. In the sample record the *Zf* is 15, thus the *Zest* is 49.0.

TABLE 11. BEST WEIGHTED ZSUM PREDICTION WHEN Zf IS KNOWN

Zf	Zest	Zf	Zest	Zf	Zest	Zf	Zest
1	-	14	45.5	26	88.0	39	134.0
2	2.5	15	49.0	27	91.5	40	137.5
3	6.0	16	52.5	28	95.0	41	141.0
4	10.0	17	56.0	29	98.5	42	144.5
5	13.5	18	59.5	30	102.5	43	148.0
6	17.0	19	63.0	31	105.5	44	152.0
7	20.5	20	66.5	32	109.5	45	155.5
8	24.0	21	70.0	33	112.5	46	159.0
9	27.5	22	73.5	34	116.5	47	162.5
10	31.0	23	77.0	35	120.0	48	166.0
11	34.5	24	81.0	36	123.5	49	169.5
12	38.0	25	84.5	37	127.0	50	173.0
13	41.5			38	130.5		

♦ *b. Location Codes.* Each of the three basic location codes are tallied separately. An entry is also required for the frequency of the *S* responses. The *S* frequency *is not* subtracted from the tallies for the three basic location codes of *W, D,* or *Dd*.

♦ *c. Developmental Quality.* Frequencies are also entered for each of the developmental quality codes, disregarding the type of location used.

▲ *2. DETERMINANTS.* Each of the determinants is tallied separately, *except* when occurring in a blend. Each blend is entered in the separate section under *Blends*, and the determinants in the Blends section *are not* counted again when entering the frequencies for the single determinants in the column headed, *Single*.

▲ *3. FORM QUALITY.* There are three distributions to be entered for form quality. The first, shown by the heading **FQx** (*Form Quality Extended*), pertains to *all* of the responses in the record. It provides spaces to enter the frequencies for each of the four types of form quality, plus one for the frequency of responses in which no form quality has been coded.

The second is headed **MQual** (*Human Movement FQ*). It is for the distribution of the types of form quality for all of the Human Movement responses.

The third is headed **W+D** (*Common Area FQ*). It is for recording the *FQ* frequencies of all of the responses that have been given to *W* and *D* areas.

▲ *4. CONTENTS.* The column headed *Contents* includes each of the 27 categories. The entry for each item represents the total number of times that the content has been given in the record, regardless of whether the content is primary or secondary in the coding for the response.

▲ *5. APPROACH SUMMARY.* The upper right section of the Structural Summary contains space to record the *location approach* used by the subject. This refers to the sequence of location selections used by the client when responding to each card. For instance, in the sample record, the person gave three responses to Card I. The first was a Whole (*W*) response, the second a Common Detail response (*D*), and the third a Whole response that included the use of white space (*WS*). Thus, the entry for Card I is *W, D, WS*.

▲ *6. SPECIAL SCORES.* The last set of frequencies to be entered are those for each of the fifteen Special Scores. Two calculations are also required. The first is the *Raw Sum* of the first six Special Scores (**Raw Sum6**). This is the total for all Level 1 and Level 2 scores for *DV, INCOM, DR,* and *FABCOM*, plus the *ALOG* and *CONTAM* entries.

The second is the *Weighted Sum* for those same six special scores (**WSUM6**). Each of the six Special Scores receives a weight:

$$WSUM6 = (1) \times DV + (2) \times DV2 + (2) \times INCOM + (4) \times INCOM2 + (3) \times DR$$
$$+ (6) \times DR2 + (4) \times FABCOM + (7) \times FABCOM2 + (5) \times ALOG$$
$$+ (7) \times CONTAM$$

THE STRUCTURAL SUMMARY - LOWER SECTION

Once the data have been organized into frequencies, the *Structural Summary* can be completed by doing the various calculations that are required for the entries in the lower section, which is divided into seven data blocks. Some items appear in more than one block because they relate to more than one characteristic. At the very bottom of the lower section there are six special indices, the PTI, DEPI, CDI, S-CON, HVI, and OBS which are completed last, using the *Constellations Worksheet*, that is shown for the sample protocol at the end of this chapter.

▲ *THE CORE SECTION.* The Core Section is at the upper left of the lower section of the *Structural Summary*. It contains sixteen entries. Seven entries are frequency data. They include **R** (total number of responses), and the total number for each of the determinants *FM, m, SumC', SumT, SumV, and SumY*. The latter four include all variations, so that *SumC'* includes *FC',C'F, and C'*; *SumT* includes *FT, TF, and T*; etc..

The other nine entries are ratios and derivations. They are:

♦ *1. Lambda (L).* The second entry is for *Lambda (L)*. This is a ratio that compares the frequency of pure *F* responses to all other answers in the record. It relates to issues of economizing the use of resources. It is calculated as:

$$L = \frac{F \text{ (Number of Responses having only Pure } F \text{ determinants)}}{R\text{-}F \text{ (Total R minus Pure Form answers)}}$$

In the sample record, out of 17 responses, there are 6 Pure *F* responses and 11 answers with other determinants, which yields a $L = (6/11) = 0.55$.

♦ *2. Erlebnistypus (EB).* This is a relationship between two major variables, human movement (*M*), and the weighted sum of the chromatic color responses. It is entered as *Sum M : Weighted Sum Color*. The *Weighted Sum Color* (**WSumC**) is obtained by multiplying each type of chromatic color response by a weight. Color naming responses, *Cn*, are *not* included in the *WSumC*.

$$\textbf{WSumC} = (0.5) \times FC + (1.0) \times CF + (1.5) \times C.$$

The sample protocol contains 7 *M* responses, 3 *FC* responses, 1 *CF* answer, and 1 *C* response. Thus, **WSumC** $= (0.5) \times (3) + (1.0) \times (1) + (1.5) \times (1) = 4.0$, yielding an *EB* of 7 : 4.0.

♦ *3. Experience Actual (EA).* This is a derivation that relates to available resources. It is obtained by adding the two sides of the *EB* together, that is, *Sum M+WSumC*. In the sample protocol it is $7+4.0 = 11.0$.

♦ *4. EB Pervasive (EBPer).* This is a ratio concerning the dominance of an *EB* style in decision making activity. *EBPer* is calculated *only* when a marked style is indicated by the *EB*. This is determined by three criteria. First, the value for *EA* must be 4.0 or greater. Second, the value for *Lambda must be less* than 1.0. Finally, when the value of *EA* falls between 4.0 and 10.0, one side of the *EB* must be *at least two points* greater than the other side. If the value of *EA* is more than 10.0, one side of the *EB* must be *at least* 2.5 points greater than the other.

When all three criteria are met, *EBPer* is calculated by dividing the larger number in the *EB* by the smaller number. In the sample protocol, *EA* = 11.0, *Lambda* = 0.55, and the difference between the two values in the *EB* is 3.0. Thus, the larger *EB* value of 7 is divided by the smaller, 4.0, with a result of 1.8.

♦ *5. Experience Base (eb).* This is a relationship comparing all nonhuman movement determinants (*FM and m*) to the shading and achromatic color determinants. It provides information concerning stimulus demands experienced by the subject. It is entered as *Sum FM+m : Sum of SumC'+ SumT + SumY + SumV.*

In the sample protocol, as indicated by the entries made just below the boxed area, there is 1 *FM* and 0 *m* determinants, and 1 *vista* answer (*SumV*), and 1 *diffuse shading* (*SumY*). Thus the *eb* is 1:2.

♦ *6. Experienced Stimulation (es).* This is a derivation obtained from the data in the *eb*. It relates to current stimulus demands. It is obtained by adding the two sides of the *eb* together, that is, The sum of *FM+m + SumC'+ SumT + SumY + SumV.* In the sample record it is 1+2, thus, *es* = 3.

♦ *7. The D Score (D).* The *D Score* provides information concerning the relationship between *EA* and *es*. This concerns stress tolerance and elements of control. It is obtained by first calculating the raw score difference between the two variables, that is, *EA − es*, and including the appropriate sign. The raw difference score is then converted into a scaled difference score, based on standard deviations, in which each *SD* has been rounded to equal 2.5.

Thus, if the difference score for *EA − es* falls between +2.5 and − 2.5, there is no significant difference between the two values and the *D Score* is 0. If the difference score for *EA − es* is greater than +2.5, the *D Score* will increase by units of +1 for each 2.5 difference score points. If the difference score for *EA − es* yields a value of less than −2.5, the *D score* will decrease by units of −1 for each 2.5 points. Table 12 is the Conversion Table for obtaining the D score.

In the sample protocol, the difference, *EA − es* is 11.0 − 3 = +8.0, yielding a *D Score* of +3.

TABLE 12. EA – es D SCORE CONVERSION TABLE

Value of (EA – es)	D Score
+13.0 to +15.0	+5
+10.5 to +12.5	+4
+8.0 to +10.0	+3
+5.5 to +7.5	+2
+3.0 to +5.0	+1
–2.5 to +2.5	0
–3.0 to –5.0	–1
–5.5 to –7.5	–2
–8.0 to –10.0	–3
–10.5 to –12.5	–4
–13.0 to –15.0	–5

♦ *8. Adjusted es (Adj es).* Whereas the *D Score* provides information concerning stress tolerance and available resources, it is important to determine if the score has been influenced by situational elements. The first step in doing this is to subtract from the *es* most of the elements that are related to situational phenomena. The tactic is simple. All but 1 *m* and 1 *SumY* are subtracted from the *es* to create the *Adj es*. In the sample record there are no *m* determinants and only 1 *Y* determinant. Thus, nothing is subtracted, and the *Adj es* has the same value as *es*, 3.

♦ *9. Adjusted D Score (Adj D).* The Adj D is obtained by using the formula *EA – Adj es*. The result is applied against the *D Score Conversion Table*. In the sample record, the result is the same as for the *D Score*, that is, 11.0 – 3 = +8.0, yielding an Adj D of +3.

▲ *THE IDEATION SECTION.* This section contains nine entries. Five of the nine are frequency data that are transcribed from the upper section of the *Structural Summary*. They are the frequencies for *MOR, Sum6, Level 2* Special Scores, *M–* and *M* responses that contain no form. A sixth entry (*WSum6*) has already been calculated and should also be transcribed from the upper portion of the *Structural Summary*. The remaining three items consist of two ratios and one index. They are:

♦ *1. Active:Passive Ratio (a:p).* This relationship concerns flexibility in ideation and attitudes. It is entered as the total number of *Active* movement answers (*Ma+FMa+ma*) on the left and the total number of *Passive* movement responses (*Mp+FMp+mp*) on the right. Movement determinants with [a-p] superscripts are added to both sides. The sample record shows an *a:p* of 6:2.

♦ *2. M Active:Passive Ratio (Ma:Mp).* This variable concerns some characteristics of thinking. It includes *only* human movement responses with total *Active* entered on the left and total *Passive* entered on the right. M^{a-p} answers are added to both sides. The sample record has an *Ma:Mp* of 5:2.

♦ *3. The Intellectualization Index - 2AB+(Art+Ay).* This index includes the Special Score *AB* (Abstract) and the contents *Art* and Anthropology (*Ay*). It is calculated as two times the number of *AB* answers plus the number of *Art* and *Ay* contents. In the sample record there are 2 *AB* responses, plus 1 *Art* content, yielding an Index value of 5.

▲ *THE AFFECT SECTION.* This section includes seven entries. Three are frequencies, and the data for those items (*Pure C, S*, and *CP*) are transcribed from the upper portion of the *Structural Summary*. The remaining four entries are the ratios described below.

♦ *1. Form-Color Ratio (FC:CF+C).* This ratio relates to the modulation of affect. It is entered as shown, with the total number of *FC* determinants on the left and the sum of the *CF+C+Cn* determinants on the right. Each of the chromatic color determinants are weighed equally in this ratio, as contrasted with the **WSumC** used in the *EB* and *EA* in which *Cn* responses are not included. The sample protocol contains 3 *FC* responses, 1 *CF* response, and 1 Pure *C* answer. Thus, the ratio is 3:2.

♦ *2. Constriction Ratio (SumC':WSumC).* This ratio relates to excessive internalization of affect. It is entered with the total number of *C'* determinants (*SumC'*) on the left and the weighted sum of chromatic color (*WSumC*) on the right. The sample protocol has no *C'* responses and a **WSumC** of 4.0. Thus, the ratio is 0:4.0.

♦ *3. Affective Ratio (Afr).* This is a ratio that compares the number of answers to the last three cards with those given to the first seven cards. It relates to interest in emotional stimulation. It is calculated as:

$$Afr = \frac{\text{Number Responses to Cards VIII+IX+X}}{\text{Number Responses to Cards I+II+III+IV+V+VI+VII}}$$

In the sample record the subject gave 6 responses to the last three cards and 11 responses to the first seven cards, yielding an *Afr* = (6/11) = 0.55.

♦ *4. Complexity Ratio (Blends:R).* This relationship is *not* reduced to a ratio. Instead, it is entered as indicated, with the total number of blends on the left and the number of responses on the right. In the sample record there are five blends yielding a ratio of 5:17.

▲ *THE MEDIATION SECTION.* This section contains seven entries. Two are frequency data that must be calculated directly from the *Sequence of Scores*. One is for the number of Popular (*P*) responses. The second is the number of *minus* answers in which white space (*S*) has been used as part or all of the location. The remaining five items in this section are percentages.

♦ *1. Form Appropriate Extended (XA%).* This variable concerns the proportion of responses in which there is an appropriate use of form features. It is calculated as:

$$XA\% = \frac{\text{Sum of responses that have an } FQ \text{ coding of } +, \text{o, or u}}{R}$$

The sample record contains 17 responses of which none are *plus*, 9 are *ordinary*, and 3 are *unusual*. This calculates as 12 divided by 17, which yields an *XA%* of 0.71.

♦ *2. Form Appropriate - Common Areas (WDA%).* This variable concerns the proportion of responses given to *W* and *D* areas in which there is an appropriate use of form features. It is calculated as:

$$WDA\% = \frac{\text{Sum of } W{+}D \text{ responses that have an } FQ \text{ coding of } +, \text{o, or u}}{\text{Sum of } W{+}D}$$

The sample record contains 15 answers with *W* or *D* locations. Twelve of the 15 responses have *FQ* codings of **o** or **u**. This calculates as 12 divided by 15, which yields a *WDA%* of 0.80.

♦ *3. Distorted Form (X-%).* This variable concerns the proportion of answers in which form use is not commensurate with the blot features. It is calculated as:

$$X\text{--}\% = \frac{\text{Sum FQx--}}{R}$$

The sample record of 17 responses includes 4 minus answers, which leads to an *X-%* of 0.24.

♦ *4. Conventional Form Use (X+%).* This variable concerns the extent to which the appropriate use of form features has included common object definitions. It is calculated as:

$$X{+}\% = \frac{\text{Sum FQx + and o}}{R}$$

In the sample record, there are no + answers and 9 *ordinary* responses, yielding an *X+%* of 0.53.

♦ *5. Unusual Form Use (Xu%).* This variable concerns the extent to which the appropriate use of form features has included uncommon object definitions. It is calculated as:

$$Xu\% = \frac{\text{Sum FQxu}}{R}$$

In the sample record there are 3 *unusual* responses, yielding an *Xu%* of 0.18.

▲ *THE PROCESSING SECTION.* This section contains seven entries, four of which, (*Zf, PSV, DQ+,* and *DQv*) are frequency data to be transcribed from the upper portion of the *Structural Summary*. Two of the remaining three express relationships, and the third is a difference score.

♦ *1. Economy Index (W:D:Dd).* This relationship is entered as shown, with the total number of *W* responses on the left, the total number of *D* responses in the center, and the total number of *Dd* answers at the right.

♦ *2. Aspirational Ratio (W:M).* This relationship is not reduced to a ratio but, instead, entered as indicated with the total number of *W* responses on the left and the total number of *M* answers at the right.

♦ *3. Processing Efficiency (Zd).* The *Zd* is a difference score obtained by the formula *ZSum − Zest*, with the appropriate sign recorded. In the sample protocol, the *ZSum* = 51.0 and the *Zest* = 49.0, yielding a *Zd* score of +2.0.

▲ *THE INTERPERSONAL SECTION.* This section contains ten entries. Five of the 10 are frequency data transcribed directly from the upper portion of the *Structural Summary* (sum of *COP* responses, sum of *AG* responses, sum of *Food* contents, sum of Pure *H* answers, and the number of *PER* Special Scores).

A sixth item displays a relationship (*GHR:PHR*) using frequency data from the upper portion of the *Structural Summary*, with the sum of *GHR* entered on the left and the sum of *PHR* entered on the right. A seventh item, *SumT*, is transcribed from the Core Section, and an eighth, *a:p* is transcribed from the Ideation Section. The remaining two items require some calculations.

♦ *1. Interpersonal Interest (Human Cont).* This entry provides information about interest in people. The entry is calculated as:

Human Cont = The sum *H+(H)+Hd+(Hd)* [*Hx* is not included]

In the sample protocol there are 2 *H*, 1 *(H)*, 4 *Hd*, and 1 *(Hd)*. Thus, *Human Cont* = 8.

♦ *2. Isolation Index (Isolate/R).* This variable is related to social isolation. It involves the contents in five categories (Botany, Clouds, Geography, Landscape, and Nature), with the raw sum for two categories being doubled. It is calculated as:

$$Isolate/R = \frac{Bt+2Cl+Ge+Ls+2Na}{R}$$

The sample record contains 1 *Ls* and 1 *Na* for a weighted sum of 3, which yields an Index value of 0.18.

▲ *THE SELF PERCEPTION SECTION.* This section contains seven entries, four of which are frequencies, or the sum of frequencies from the upper portion of the *Structural Summary*. They include the sum *Fr+rF*, the number of Form Dimension (*FD*) responses, the number of Special Scores for morbid content (*MOR*), and the sum of Anatomy (*An*) and X-ray (*Xy*) contents. The fifth entry, *SumV*, is transcribed from the Core Section.

The sixth entry is a ratio *H:(H)+Hd+(Hd)* in which the number of Pure *H* contents is entered on the left, and the sum of *(H)+Hd+(Hd)* is entered on the right. In the sample record, there are 2 responses that contain a Pure *H* content and 6 answers that contain other types of human content. Thus, the ratio is expressed as 2:6.

The seventh item requires some calculation.

♦ *1. Egocentricity Index (3r+(2)/R).* This index relates to self esteem. It represents the proportion of reflection and pair responses in the total record, with each reflection determinant weighed as being equal to three pair responses. It is calculated as:

$$3r+(2)/R = \frac{3x(Fr+rF) + Sum\ (2)}{R}$$

The sample record contains 1 reflection answer and 3 pair responses leading to an Egocentricity Index = [(3)x1 + 3]/(17) = 0.35.

SPECIAL INDICES. At the bottom of the *Structural Summary* there are six special indices, the Perceptual-Thinking Index (*PTI*), the Depression Index (*DEPI*), the Coping Deficit Index (*CDI*), the Suicide Constellation (*S-CON*), the Hypervigilance Index (*HVI*), and the Obsessive Style Index (*OBS*).

The variables included for each are shown on the *Constellations Worksheet* (see next page) with boxes provided to check each item that is positive. The total number of positive variables should be entered at the bottom of the *Structual Summary* for the *PTI, DEPI, CDI*, and *S-CON*. Notations of *Yes* or *No* should be entered for the *HVI* and the *OBS*.

When working with the protocols of younger people, it is important to note that there are some age adjusted cutoff values for four variables. One (*WSum6*) appears in the *PTI*. A second (*3r+(2)/R*) appears in the *DEPI*, and the third, (*Afr*) is in both the *DEPI* and the *CDI*. Each is noted on the *Constellations Worksheet* with an *, and the cutoff values to be applied are shown below by age groups.

Age Adjustments for Egocentricity Index

Age	Significant if $3r+(2)/R$ is less than	Significant if $3r+(2)/R$ is more than
5	.55	.83
6	.52	.82
7	.52	.77
8	.48	.74
9	.47	.69
10	.47	.61
11	.46	.58
12	.46	.58
13	.41	.55
14	.37	.54
15	.33	.50
16	.33	.48

Age Adjustments for WSum6

If R is 17 or more:

Ages 5 to 7:	*WSum6* > 20
Ages 8 to 10:	*WSum6* > 19
Ages 11 to 13:	*WSum6* > 18

If R is less than 17

Ages 5 to 7:	*WSum6* > 16
Ages 8 to 10:	*WSum6* > 15
Ages 11 to 13:	*WSum6* > 14

Age Adjustments for the Affective Ratio

Ages 5 & 6:	*Afr* < .57
Ages 7 to 9:	*Afr* < .55
Ages 10 to 13:	*Afr* < .53

CONSTELLATIONS WORKSHEET

S-Constellation (Suicide Potential):

☐ Check Positive if 8 or more conditions are true:
Note: Applicable only for subjects over 14 years old.

- ☐ FV+VF+V+FD > 2
- ☒ Color-Shading Blends > 0
- ☐ 3r+(2)/R < .31 or > .44
- ☐ MOR > 3
- ☐ Zd > +3.5 or Zd < -3.5
- ☐ es > EA
- ☐ CF+C > FC
- ☒ X+% < .70
- ☒ S > 3
- ☐ P < 3 or P > 8
- ☐ Pure H < 2
- ☐ R < 17

PTI (Perceptual-Thinking Index):

- ☐ XA% < .70 and WDA% < .75
- ☐ X-% > .29
- ☐ LVL2 > 2 and FAB2 > 0
- ☐* R < 17 and WSUM6 > 12
  OR R > 16 and WSUM6 > 17
- ☐ M- > 1 OR X-% > .40

___0___ Sum PTI

DEPI (Depression Index):

☒ Check Positive if 5 or more conditions are true:

- ☒ (FV+VF+V > 0) OR (FD > 2)
- ☒ (Col-Shd Blends > 0) OR (S > 2)
- ☐* (3r+(2)/R > .44 and Fr+rF = 0)
  OR (3r+(2)/R < .33)
- ☐* (Afr < .46) OR (Blends < 4)
- ☒ (SumShading > FM+m) OR (SumC'>2)
- ☒ (MOR > 2) OR (2xAB+Art+AY > 3)
- ☒ (Cop < 2) OR
  ([Bt+2xCl+Ge+Ls+2xNa]/R > .24)

CDI (Coping Deficit Index):

☐ Check Positive if 4 or 5 conditions are true:

- ☐ (EA < 6) OR (AdjD < 0)
- ☒ (COP < 2) and (AG < 2)
- ☐ (Weighted Sum C < 2.5) OR *(Afr < .46)
- ☐ (Passive > Active+1) OR (Pure H < 2)
- ☐ (Sum T > 1)
  OR (Isolate/R > .24)
  OR (Food > 0)

HVI (Hypervigilance Index):

☒ Check Positive if condition 1 is true and at least 4 of the others are true:

- ☒ (1) FT+TF+T = 0
- -
- ☒ (2) Zf > 12
- ☐ (3) Zd > +3.5
- ☒ (4) S > 3
- ☒ (5) H+(H)+Hd+(Hd) > 6
- ☒ (6) (H)+(A)+(Hd)+(Ad) > 3
- ☒ (7) H+A: Hd+Ad < 4:1
- ☐ (8) Cg > 3

OBS (Obsessive Style Index):

- ☐ (1) Dd > 3
- ☒ (2) Zf > 12
- ☐ (3) Zd > +3.0
- ☐ (4) Populars > 7
- ☐ (5) FQ+ > 1

- -

☐ Check Positive if one or more is true:

- ☐ Conditions 1 to 5 are all true
- ☐ 2 or more of 1 to 4 are true AND FQ+ > 3
- ☐ 3 or more of 1 to 5 are true AND X+% > .89
- ☐ FQ+ > 3 AND X+% > .89

*Note: Should be adjusted for younger clients.

PART II

WORKING TABLES

AND

DESCRIPTIVE STATISTICS

10 ❖ Working Tables

This section contains two tables, one of which is used very frequently in coding decisions concerning responses. It is *Table A*, which includes figures of each of the 10 blots showing the location numbering for the common and unusual detail areas. The bulk of Table A is comprised of listings of responses, by card and location area. Each is designated as **o** (*ordinary*), **u** (*unusual*), or − (*minus*), depending on whether it meets the frequency or judgement criteria described in Chapter 4.

Table A could be expanded considerably with the addition of a large number of minus responses, selected either from the more than 205,000 responses against which the frequency criteria were applied, or from psychotic or schizophrenic records not included in that data base. However, the overwhelming majority of those answers occur with a very low frequency, typically less than once per 500 records. Their inclusion would probably detract, more than assist, in the usefulness of the table by making it much longer. Thus, a frequency criterion of 4 or more has been used in selecting the minus responses that are included for the *W* and *D* areas, and 3 or more for inclusion in the listings for *Dd* areas.

Table B provides some illustrations of responses in which the form features have been articulated more extensively than is common, thus warranting the *FQ* coding of +. As noted in Chapter 4, the decision to code a response as *FQ*+ involves some subjective judgement. Answers coded + reflect an unusual detailing of form features that may be the product of creativeness, or may simply represent a tendency toward greater preciseness. Any of the answers presented in Table B could be delivered with less articulation of the specific form elements and, if so, would be coded as **o**. In each of the examples in Table B, the person has gone well beyond the normal requirements for form specification and, in doing so, has enriched the answer by being more precise or detailed.

It may be important to note again, that the coding of + is restricted to answers that, with less elaborate form articulation, would be coded **o**. This is an empirically based rule. The vast majority of responses that include an unusual elaboration of form elements, and thus are coded +, also meet the criterion to be coded **o**. It is true that some uncommon answers, coded **u**, are especially creative and include an elaborate specification of the form features. Even so, an *FQ* coding of + is not assigned because of the **u** coding. This is to insure that the calculations for the *X+%* and *Xu%* accurately reflect the extent to which answers in which form has been used appropriately are differentiated as being conventional or uncommon.

Some examiners may wish to note the presence of elaborate form articulation in responses for which the *FQ* is **u** by using a special notation of **u/+** to call attention to the elaborated form use. In some instances, such notations may contribute to interpretive postulates, especially if such responses occur often in a record. But if the u/+ code is assigned, the response should continue to be treated as **u** in all of the structural calculations.

▲ *USING TABLE A.* In a broad context, Table A can be thought of as the basic source from which to determine the correct form quality coding for an answer. The task would be reasonably straightforward if all answers were simply differentiated into two categories, one for appropriate form use (*good fit*) and one for inappropriate form use (*poor fit*). Rorschach used that approach in his investigations, and several distinguished Rorschachers, responsible for the development of the test, also applied a similar model. The Comprehensive System builds on the basic distinction between good and poor form fit, by adding a second layer of differentation to glean more information about perceptual and mediational operations, and their influence on cognitive functioning. This second layer of differentiation focuses only on those responses in which form has been used appropriately. The goal is to sort out those answers which are reasonably common (*ordinary*) from those which are considerably less common (*unusual*).

The listing of responses in Table A is fairly extensive, and the *FQ* decision will be made easily for most answers. However, some items may not appear in the table with the same specificity that occurs in a response. When an item does not appear in the table for a given location area, it is necessary to attempt *conservative but reasonable* extrapolation from the Table A data.

Some extrapolation is very straightforward. For instance, a person may have given the response, *A cougar* to the *D1* area of Card VIII. An examination of Table A reveals that some specific animals appear in the listing for the *D1* area but *cougar* is not in the list. However, under the heading *animal*, which is listed as **o**, it is noted that this item deals with a class of four legged animals that have shapes appropriate to the *D1* contours. The notation also includes several commonly reported animals including *cat*. Thus, it is not difficult to extrapolate from the notation to select the appropriate coding of **o** for *cougar*.

Other extrapolation efforts require more effort and good logic. For example, a person may report, *Some cherries, four of them*, to the *D6* area of Card IX. *Cherries* are not listed for the *D6* area in the table. The first step is to review items in the listing for *D6* searching for similarities. That review yields three possibilities (*apples*, *radishes*, and *raspberries*), but they do not all have the same *FQ* code. *Apples* are listed as **o**, whereas *radishes* and *raspberries* are listed as **u**. A scorer might be tempted to make a decision at this point, but one more step should be taken before any decision is reached. It is a review of the listing of items for the *D4* area, because the person has noted that there are *four of them*, and one includes the *D4* area. This review finds that *cherry* is not listed for *D4*, but both *apple* and *raspberry* are listed as **o**.

The decision concerning this answer, whether four *cherries* should be coded as **u** or o, might be addressed concretely by some scorers who assume that if cherries are not listed either for *D6* or *D4* the scoring should be **u**. But that *is not* reasonable extrapolation. A cherry is like a small apple, and not very unlike a raspberry. Reasonable extrapolation suggests that the coding of **o** is more appropriate. The decision follows the same logic used in the extrapolation described earlier concerning the cougar response. Namely, if the scanning of the list reveals an item similar to that given in the answer, it is correct to assign the same code for the unlisted item.

Conversely, if the specific objects listed are not comparable in form to the object in question, the coding decision will remain more subjective using the following principles that are derived from the *FQ* criteria:

(1) If a specific item is not listed and extrapolation does not occur easily, it should be coded either as **u** or **minus** by applying principles 2 or 3.

(2) If a specific item does not appear in the list and extrapolation is impossible but the object can be perceived *quickly and easily* and involves no substantial contour distortions, it should be coded **u**.

(3) If a specific item is not in the list, and extrapolation is impossible, and the object can be perceived only with difficulty, or not at all, it should be coded as **minus**.

As with the "cherry" example, it may be necessary to review the lists for more than one location before reaching a decision. For instance, a response might involve several specific anatomy objects. The list for the total area might indicate an *FQ* code for anatomy (*Unspecified*). In this case the lists for the areas used for each of the anatomy objects should be reviewed to determine if codes are available for any of those items.

As noted in Chapter 4, some multiple object responses, not listed in Table A, will also require a review of more than one location list before making a decision about the *FQ* coding. When that is the case, the lowest *FQ* value should be assigned to the response, *if the object listed with a lower value is considered important to the overall answer*. For example, the Card II, *D1* areas, are Popular for bears, and usually assigned an *FQ* coding of **o**. However, if a response were, *Two bears (D1) standing behind a red flower (D3)*, the *FQ* coding would be **u** because *flower* is listed as **u** in Table A, and it is important to the response. However, caution must be exercised when applying this rule to insure that an object with a lower *FQ* is really *important*, and not just a casual addition, to the overall answer.

Caret marks (**< v >**) are included for some responses to indicate the direction of the apex of the blot. If no caret mark appears next to an item, it signifies that the FQ coding listed is appropriate only when the apex of the card is in the upright position, *or when the object reported is described in a manner that is commensurate with the description that would be given of that object if the card were in the upright position.*

TABLE A: FIGURES SHOWING COMMON (D) AND UNUSUAL (Dd) LOCATION AREAS BY CARD, LISTINGS OF ORDINARY (o), UNUSUAL (u), AND MINUS (–) RESPONSES AND RESPONSE CLASSES BY LOCATION AREAS, PLUS POPULARS AND Z VALUES FOR EACH CARD

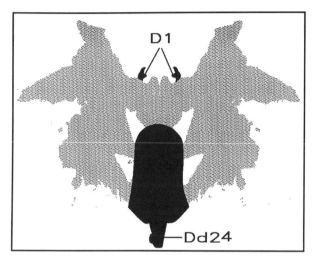

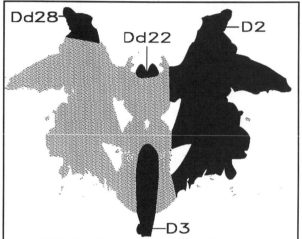

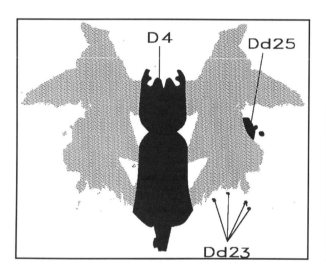

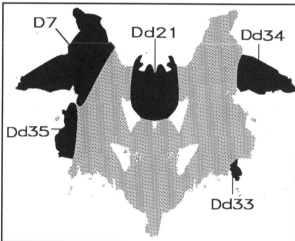

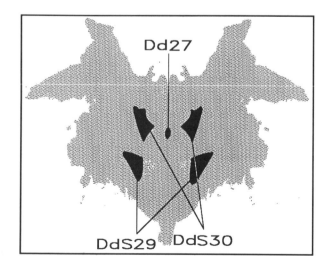

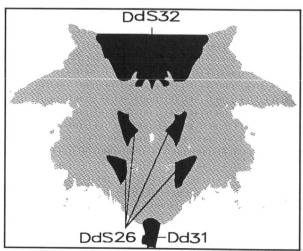

TABLE A: FIGURES SHOWING COMMON (D) AND UNUSUAL (Dd) LOCATION AREAS BY CARD, LISTINGS OF ORDINARY (o), UNUSUAL (u) AND MINUS (-) RESPONSES AND RESPONSE CLASSES BY LOCATION AREAS, PLUS POPULARS AND Z VALUES FOR EACH CARD

CARD I

Popular is to W: BAT OR BUTTERFLY

Z Values: W = 1.0 ADJACENT = 4.0 DISTANT = 6.0 SPACE = 3.5

W

- – Abacus
- – Abalone
- – Abdomen
- u Abstract
- u Airplane (Top view)
- – Airplane (Front view)
- – Albacore
- u Amoeba
- – Anchor
- o Angel
- o Angels (2 with D4 another object)
- – Animal (Not winged) (Note: This class of response includes a large group of animals which do not have wings or flappers such as bear, cat, dog, lion, etc)
- u Animal (Winged but unspecified)
- – Ant
- – Anteater
- u Art (Abstract)
- u **v** Astrodome
- – Australia
- – Baboon
- o Badge
- o Bat
- – Battleship
- – Bear
- – Beard
- u Bee
- u Beetle (Winged)
- – Bell
- u **v** Bellows
- – Bib
- o Bird
- u **v** Bird (Prehistoric)
- – Blanket

- – Boat
- – Body
- – Body (Split)
- – Book
- – Bookmark
- u Bone (Skeletal)
- u Bowl (With handles)
- – Brain
- u Brain (Cross section)
- – Brain (Top view)
- – Breast
- – Bridge (Man made)
- u Bridge (Natural)
- – Buckle
- o Bug (Smashed)
- o Bug (Winged)
- – Bug (Unspecified, not winged)
- u **v** Building
- – Bullet
- o Butterfly
- u **v** Cabin
- – Cactus
- – Cage
- – Cake
- u **v** Cap (Snow)
- u Cape
- – Car
- – Cart
- u **v** Castle
- – Cat
- u **v** Catamaran (Front view)
- – Cattle (Herd)
- u **v** Cave (Front view)
- o **v** Chandelier
- – Chest
- – Chevron
- – Chinese Art
- u **v** Chinese House
- u Cinder
- u **v** Circus Tent
- – Cistern
- – Citrus Tree

- – Clamp
- – Clitoris
- u Cloak
- – Clock
- u Cloud(s)
- – Clove
- u Coal (Piece)
- – Coat
- u Coat of Arms
- u Cocoon (With winged insect emerging)
- – Codfish
- u Coral
- – Cow
- u Crab
- – Crate
- – Crater
- u Crawfish
- o Crow
- o **v** Crown
- o Dancer (As D4 in costume or cape)
- – Dandelion
- u Demon (In cape or with wings)
- u Design
- – Dirigible
- u Dirt
- o Disc (Anatomy)
- u **v** Dome
- – Door
- u Dracula
- u Dragon (Usually with wings)
- u Dragonfly
- – Dream
- – Dress
- – Drill
- u **v** Drillpress
- u Duck
- u Dust (Speck)
- o Eagle
- – Egg

W (Continued)

- Elves
o Emblem
- Explosion

FACE:
(Note: Most faces are o or u, provided Dd34 is used as ears, and DdS29 & 30 are used for eyes & mouth and the content is (Hd), Ad or (Ad), however, some faces are inappropriate for the contours. A partial list is given below.)

o Face, Animal (Unspecified)
u Face, Animal w/ horns
- Face, Ant
u Face, Bear
- Face, Bird
u Face, Bug
o Face, Cat
u Face, Cow
u Face, Dog
- Face, Fish
o Face, Fox
- Face, Goat
- Face, Horse
- Face, Human
- Face, Insect (Specified)
u Face, Insect (Unspecified)
u Face, Monster (Gremlin, evil, alien)
u Face, Mouse
u Face, Rabbit (Floppy ears)
- Face, Racoon
u Face, Robot
u Face, Skeleton (Animal)
- Face, Skeleton (Human)
o Face, Tiger
- Face, Turtle
u Face, Witch
o Face, Wolf
- Fan
- Fern
- Fiddle
- Fire
- Flag
u Flea

u Fly
u Fog
- Foliage
- Food
- Forest
u Fossil
o v Fountain
- Frog
u Fur (Piece)
u Fuzz (Piece)
- Garden
u v Gazebo
u Gnat
o Girls (Dancing or standing in a circle)
u v Hair (Styled)
o v Hat (Woman's)
  Head (See Face)
o v Headdress
- Helicopter
o v Helmet
u v Hill
- Hive (Insect)
u v House
- Human
o Human (Winged or caped)
u Humans (2 Facing midline)
- Humans (2 Turned away)
o Humans (3, one at D4)
- Ice
u Ink
u Inkblot
- Insect (Not winged)
o Insect (Winged)
u Island
- Jellyfish
- Keel (Boat)
- Kidney(s)
u Kite
- Lamp
u Landscape
  (Note: This category includes rocks, rocky terrain and broad landscape expanse such as a mountainside)
o Leaf
- Lobster
- Lungs
- Map (Specified)
u Map (Unspecified)
o Mask
  (Note: This category includes

a wide variety of animal, Halloween, monster, party, voodoo, etc. masks)
- Mat (Door)
- Meat
u Medusa
- Melon
u v Monster
u Mosquito
o Moth
u v Mountain
u Mud
- Neck
- Neckbone
- Nest
- Net
- Nose
- Note (Musical)
o Opera Singers (2 or 3)
o Ornament
- Owl
- Pau (Cooking)
- Parking Meter
o Pelvis
o People (2) Dancing
- Pick (Guitar)
- Plant
- Plymouth Emblem
- Pot
- Printing Press
- v Pumpkin
- Rib(s)
- Roadmap
u Robot
u v Rock
u v Rocketship
u Rower (In boat)
- Rudder
- Rug
- Sailboat
- Sawhorse
o Sea Animal (With D2 or Dd34 as flappers)
- Seed
- Ship
- Shrimp
- Skeleton (Unspecified)
o Skull (Human or animal)
- Smile
- Snowflake
u v Spaceship
- Sperm
- Spider

W (Continued)

- – Sponge
- – Spring (Metal)
- u Squirrel (Flying)
- o Statues (2 or 3)
- – Steeple
- u Stone (Carved)
- – Stove
- – Sundial
- – Tank (Army)
- u **v** Tent
- – Tornado
- o Totem (Winged)
- u **v** Train (As D4 crossing a trestle)
- – Tree
- – Tuning Fork
- – Turtle
- u Urn
- – Valve
- u Vase
- – Washing Machine
- u Wasp
- – Wave
- – Weather Vane
- – Weed
- o Witches (2 or 3)
- o Woman (Winged or caped)
- – Wood
- o X-ray (Chest)
- – X-ray (Heart)
- – X-ray (Lungs)
- o X-ray (Pelvis)
- – X-ray (Stomach)
- o X-ray (Unspecified)
- – Yacht

D1

- – Ants
- o Antennae
- u Antlers
- – Apes
- o Bird Heads
- – Birds
- – Bones
- – Bugs
- u Butterflies

- o Claws
- – Clip
- – Crabs
- u Dancers
- u Devils
- u Duck Heads
- u Eagle Heads
- – Elves
- o Feelers
- o Fingers
- – Flags
- – Fork
- u Ghosts
- – Gun
- o Hands
- – Heads (Animal)
- o Heads (Birds)
- u Heads (Insects)
- u Heads (Monster)
- u Heads (Reptile)
- o Horns
- o Humans or human-like figures
- – Insects
- o Mittens
- u Monsters
- – Penis
- o Pincers
- u Puppets
- – Rocket
- u Rocks
- – Roots
- u Sculpture (Abstract)
- – Shrimp
- u Thumb
- – Tooth
- – Tree
- – Waves

D2

- o Acrobat
- – Airplane
- – Anatomy
- o Angel
- o Animal (Specified as long eared, such as donkey, elephant, some varieties of dogs)

- – Animal (Specified as short eared such as cat, cow, and some varieties of dogs)
- o Animal (Cartoon)
- u Animal (Unspecified)
- – Bat
- – Beetle
- o Bird (With Dd34 as wings)
- – **v** Boots
- u Bug (With Dd34 as wings)
- – Bug (Not winged)
- – Cat
- – Chicken
- u Cloud
- – Cow
- o Dancer
- o Demon
-    Dog (See Animal)
- – Dragon
- o Face (Animal, bird, cartoon or monster with Dd34 as nose)
- – Face (Animal, bird, cartoon or monster with Dd34 as ear)
- – Face, Human
- – Fish
- u Gargoyle
- o Head, Bird
- o Human
- o Human-like Figure
- o Landscape
- u Leaf
- – Map (Specified)
- u Map (Unspecified)
- o Pegasus
- – Pig
- u < Rabbit
- – Rodent
- – Sky
- u Smoke
- – Tree
- u < Tree(s) & foliage
- o Wing(s)
- – Wolf
- u Woodpecker (Profile)
- – X-ray (Specified or unspecified)

D3

u Alligator
u < Alligator (Reflected)
o **v** Bowling Pin
– Brain Stem
– Candle
– Candle Holder
– Face
– Gun
o Human (Lower half)
– Insect
o Legs
o Mummy Case
– Nose
– Ornament
– Penis
u Robot
– Snake
u Spaceship
u Spinal Cord
o Statue
o Totem Pole
– Tree
– Vagina
o Vase
u Violin

D4

– Alligator
– Anatomy
– Animal (Unspecified)
– Ant
u Baboon
– Bee
o Beetle
– Bird
– Bone Structure
o Bug (With D1 as antennae or feelers)
– Bullet
– Cat
o Cello
– Centipede
– Clitoris
– Crab
u Cricket

u Crown (Ceremonial)
– Door
– Face
– Fish
– Fly
– Frog
o Gorilla
o Human (Whole)
o Human (Headless)
o Humans (2)
o **v** Human-like Figure
o Insect (Unspecified with D1 as antennae or feelers)
– Island
u Jack-in-the-box
– Lamp
– Lobster
u Man
o Monster
u Monument
– Nose
– Plant
– Reptile
u **v** Rocket
u **v** Rocketship
u Space Creature
– Spider
– Spine
o Statue
u **v** Tree
– Turtle
– Wasp
o Woman
u Vase
u Viola

D7

– Animal (Not winged)
o Animal (Winged)
u Arrowhead
o Bird
– Bone
u Cliff
u Cloud
o Crow
u Duck
o Eagle
u Ears (Animal)
u Face, Animal (With Dd34

as nose)
u Face, Cartoon (With Dd34 as nose)
– Face, Human
u Face, Witch
– Hat
u Head (Bird, duck, horse)
– Horn
– Insect (Not winged)
u Insect (Winged)
o Landscape
– Map (Specified)
u Map (Unspecified)
u Nest
– Plant
u Pot (Dd34 as handle)
u Rock
– Skull
o Sphinx
o Statue (Bird)
u Weather Vane
u Wing (Airplane or bird)
o Wings

Dd21

– Anatomy
o Bug (D1 as feelers)
u Crab
– Foliage
– Heart
– Jellyfish
u Landscape
o Nest
– Sea Animal
u Shield
– Statue

Dd22

- – Balls
- u Breasts
- u Boulders
- – Buttocks
- u Eyes, bug or frog
- – Ghosts
- – Heads (Animal)
- u Heads (Human)
- o Hills
- u Hump (Camel)
- u Labia
- o Mountains
- – Trees
- – Warts

Dd23

- – Airplanes
- u Birds
- – Dots
- – Flies
- u Insects
- o Islands
- – Notes (Musical)
- – Symbols

Dd24

- o Bell
- – Bug
- o Cello
- u Dress
- u Emblem
- – Head
- u Helmet
- – Human (Whole)
- u Human Figure (Lower half)
- u Lamp
- u Lantern
- u Monster

- – Plant
- u Skirt
- – X-ray

Dd25

- – Animal
- – Animal Rump
- u Face, Human-Abstract
- u Face, Human
- – Trees

DdS26

- o Clouds
- o Eyes
- o Ghosts
- o Mask Details
- u Snow
- – Trees
- o Windows

Dd27

- u Boat (With midline)
- o Buckle
- u Elevator (With midline)
- – Face
- – Head
- – Heart
- u Shield
- u Spaceship
- – Top
- – Ulcer

Dd28

- u Arrowhead
- – Bird (Whole)
- u Hat
- – Head (Animal)
- o Head (Bird)
- – Head (Human)
- u Head (Human-like w/hat)
- – Pole
- – Shoe
- u Tree

DdS29

- o Eyes (Abstract)
- – Eyes (Human)
- u Flying Saucers
- o Ghosts
- o Holes
- u Mountains
- u Pyramids
- u Snow
- u Spaceships
- u Tents
- u Triangles
- u Wings

DdS30

- o Eyes
- o Ghosts
- u Human (In costume)
- – Lungs
- u Snow
- – Trees

Dd31

u   Feet
–   Hammer
u **v** Head (Rabbit)
–   Head (Unspecified)
u **v** Mountain peak
–   Nose
–   Root
–   Skull
–   Stinger
u   Tooth
u **v** Volcano

DdS32

u   Bay
–   Bird
u   Canyon
–   Mask
–   Vase

Dd33

–   Ball
–   Bell
–   Bone
–   Head (Animal)
u **v** Head (Human)
–   Lamp
u **v** Mushroom
u **v** Poodle Tail
u   Tail
o **v** Tree

Dd34

u   Arrowhead
u   Blade (Knife)
o   Cliff
–   Face
o   Fin
u <Ghost
–   Head
–   Insect
o <Mountain
u   Nose (Cartoon)
u   Rock
u   Saw
u <Seal
u <Shrub
u <Tower
o <Tree (Fir)
u <Tree (Unspecified)
u <Umbrella (Closed)

Dd35

u <Dog
–   Face (Animal)
–   Face (Bird)
u **v** Face (Human)

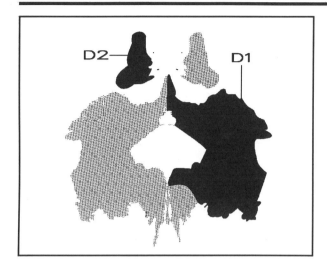

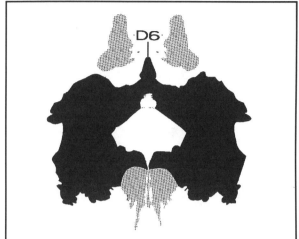

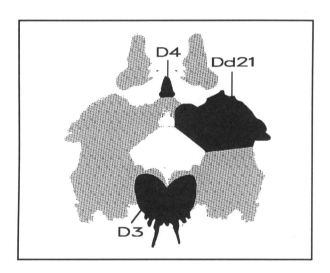

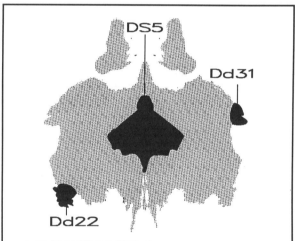

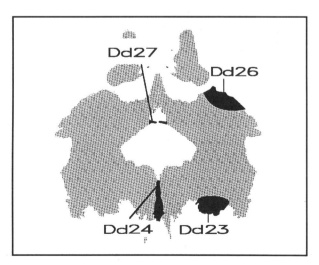

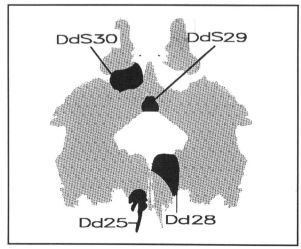

C A R D
II

Popular is to D1: BEAR, DOG, ELEPHANT OR LAMB, HEAD OR WHOLE ANIMAL

Z Values: W = 4.5 ADJACENT = 3.0 DISTANT = 5.5 SPACE = 4.5

W

-   Anatomy (Specific)
- u Anatomy (Unspecified)
- u Animals (Unspecified)
- u Art (Abstract)
-   Badge
-   Bat
- o Bears
-   Bird
- u Birds (2)
-   Body
- u Bookends
-   Bug (Smushed)
- u **v** Bug (Winged)
- o **v** Butterfly
- o Cartoon Characters (Human or animal)
- u Cave
- u Chickens
- o Dancers
- u Design (Abstract)
- o Devils
-   Disc (Anatomy)
- u Dogs (With D3 as blood or separate object)
- u Ducks
- u Emblem
- o **v** Explosion
-   Face (Human or animal)
- o Fire & Smoke
-   Flower
-   Fly
- u Gorillas
-   Heart
- u Hole (Bullet)
- o Humans or Human-like Figures
-   Insect (Not winged)
- u Insect (Winged)
-   Intestines
-   Kidneys
- u Kite
- u Lamp (Ornamental)
-   Lungs

-   Map
- u Mask
- (Note: This category includes a variety of animal, cartoon, Halloween, party etc. masks)
-   Meat
- u Monster
- u **v** Moth
-   Mouth
- o Ornament
- u **v** Pelvis
- u Penguins (2)
- u **v** Phoenix
-   Plant
-   Rectum
-   Spaceship
- o Statues (Human or animal)
-   Stomach
-   Throat
- u **v** Torches (With smoke)
-   Tornado
- u Turkeys
-   Vagina
- u Volcano
- u **v** Volcano (Erupting)
- - **v** Wreath (Xmas)
-   X-ray

D1

-   Amoeba
- u Animal (Stuffed)
- u Animal (Unspecified)
- u Baboon
- o Bear
-   Bird
- u <Buffalo
- o <Cat
-   Chicken (No head)
- u Cloud
-   Clown

- u **v** Coat
- o Cow
- o **v** Demon
- o Dog
- u **v** Dog
- o Elephant
-   Fish
- u **v** Gorilla
- o <Hamster
-   Hat
-   Heart
-   Hippo
-   Human
- o **v** Human
- u Insect
- o Lamb
- u Landscape
-   Leaf
-   Machine
-   Map
- o **v** Monster
-   Monument
- o **v** Mountain(s)
-   Pig
- o <Rabbit
- u Rock
- u Smoke
-   Sponge
- u Tiger
-   Tree
-   Turtle
- u Warthog
-   Wing

D2

-   Anatomy
- u Angel
-   Animals (Unspecified)
- o Bird
- u >Bird
- o Blood

D2 (Continued)

–	Boot
–	Bug (Not winged)
u	Bug (Winged)
o	Butterfly (Side view)
–	Candle
o	Cap
–	Cell (Blood)
u	Chicken
o	Creature (Cartoon)
u	Devil
u	Finger Painting
–	Fingerprint
o	Fire
o	Flame
u **v**	Footprint
–	Hand
o	Hat
–	Head (Animal)
u	Head (Bird)
–	Head (Human)
u	Head (Human-like)
u **v**	Holster
u **v**	Hummingbird
u **v**	Italy (Map)
–	Kidney
–	Lantern
u	Lava
–	Leg
u	Lipstick Smear
o	Mask (Animal, bird, cartoon, human-like)
u	Meat
–	Mitten
–	Penis
o	Puppet (Hand)
u	Rabbit
–	Rat
u	Rooster
o	Seal
–	Shoe
u	Snail
u **v**	Sock
u **v**	South America (Map)
–	Termite
u	Thumb
–	Tongue
–	Tooth
o	Torch
–	Vase
u	Walrus

D3

u	Anemone (Sea)
–	Ant
–	Anus
u	Bagpipes
–	Beetle
o	Blood
–	Bug (Not winged)
o	Bug (Winged)
o	Butterfly
–	Clamp
u	Coral
o	Crab
–	Crawfish
u	Embryo
o **v**	Explosion
–	Face (Animal)
u **v**	Face (Devil or monster)
–	Face (Human)
u	Fan
o	Fire
–	Fish
u **v**	Flower
–	Fly
–	Hair Ribbon
u **v**	Head (Animal, horned)
–	Head (Animal, not horned)
–	Head (Bird)
–	Head (Human)
u **v**	Headset (Radio)
–	Heart
u	Insect
u	Jellyfish
–	Kidney
–	Lobster
–	Lung
u	Manta Ray
–	Mask
u	Meat
u	Menstruation
u	Monster
u	Moth
o	Paint
u	Plant
u	Snail
u	Spaceship
o **v**	Sun
o **v**	Torch
o	Vagina

o	Volcano
–	Uterus

D4

o	Arrow
o	Arrowhead
–	Bat (Baseball)
–	Bell
–	Bottle
o	Bullet
u	Candle
o	Capsule (Space)
u	Castle
u	Clippers
–	Crucifix
–	Crucifixion
u	Dome
–	Door
u **v**	Drill
–	Face
u	Hands (Praying)
u	Hat
–	Head
u	Helmet
–	Knife
o	Missile
u	Monument
–	Mountain
–	Nose
u	Penis
u	Penpoint
u	Pliers
u	Pyramid
u	Robot
o	Rocket
–	Snake
o	Spaceship
u	Spear (Tip)
o	Steeple
–	Tail
o	Temple
o	Tower
u	Tree (Fir)
–	Tree (Unspecified)
–	Vase
u	Weapon

DS5

o	Airplane
u	Archway
u	Basket
–	Bat
u	Bell
–	Bird
–	Boat
u	Bowl
–	Butterfly
o	Castle (May include D4)
o	Cave
o	Chandelier
o	Church
u	Crown
u	Diamond
u	Dome
–	Dress
u	Drill
u	Fountain
u	Glass
u	Goblet
u	Hat (Woman's)
–	Heart
u	Helmet
o	Hole
u	Island
u	Kite
o	Lake
o	Lamp
o	Light
–	Mask
o	Missile
–	Mouth
o	Ornament
u	Pendant
o	Rocket
u	Silhouette (Human, dancer or skater in costume)
u	Snowflake
o	Spaceship
u	Steeple
u v	Sting Ray
–	Stomach
u	Temple
o	Top
o	Tunnel
u	Vagina
o	Vase
u	Well

D6

–	Anatomy
u	Animals (2 Unspecified)
o	Animals (2, meeting criterion for o as D1)
–	Backbone
–	Bat
–	Bird
u	Butterfly
u	Cloud(s)
u	Doughnut
u	Drainpipe (with DS5)
–	Humans (2)
o v	Humans (2)
–	Insect (Not winged)
u	Insect (Winged)
u	Island
u	Landscape (Often with DS5 as lake)
–	Lungs
–	Map (Specified)
u	Map (Unspecified)
u	Moth
u	Mountain
o v	Pelvis
–	Rug
u	Spaceship (Usually with reference to DS5)
u	Spinal Cord (Slice, may include DS5)
–	Stomach
o v	X-ray (Pelvic)
–	X-ray (Specific other than pelvic)
–	X-ray (Nonspecific)

Dd21

–	Beak
–	Bird
–	Ear
–	Frog
o	Head (Animal)
–	Head (Bird)
–	Head (Fish)
–	Head (Human)

o	Mountain
–	Nest
–	Seal
–	Shrub
–	X-ray

Dd22

o v	Bush
–	Chicken
–	Head (Animal)
u v	Head (Human)
u v	Rabbit
u v	Rock
–	Tree

Dd23

u v	Bush
–	Frog
–	Head
u v	Mountain
u v	Rock
–	Tree

Dd24

u	Anus
u	Bowling Pin
u	Bullet
u	Candle
–	Face
u	Ghost
–	Human
u	Human-like Figure
u	Penis
u	Rocket
–	Tooth
u	Totem
o	Vagina
u v	Waterfall

Dd25

o Antennae
o Antlers
u Feelers
o Horns
u Icicles
u Needle
u Spear
u Spike
u Stick
– Tail
– Tusk

Dd26

o Blood
u Caterpillar
o Fire
u Sunset
– Walrus
u Worm

Dd27

u Bridge
u Claw
– Nail
– Tail
– Wall

Dd28

u Bloodstain
– Head
– Turtle
u Varnish
u Wood (Stained)
– X-ray

DdS29

u Cave
u Cup
u Dome
u v Goblet
u Pottery
u Tunnel

DdS30

– Clam
– Eyes
– Head
u Inlet
– Oyster

Dd31

u Beak
– Claw
u v Ears (Animal)
u Faces
– Head (Animal)
u Head (Human)
u Head (Human-like)
u <Mountains
u Stone Sculpture
– Trees

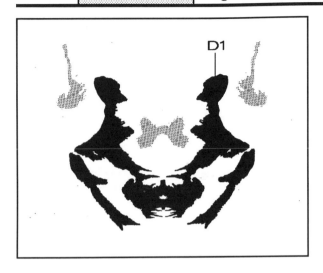

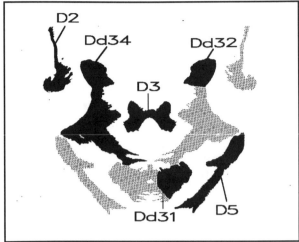

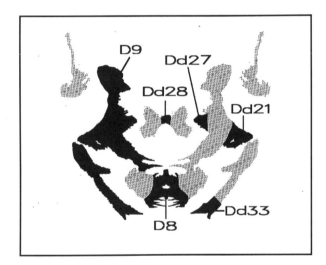

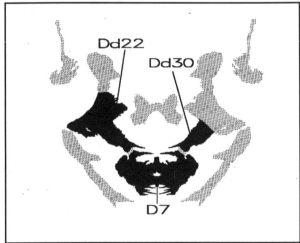

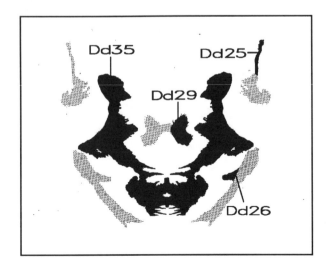

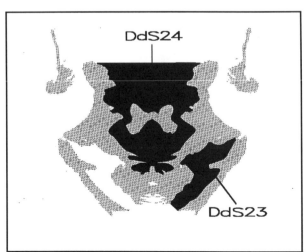

CARD III

Popular is to D1 or D9: Human Figure or Representation Thereof

Z Values: W = 5.5 ADJACENT = 3.0 DISTANT = 4.0 SPACE = 4.5

W

(Note: Most W responses that involve a single object will be coded - as the blot is broken. In a few instances, response frequencies argue in favor of a u coding for answers which conform to the contours and are not largely dependent on arbitrarily created contours. W responses coded o will usually involve multiple objects)

-   Anatomy
-   Animal
- o Animals (As D1 in a scene with other objects, such as in a circus. All other objects included must be codeable as o if reported separately)
-   Ant
- u Art (Abstract)
- u Badge
- o Birds (As D1 in a scene with other objects such as in a cage. All other objects included must be codeable as o if reported separately)
- u Bowl (With handles and design)
-   Bug
-   Butterfly
-   Cat
- u Chandelier
-   Crab
- u Emblem
-   Face
-   Flower
-   Fly
-   Frog
- u Frog (Dissected)
-   Gorilla

-   Human
- o Humans or Human-Like Figures (As D1 in a scene with other objects each of which would be coded as o if reported separately, such as in ceremonies, parties, playgrounds, etc.)
-   Insect
- u **v** Islands
-   Jack-O-Lantern
-   Jellyfish
- u **v** Landscape
-   Map (Specific)
- u Map (Unspecified)
- u **v** Monster
-   Noose
-   Rib Cage
-   Skeleton
-   Spider
- u **v** Vase (With handles and design)
-   X-ray

D1

-   Animal
- u Animals (2 Unspecified)
-   Ant
- u **v** Arch
-   Bird
- o Birds (2)
- o Bone Structure
-   Bug
- u **v** Cave Entrance
-   Dog
- o Dogs (2 with D7 as separate object)
- o Dolls (2)
- u Frog (Dissected)
- u **v** Gremlin
-   Human

- o Humans (2 with D7 as separate object)
-   Humans (2 with D7 or Dd31 included as a part of the human figure)
- u **v** Humans (With D5 as arms)
-   Insect
- u Keel (Boat with D5 as supports)
- o **v** Landscape
-   Lobster
-   Map (Specific)
- u Map (Unspecified)
- o Monkeys (With D7 as separate object)
- u **v** Monster (Alien, robot)
- u **v** Mountain (Usually with snow)
- o Ostrich (2)
- o Pelvic Structure
- o Sheep (2, or lambs)
-   Skeleton
-   Skull
-   Spider
-   Trees
-   Tunnel
- u Vase
- o X-ray (Pelvis)
- u X-ray (Unspecified)

D2

- u Amoeba
-   Anchor
- o Animal (Long tailed)
-   Animal (Not long tailed)
-   Artery
-   Berries
- o Bird
- o Blood

D2 (Continued)

- – Bone
- – Brain
- – Bug
- u Chandelier
- o Chicken (Hanging)
- – Club
- – Cocoon
- u Coral
- o Decoration (Unspecified)
- o Devil
- – Dog
- – Dragon
- – Duck
- o Embryo
- u Esophagus
- u Fetus
- o Fire
- – Fish
- u Fishhook
- o v Flamingo
- – Flesh
- u v Flower
- – Fly
- u Germ
- u Guitar
- o Hat (Clown or Costume)
- – Head (Animal)
- – Head (Bird)
- – Head (Human)
- u Head (Human-like)
- – Heart
- u Hook
- o Human (This class of response includes many varieties of the human figure with the blot held in various positions, such as acrobat, child, gymnast, etc.)
- o Human-Like Figure (This class of response includes many variations of cartoon, mythological, or science fiction figures such as devil, dwarf, elf, imp, etc.)
- – Insect
- – Intestine
- u Island
- u Kidney
- u Lantern

- – Lung
- o Meat (Hung)
- o Monkey
- o Neuron
- u Note (Musical)
- o v Parrot
- u v Pipe
- u v Plant
- o Pot (Hanging)
- o v Puppet
- – Rabbit
- – Raindrops
- u Robot
- u Rope (Vine)
- u Sea Horse
- – Snail
- – Snake
- u Statue (Abstract)
- u Statue (Animal)
- o Statue (Human)
- – Stick
- u Stomach
- o Symbol (Abstract)
- u v Tree
- o Umbilical Cord (With placenta)
- – Vase

D3

- – Antennae
- – Antlers
- – Bat
- u Bellows
- – Bird
- o Blood
- u Bone
- o Bow
- – Brain
- u Brassiere
- – Breasts
- – Breastbone
- o Butterfly
- u Chair (Back of typists)
- – Crab
- u Dam (Between hills)
- o Decoration (Unspecified)
- – Dragonfly
- u Dumbbell

- u Emblem (Abstract)
- u Exercise Apparatus
- – Eye Glasses
- u Eye Shades
- o Fire
- – Fly
- u Fossil
- – Girdle
- u Hang Glider
- – Heart
- – Helmet
- – Human(s)
- – Insect (Not Winged)
- u Insect (Winged)
- – Intestine
- u Island
- u Kidney
- u Kite
- – Lips
- o Lungs
- – Mask
- u Mosquito
- o Moth
- – Mouth
- – Nose
- u Noseguard
- – Nostrils
- – Oranges
- o Pelvic Structure
- o Ribbon
- – Seed
- – Skeleton
- u Slingshot
- u Spinal Cord (Cross Section)
- u Sun Glasses
- – Testicles
- – Trees
- u Wasp
- u Wing
- – Wishbone

D5

- u Arm
- u Arrow
- – Bird
- u Bomb
- – Bone
- – Bug

D5 (Continued)

u	Bullet
u	Claw
u	Club
o	Fish
–	Gun
–	Hand
–	Horn
u	Island
o	Leg (Animal)
o	Leg (Bird)
o	Leg (Human)
u	Leg (Insect, usually spider)
u	Limb (Tree)
u	Log
–	Map
u	Missile
–	Pen
u	Peninsula
u	Rocket
o	Shark
–	Snake
u	Spaceship
u	Spear
u	Stick
u	Torpedo
–	Tree
–	Vine

D7

–	Anatomy
–	Animal
o	Basket
–	Beetle
o	Bones
–	Buckle
–	Butterfly
–	Cactus
o	Cauldron
u	Coal (Piece)
o	Crab
u	Drum
–	Ducks
–	Eye Glasses
–	Face
o	Fireplace
u	Gate

–	Head
u	Head (Monster)
–	Heart
u	Island
–	Kidney
–	Lungs
u v	Mushrooms
o	Nest
o	Pelvis
u	Pumpkin (Halloween)
–	Ribs
o	Rock(s)
u	Shadows
u	Smoke
–	Stomach
u	Table
– v	Tornado
o v	Trees (DdS24 Lake)
–	Vagina
u	Vertebrae
o	X-ray (Pelvis)
–	X-ray (Specific other than pelvis)
u	X-ray (Unspecified)

D8

u v	Basket
o	Bones
–	Brain Stem
–	Chest
u	Crab
–	Dragon
u	Face (Alien, monster)
u	Hour Glass
u	Lake (In Mountains)
u	Lamp
u	Monster
–	Pumpkin
o	Ribs
–	River
u	Skeletal (Specific other than ribs)
o	Skeletal (Unspecified)
u	Stone
u v	Torch
–	Vagina
u v	Vase

u v	Wine Glass
–	X-ray

D9

–	Anatomy
u	Animal (Unspecified)
–	Ant
o	Bird
–	Bug
o	Cartoon Figure
u	Chicken
u	Cloud
u	Demon
o	Dog
o	Doll
u	Duck
–	Foliage
u	Ghost
o	Human
–	Insect
u	Jack-In-The-Box
–	King Kong
o	Lamb
u v	Landscape
o	Monkey
u	Monster
u v	Mountain
u	Parrot
o	Puppet
–	Rabbit
–	Root
o	Sheep
u	Skeleton
–	Spider
u	Statue
–	Tree
o	Witch
–	X-ray

Dd21

u	Bird
–	Bomb
u	Cliff

Dd21 (Continued)

- – Dog
- – Head (Animal)
- o Head (Bird)
- o Head (Fish)
- – Head (Human)
- u Landscape
- o **v** Mountain
- u Peninsula
- u **v** Tree

Dd22

- – Animal
- o Bird
- – Bone
- u Cloud
- u Human (Upper Half)
- u **v** Landscape
- – Rodent
- u Statue

DdS23

- u Bird
- u Cloud
- u Ghost
- – Head
- u Water

DdS24

- u Bowl
- – Head
- u Lake
- u **v** Lamp
- u **v** Mushroom
- u Snow
- u **v** Statue
- u Vase

Dd25

- u Esophagus
- – Face
- – Head
- u Root
- u Rope
- – Spear
- u Stick
- u String
- u Tail
- – Tool
- u Tube
- u Umbilical Cord
- u Worm

Dd26

- u Duck Bill
- u Fin
- – Head
- – Leg
- o Penis
- u Stump

Dd27

- o Breast
- – Building
- o Head (Animal)
- o Head (Bird)
- u Head (Fish)
- – Head (Human)
- u **v** Mountain
- u Nose
- – Skull

Dd28

- u Corset
- u Dam
- u Doors (Swinging)
- – Face
- – Head
- u Net
- – Tooth

Dd29

- – Airplane
- – Arrow
- u Arrowhead
- u Bird
- u Breast
- u Butterfly
- u Cartoon Character
- – Fetus
- – Head
- – Heart
- – Human
- – Insect
- – Kidney
- – Tent
- u **<** Valentine

Dd30

- u Arm
- – Club
- – Foot
- – Hand
- – Head
- u Icicle
- u Log
- – Missile

Dd31

- – Anatomy
- u Animal
- o Ball
- u Balloon
- o Basket
- u Bones
- u Boxing Glove
- u Cloud
- – Earmuffs
- – Embryo
- – Eyes
- – Face
- – Fan
- u Feather Duster
- u Gourd
- – Hat
- – Head (Animal)
- o **v** Head (Human)
- o **v** Head (Skeletal)
- u Kettledrums
- – Lamp
- – Lungs
- u Mittens
- – Mountains
- o Pot
- – Shoes
- o Skeletal
- o **v** Skull
- u Smoke
- o Stones
- o **v** Trees
- – Turtle
- – Womb

Dd32

- – Animal
- – Ball
- u Clam
- u Coconut
- – Egg
- – Eye
- – Fish
- – Head (Animal)
- o Head (Bird)
- o Head (Human)

- u Mask
- u Oyster
- u Rock
- u Statue

Dd33

- u Claw
- u Finger
- u Foot
- – Fork
- u Hand
- – Head (Animal)
- u Head (Bird)
- – Head (Human)
- o Hoof
- – Penpoint
- o Shoe
- – Spear

Dd34

- – Animal
- o Bird
- – Fish
- o Human (Upper part)
- – Insect
- o **v** Landscape
- o **v** Mountains
- – Skeletal
- – X-ray

Dd35

- u Arch
- o Birds (2)
- u Bones
- u Bowl
- – Crab
- – Frog
- u Islands
- o **v** Landscape
- u Mountains (Aerial view)
- o Pelvis
- – Trees
- u Vase
- o X-ray (Pelvis)
- – X-ray (Specific other than pelvis)
- u X-ray (Unspecified)

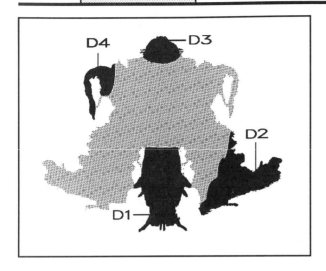

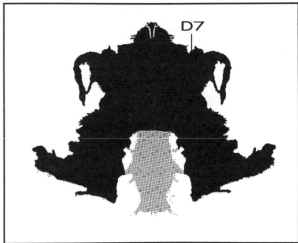

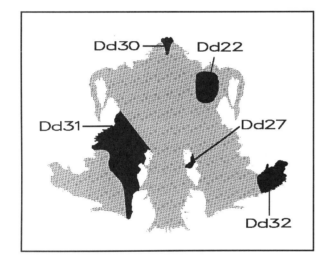

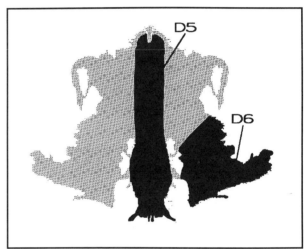

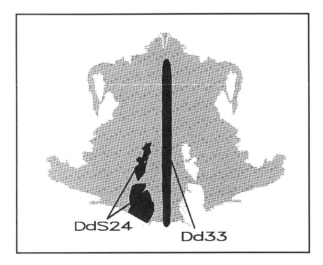

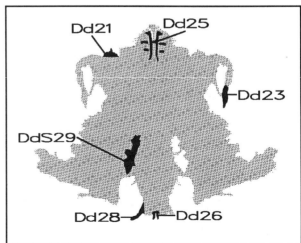

CARD IV

Popular is to W or D7: HUMAN OR HUMAN-LIKE FIGURE

Z Values: W = 2.0   ADJACENT = 4.0   DISTANT = 3.5   SPACE = 5.0

W

- – Amoeba
- o **v** Anchor
- o Animal
- u Animal (Squashed)
- u Anteater
- o **v** Badge
- o **v** Bat
- u Bell
- u **v** Bird
- o Boots (On pole)
- – Brain
- – Bug (Flattened)
- u **v** Bug (Winged)
- – Building
- – Bull
- o Bush(es)
- o Butterfly
- – Candle
- u Canyon (Often with center area as river)
- u Carcass (Animal)
- – Cave
- u **v** Chandelier
- u Cloud(s)
- o Coat (On pole)
- – Coral
- – Crab
- o **v** Crest
- u Design (Abstract)
- u Dinosaur (Front view)
- u Dirt
- u Dog (Sitting, usually facing away)
- u Dragon (Front view)
- u **v** Eagle
- – Elephant
- o **v** Emblem
- – Embryo
- u **v** Explosion
- – Face
- u **v** Flower
- u Forest (Top view)
- u Fossil
- u **v** Fountain

- u Frog
- u Fungus
- o Giant
- o Gorilla
- u Groundhog
- u Head (Animal)
- – Head (Bird)
- – Head (Human)
- u Head (Reptile)
- – Helmet
- o Hide (Animal)
- o Human
- (Note: This class of response may involve W as the human figure or D7 as the human figure with D1 as a second object, such as bike, seat, stump, etc. The card must be upright).
- o Human-like Figure
- u Humans (2, leaning against center object)
- o Hunchback
- u Ice Cream Cone
- – Insect
- u **v** Insect (Winged)
- u Island (Unspecified)
- – Jello
- – Jellyfish
- u Kite
- o Landscape
- o <Landscape (Reflected)
- o Leaf
- – Lettuce
- – Lobster
- – Lung(s)
- – Map (Specific)
- o Map (Topographic, nonspecific)
- u Map (Unspecified)
- u Mask (Usually science fiction)
- – Meat with bone
- o **v** Monster
- u **v** Moth
- u Mountain
- u Mud

- o Pelt
- o **v** Pelvis
- o **v** Plant
- u Robe
- u Robot
- u Rock
- – Rocket
- – Root
- o Rug
- u Scarecrow
- o Sea Animal
- u Seaweed
- o Skin (Animal)
- – Skull (Animal)
- u Smoke
- – Snail
- – Snowflake
- u Sponge
- u Squid
- u Squirrel (Flying)
- u Squirrel
- u Statue
- o **v** Sting Ray
- u Teenage Mutant Ninja Turtle
- u Temple
- o Tree
- – Tornado
- – Turtle
- u **v** Urn
- u Volcano
- u **v** Waterfall (As D1 with landscape around)
- o X-ray (Pelvis)
- – X-ray (Specific other than Pelvis)
- u X-ray (Unspecified)

D1

- – Alligator
- – Animal
- u Bug
- o Bush(es)
- o **v** Cactus
- u **v** Candle
- u **v** Castle
- o Caterpillar
- – Crab
- – Crawfish
- u **v** Crown
- – Fish
- o **v** Head (Animal, horned or horse)
- – **v** Head (Animal, specific not horned or horse)
- u **v** Head (Animal, not specific)
- u **v** Head (Bird)
- u Head (Dragon)
- – **v** Head (Human)
- o **v** Head (Insect)
- u **v** Head (Monster)
- – **v** Head (Reptile other than turtle)
- u **v** Head (Turtle)
- u **v** Head (Snail)
- – Human
- u **v** Hydrant
- o Insect
- – Intestines
- – Lamp
- u **v** Lighthouse
- u Medulla
- – Nose (Human or animal)
- u Nose (Fictional human or animal)
- – Penis
- – Shell
- o Shrub
- – Skull
- u Snail
- – Snake
- o Spinal Cord
- o Stool
- u **v** Stove (Wood burning)
- o Stump
- u Tail

- o Tree Trunk
- o Vertebrae
- – Worm
- – X-ray

D2

- o <Bear
- – Boat
- – Bone
- u Cliff
- u Cloud
- – Cow
- o **v** Dog
- – Emblem
- o Foot
- o <Head (Animal, flat or stubby nose such as bear, dog, pig, seal, etc.)
- u <Head (Animal, not specific)
- – Head (Bird)
- u **v** Head (Camel)
- o <Head (Human)
- – Head (Insect)
- – Head (Reptile)
- u Landscape
- u Map (Africa or South America)
- – Map (Specific other than Africa or South America)
- u Map (Unspecified)
- u Peninsula
- o <Pig
- u Rock
- o <Seal
- o Shoe
- u Sphinx
- u Statue
- u <Totem
- u <Wave
- u Wing
- – X-ray

D3

- – Anus
- u Brain
- – Beak (Bird)
- o Bud (Flower)
- u Bush
- u Butterfly
- u Cabbage
- u Clam
- u Crown
- – Face
- u Fan
- o Flower
- o Head (Animal, flat faced such as cat, monkey, owl, etc.)
- – Head (Animal, specific but not flat faced)
- u Head (Animal, unspecified)
- u Head (Bird)
- – Head (Human)
- u Head (Monster or science fiction)
- – Head (Reptile)
- – Insect (Not winged)
- u Insect (Winged)
- u Leaf
- u Mountain
- u Mushroom
- o Sea Shell
- u Shrub
- u Tam o' Shanter
- u Tree (Top)
- u Vagina

D4

- – Animal
- u Arm (Deformed)
- – Arrow
- o Bird (Long necked)
- o Branch (Tree)
- u Cap (Stocking)
- o Claw
- o Diver (Back flip)

D4 (Continued)

-   Ear
- u Eel
-   Fish
- u **v** Fish hook
-   Flower (Dead)
- o Handle
-   Head (Animal)
- o Head (Bird)
- u Horn (Animal)
- o Human (Bending or diving)
- o Icicle
-   Leg
- o Lizard
- u Nail (Bent)
- u Peninsula
-   Penis
- u Root
- o Snake
- u Tail
- u Trunk (Elephant)
- o Vine (Hanging)

D5

- o Bone (Skeletal)
- o Canyon
- o Column
-   Crayfish
- u Drill
-   Fish
- u **v** Fountain
- o Gorge
-   Insect
- o Pole
- o River
-   Rocket
- o Spinal Cord
-   Statue
- u Totem
-   Tree
- o Vertebrae
- o Waterway
- u Worm
- u X-ray (Specific other than spine)

- o X-ray (Spine)
- u X-ray (Unspecified)

D6

- o <Animal (As D2 on hill or rock)
- o Boot
-   Face
- o Foot
- u **v** Head (Camel)
- u **v** Head (Cartoon animal)
- o <Human (As D2 sitting in a chair or on a hill)
-   Italy
- o Leg
- u Map (Italy)
-   Map (Specific other than Italy)
- u Map (Unspecified)
- u Rudder
-   Sea Animal
- u Shoe
- u Smoke
- u **v** Wing

D7

- u **v** Anchor
- o Animal
- u **v** Badge
- o **v** Bat
- u Bird
-   Bug
-   Crab
-   Face
- u Fossil
- u Frog
- o Giant
- o Gorilla
-   Head
- u Helmet
- o Hide (Animal)
- o Human
- o Hunchback

- u Island
- o Mask
- o Monster
- u Mountain
- o **v** Pelvis
- u Squirrel
- u Statue

Dd21

-   Apple
- u Crown
- o Face (Human, profile)
-   Fist
-   Head (Animal)
- o Head (Human)
- u Hut
- u Landscape
- u Temple
- u Tent
-   Wart

Dd22

-   Eye
-   Face
-   Head
-   Moon
-   Shrub

Dd23

- u Beak
-   Head (Animal)
- o Head (Bird)
-   Head (Human)
- u Head (Reptile)

DdS24

u   Clouds
u   Ghosts
–   Head(s)
u   Snow

Dd25

–   Face
–   Human(s)
–   Human-Like Figure(s)
u   Landscape (Aerial view)

Dd26

–   Clitoris
u   Feet
u   Fingers
u **v** Ghosts
–   Heads (Animal)
u   Heads (Bird)
–   Heads (Human)
–   Humans
u **v** Human-Like Figures
u   Legs
u   Snakes
–   Teeth
–   Trees
u   Worms

Dd27

u   Bridge
u   Cliff
–   Foot
–   Tail

Dd28

o   Antennae
–   Claws
–   Feet
u   Horns
–   Legs
–   Roots
u   Stingers (Insect)

DdS29

u   Clouds
u   Ghosts
u   Lakes
u   Monsters

Dd30

u   Beak
–   Face
u   Flower
–   Heart
–   Human
u   Nail
o **v** Rocket
u   Tack
o   Tee (Golf)
–   Tongue
u   Tooth
u   Waterfall

Dd31

–   Animal
–   Bird
u   Ghost
–   Head (Animal)
–   Head (Bird)
–   Head (Human)
u **v** Head (Human-like)
–   Human
–   Rock
–   Root
u **v** Seal
u **v** Statue
–   Tree
u **v** Witch

Dd32

–   Fist
u **<** Head, Animal
u **v** Head (Animal with flat or stubby nose)
u **v** Head (Human)
u   Rock
u   Toe

Dd33

o   Bone (Skeletal)
o   Crayon
u   Drill
o   Gorge
u   Pole
o   River
o   Spine
o   Waterway

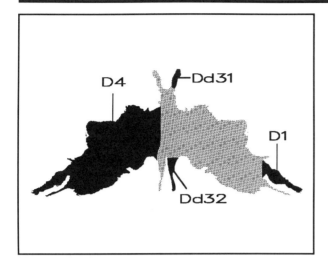

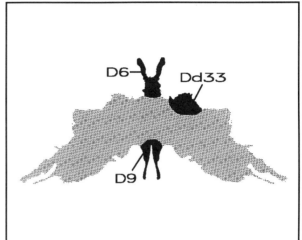

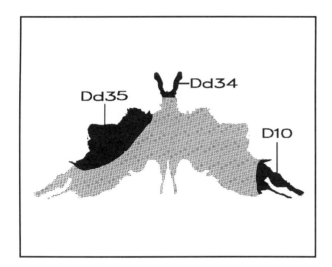

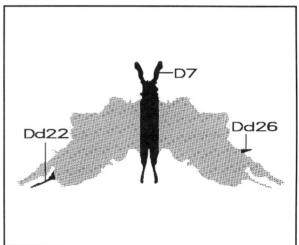

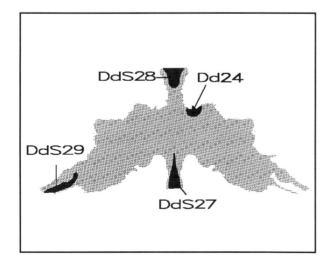

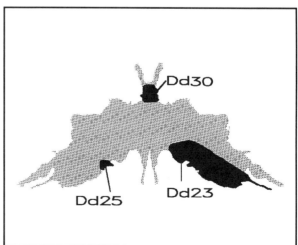

CARD V

Popular is to W: BAT OR BUTTERFLY

Z Values: W = 1.0   ADJACENT = 2.5   DISTANT = 5.0   SPACE = 4.0

W

u v Acrobat (Doing handstand)
u Airplane
– Anatomy
– Anchor
u Angel
– Animals
o Animals (2 Butting heads)
– Badge
– Banana
o Bat
– Beetle
o Bird (Beak D6)
u Bird (Beak D9)
o < Bird (To midline, being reflected)
u Bookends
u Boomerang
– Bug (Not winged)
u Bug (Winged)
o Butterfly
u Cape
– Cat
u Cloth (Piece)
u Cloud(s)
– Clove
u Coal (Piece)
– Coat
– Coral
o Crow
o Dancer (In costume)
u Demon
u Devil (Sometimes winged)
o Dracula
u Duck
u Eagle
– Elves
– Explosion
u Fairy
– Fern
– Flag
u Flea
u Fly

u Flower
u Foliage
u Fur
– Gnat
u Goose
– Grasshopper
– Hairpiece
– Head
u Hill (With trees)
u Hornet
– Human
o Human (In costume)
o Human (Hang gliding)
o Humans (Back to back)
u Human-Like Figure (Specified with giant arms or wings)
– Ice
– Insect (Not winged)
o Insect (Winged)
– Kangaroo
– Kidney
u Kite
o Landscape
u Leaf
– Lung(s)
– Machine
– Map
– Microorganism
u Monster
u Mosquito
o Moth
u Mountain
u Mustache
– Neckbone
u Ornament
u Ostrich
u Peacock
u Pelvis
o v Pelvis
– Propeller
u Pterodactyl
– Pump
– Ribs
u Rower (In boat)
– Sailboat

– Skeleton
u v Smoke
u Spaceship
– Spider
u Stole (Fur)
u Stone
– Tent
– Tree Stump (Reflected)
u < Tornado (Reflected)
– Umbrella
o Vampire
u Vulture
u Wasp
u Wings
u v Wok (Cooking)
o X-ray (Pelvis)
– X-ray (Specific other than pelvis)
u X-ray (Unspecified)

D1

u Arm
– Arrow
o Bone
– Cylinder
– Eel
– Fish
u Foot (Animal)
– Foot (Human)
– Head (Animal)
u Head (Cartoon animal)
– Head (Human)
o Head (Reptile)
o Leg (Animal)
o Leg (Human)
u Limb (Tree)
u Log
u Muscle
– Nose
u Root

D1 (Continued)

u Skull (Animal)
- Spear
u Stick
- Wrench

D4

- Alligator
o Animal (With head at D7)
- Anteater
u Blanket
o Bush(es)
u Cloud
- Crab
- Driftwood
u Fan
u Head (Alligator)
- Head (Animal)
- Head (Bird)
o Head (Human, profile)
o Human (Reclining)
- Insect
- Jellyfish
- Kangaroo
u Landscape
- Leaf
- Leg
u Leg (As D1 in clothing)
u Leg (Chicken or turkey cooked)
u Map
- Mud
u Plant
o Rock
u Shoulder Pad (Football)
- Skin
u Sleeping Bag
o **v** Smoke
u <Swan
- Tree
u Weed
u <Wing

D6

u Antennae
u Badge
- Bird
u Clippers
u **v** Elves
o Face (Animal, long eared)
- Face (Human)
o Face (Human with mask)
- Face (Unspecified)
u Fingers (2, As in victory sign)
u **v** Forceps
u Hat (Mickey Mouse)
o Head (Animal, with horns or long ears)
u Head (Animal)
u Head (Insect)
- Head (Human)
o Head (Human, In costume or with mask)
u <Head (Reptile)
- Head (Reptile)
u Human (Lower half)
u Insect (With antennae)
u Pliers
u **v** Robot
u **v** Sawhorse
u Scissors
u Slingshot
u Statue
- Tuning Fork
u Tweezers
- Vase
u Wishbone

D7

u Alien
o Animal (Horned or long eared)
- Animal (Not horned or long eared)
u Ballerina (In costume)
- Beetle
- Bone

u Bug (With antennae)
o Demon
o Devil
- Fish
- Human (2)
o Human (In costume)
u Humans (2, with arms raised)
u Human (Mythological)
u Insect (With antennae)
u Monster
o Rabbit
- Skeleton
u Snail
- Tree

D9

u Beak
u **v** Bells
o **v** Birds (2, long-neck)
u **v** Brooms
u Chopsticks
u Clamp
u Cleaners (Vacuum)
- Feet (Animal)
o Feet (Bird)
- Feet (Human)
o **v** Flamingos
o **v** Geese
u <Head (Alligator)
- Head
u Heads (2, Birds)
- Insect(s)
u Legs (Animal)
o Legs (Bird)
- Legs (Human)
u Pliers
- Stethoscope
o Swans
u Tail(s)
o Tweezers
- Vagina
o Wishbone

D10

- u Bones
- − Coral
- − Head (Animal)
- u Head (Bird)
- u Head (Cartoon)
- o Head (Reptile)
- − Insect
- u Legs (Animal)
- − Legs (Bird)
- u Legs (Human)
- − Nose
- u Peninsula
- u Pincers (Crab)
- u Pipe Wrench
- o Roots
- u Wood (Driftwood, logs or sticks)

Dd22

- o Arrow
- u Bayonet
- u Crutch
- − Finger
- − Head (Animal)
- u Head (Bird)
- − Head (Human)
- − Insect
- − Leg (Animal)
- u Leg (Bird)
- − Leg (Human)
- o Limb (Tree)
- o Reptile
- o Spear
- o Sword
- o Tail

Dd23

- u Coastline
- − Head (Animal)
- − Head (Human)
- u Landscape

Dd24

- u Bird
- − Breast
- u Ghost
- − Human
- u Monster
- u Nipple
- u Tent
- u Tree

Dd25

- u Cannon
- − Hat
- − Penis
- u Rock
- − Thumb
- − Tree

Dd26

- u v Bird (In flight)
- u Branch (Tree)
- − Head
- − Reptile
- − Tree

DdS27

- u Cone
- u Ghost
- u Inlet
- u Spike
- u Tower
- u v Vase

DdS28

- u v Bell
- u Cup
- − Helmet
- u v Hill
- u Inlet
- u v Mountain
- u Vase

DdS29

- u Inlet
- u River
- − Snake

Dd30

- − Ball
- − Face (Animal except cat or rabbit)
- u Face (Bird)
- u Face (Cat)
- − Face (Human)
- u Face (Rabbit)
- u Head (Animal)
- u Head (Bird)
- − Head (Human)
- o Mask
- − Skull

Dd31

- o Bone
- u Ear (Animal)
- u Elf
- u Finger
- – Foot
- – Head
- – Human
- u Leg
- u Penis
- u Stick
- – Tree
- u Worm

Dd32

- u Antennae
- o Beak
- o **v** Bird (Long neck)
- u Bone
- u Club
- – Finger
- o Head (Bird)
- – Match
- – Root
- – Snake
- o **v** Swan
- – Tree

Dd33

- – Breast
- – Head (Animal)
- – Head (Human)
- u Head (Human-Like)
- o Hill
- o Mountain
- u Shrub(s)

Dd34

- o Antennae
- u Beak
- u Bones
- u Clippers
- u Elves
- – Heads (Animal)
- – Heads (Birds)
- – Heads (Human)
- u Heads (Insect)
- u Heads (Reptile)
- o Horns
- – Humans
- u Human-Like Figures
- u **v** Legs
- u **<** Mouth (Animal or bird)
- u Pliers
- u Scissors
- u **v** Stool
- – Trees

Dd35

- – Breast
- – Head (Animal)
- – Head (Bird)
- o Head (Human, profile)
- u Human (Sitting or lying)
- o Landscape
- u Mask (Profile)
- o Mountains
- – Nose
- u Rocks

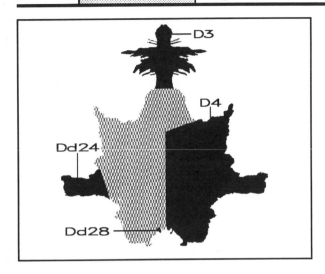

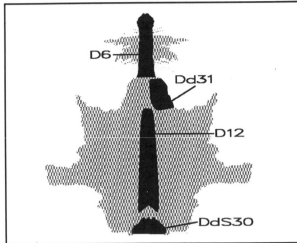

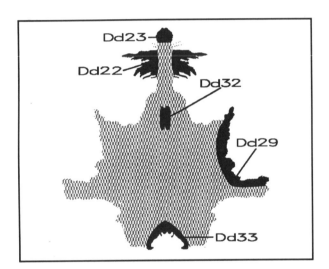

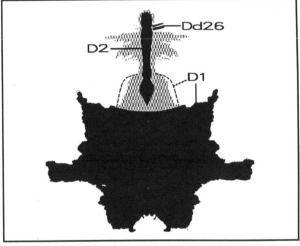

NOTE: The D1 location may also include the dashed area.

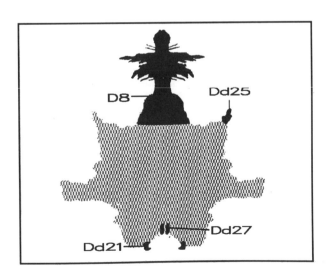

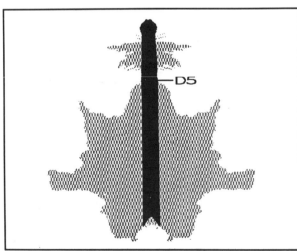

CARD VI

Popular is to W OR D1: ANIMAL SKIN, HIDE, PELT OR RUG

Z Values: W = 2.5 ADJACENT = 2.5 DISTANT = 6.0 SPACE = 6.5

W

u Abstract Drawing
u Airplane
– Amoeba
– Anchor
u Animal (In natural form, canine or feline, such as cat, dog, lynx, tiger, wolf, etc.)
– Animal (In natural form, not canine or feline such as anteater, elephant, giraffe, etc.)
o Animal (In unnatural form such as flattened, skinned, etc.)
u Animal (Sea, such a ray with D3 as head or tail)
o Animal Pelt or Skin
– Animal (Winged)
– Artichoke
u Artifact (Indian)
– Badge
– Bat
– Bear
o Bearskin
– Bee
– Beetle
u Bird
u Bird (Prehistoric)
– Body
– Brain
– Brainstem
– Bug (Not winged)
u Bug (Winged)
– Butterfly
o Candle (With D1 as base)
u Cello
– Chest
– Club
o v Coat (Hanging on Post)
u Coat (With hanger as D3)
u Cocoon (With butterfly or larvae as D3)

– Crab
– Crow
– Crown
u Design (Abstract)
– Doll
u Dragon (Flying)
– Dragonfly
u v Drill
u Duck
u v Duster (With handle)
– Emblem
u Explosion
– Face
o v Fan
– Faucet
– Fish (see also Animal, sea)
u v Flag
– Flea
u v Flower
– Fly
u Forest (Aerial view)
u Fountain (Abstract)
– Frog
o Fur Pelt
– Genitals (Male)
– Gnat
u Goose
u Guitar (Sometimes Dd24 is excluded)
u Gun (Space or toy)
– Hair
o <Iceberg (Reflected)
– Insect (Not winged)
u Insect (Winged)
u Island
u v Jackhammer
– Lamp
o <Landscape (Reflected)
u Leaf
u Leather (Piece)
u Lighthouse (On hill)
– Lizard (Flying)
– Lungs
– Map (Specific)
u Map (Unspecified)
u Mask (Science fiction)

u Mine Shaft (Cutaway view)
u v Mirror (Hand)
o Missile Launch (With missile at D6 and pad or smoke at D1)
u v Monster (Sometimes 2 headed)
u Monster (Animal)
u Monster (Sea)
– Mosquito
– Moth
– Mountain
– Mud
– Note (Musical)
u Ornament
– Pan
o Pelt
u v Plant
u v Pogo Stick
– Pot
u Raft
u v Road Sign
o Rocket Launch (With rocket at D3 and pad or smoke at D1)
u Rudder
o Rug
u v Scarecrow
u v Shield
o <Ship (Reflected with D3 as second object(s))
– Shrimp
– Skeleton
o Skin (Animal)
– Snail
– Spider
u v Sponge
u Squirrel (Flying)
u v Statue
u v Sting Ray
u Sword in Stone
u Tank (Top view with cannon)
– Tepee
o Totem (As D3 with D1 as hill or expanse)

W (Continued)

o **v** Tree
u Turtle
u Violin (Usually with Dd24 excluded)
– Volcano
o Waterway (As D5 with other areas landscape)
– X-ray (Specific)
u X-ray (Unspecified)

D1

u Amoeba
– Anatomy
u **v** Animals (Back to back)
– Artichoke
u Badge
u Bib
o Blanket
– Body
u Bookends
u Bowl (With handles)
– Brain
– Bug
– Butterfly
u **v** Cape
u **v** Cartoon Figures
– Chest
u Cloak
u Cloud(s)
u Coal (Piece)
o Coat
u Crevice (As middle area between rocks)
u **v** Crown
– Cup
– Disc (Anatomy)
u Doors (Swinging)
u Emblem
– Face
u Face (Monster)
u Filet (Fish or meat)
– Flesh
– Flower
u Foliage (Aerial view)
u Forest (Aerial view)

u Gate
u **v** Gorillas (Back to back)
– Head
– Heads (Animal)
u Heads (Human, profile, back to back)
u **v** Hive (Bee)
– Human
u Humans (Back to back)
u Ice
o **v** Iceberg (Reflected)
u Island
u **v** Jacket
o Landscape
o Leaf
– Liver (Anatomy)
– Lung(s)
– Map (Specific)
u Map (Topographic)
u Map (Unspecified)
u **v** Monkeys (Back to back)
u **v** Monster (Usually science fiction)
u **v** Monsters
o <Mountain Range (Reflected)
u Mud
u Ornament
o Pelt
o Pot (With handles)
u Rock(s)
o Rug
– Shell
u Shield
o Ship (Reflected)
o Skin (Animal)
– Skull
u Smoke
u Sponge
– Star
– Starfish
o Statues
– Turtle Shell
u Urn
o Waterway (As D5 with other areas as landscape)
– X-ray (Specific)
u X-ray (Unspecified)

D2

o Alligator
– Animal
o Banister Spindle
o Bedpost
u Bone
– Bug
o Candle
o Candlestick
– Caterpillar
u Club
u Crocodile
u Drill Bit
u Eel
– Fish
o Giant
o Human
o Human-Like Figure
– Insect
u Knife
o Lamp (Ornamental)
o Lamp Post
o Lamp (Street)
o Missile
u Nail
– Needle
u Pen
u Penis
u Piston
u Reptile
o Rocket
o Statue (Human-like)
u Sword
u Thermometer
o Totem Pole
u Train (Aerial view)
– Vertebrae
– X-ray (Specific)
u X-ray (Unspecified)

D3

u Airplane
– Anatomy
– Animal (Not winged)
u Animal (Winged)
o Bird

D3 (Continued)

u   Bug (Not winged)
o   Bug (Winged)
u   Butterfly
–   Coat Rack
o   Cross (Abstract or
    modern)
o   Crucifix (Abstract)
u   Crucifixion
o   Duck (Flying)
o   Emblem
–   Face
u   Flag (Torn)
u   Flower
u   Fly
u   Flying Fish
o   Goose (Flying)
u   Head (Animal, with
    whiskers)
–   Head (Bird)
–   Head (Human)
–   Head (Insect)
–   Head (Reptile)
u   Hornet
–   Human
o   Human (Abstract)
o   Human (In costume)
o   Human-Like Figure
u   Insect (Not winged)
o   Insect (Winged)
o   Lamp
–   Leaf
o   Match (With fire)
u   Object (Burning with
    Dd22 as flames)
o   Ornament
–   Owl
–   Penis
u   Pole (Electric or
    telephone)
u   Rocket
o   Rocket (With fire or
    smoke)
o   Scarecrow
u   <Shrub(s) (Reflected)
–   Skull
o   Statue
u   Streetlight (May include
    D5)
o   Totem Pole
u   Tree

–   Valve
u   Wasp
u   Weather Vane

D4

o   <Aircraft Carrier
u   **v** Animal
o   <Animal (As Dd24 and
    remainder as another
    object)
o   <Bathtub (With Dd24 as
    another object)
o   <Battleship
o   <Boat (In some instances
    Dd24 may be reported as a
    separate object)
–   Building
u   Cloud
o   <Cloud
–   Cocoon
u   Coral
u   Crib (With Dd24 as baby)
u   <Explosion
u   <Gun (Science fiction)
–   Head (Animal)
–   Head (Bird)
o   Head (Human, profile)
u   **v** Human
u   **v** Human-Like Figure
o   Iceberg
–   Insect
o   Landscape
–   Map (Specific)
u   Map (Unspecified)
o   Mask
o   <Mountain(s)
o   Rock
o   <Rower (In boat)
o   <Sailboat
o   <Ship
o   Statue
o   <Submarine
u   <Tank (Army)

D5

–   Animal
o   Backbone
o   Bone
o   Canal
o   Canyon
–   Caterpillar
u   Coat Rack
–   Eel
–   Fern
u   Foliage (Aerial view)
o   Gorge
–   Human
–   Insect
–   Knife
u   Lamp Post (Usually with
    Dd22 as light)
o   Missile Launch (With
    missile as D2 or D6 and
    remainder as smoke
    and/or fire)
u   Pole
u   Reptile
o   River
o   Road
o   Shaft
u   Snake
u   Spear
o   Spinal Cord
u   Stick
u   Thermometer
–   Tree
u   Tube
o   Waterway
u   Worm
–   X-ray (Specific, other than
    spine)
o   X-ray (Spine)
u   X-ray (Unspecified)

D6

–   Animal
u   Arm (With fist at Dd23)
o   Bullet
u   Cane
u   Carving

D6 (Continued)

u Club
u Cylinder
u Eel
– Fish
– Head (Animal)
– Head (Human)
u Head (Reptile, usually turtle)
– Human
u Insect
u Log
o Missile
u Mummy Case
– Neck
u Parking Meter
o Penis
o Pole
o Reptile
u Road
o Rocket
– Skull
u Statue
u Tower
– Valve
u Weapon (Unspecified)

D8

u Airplane
– Animal
u Bird
– Bug (Not winged)
u Bug (Winged, crawling from object)
– Butterfly
o Cross (On hill)
o Crucifix (Abstract)
o Crucifixion (On hill)
u Dragonfly
o Flower (In pot)
o Fountain
u Head (Animal, whiskered)
– Head (Bird)
– Head (Human)
– Head (Reptile)
u Human (Robed)

u Insect (Winged)
u Lamp Post
o Lighthouse
– Map
o Plant
o Rocket (With fire or smoke)
o Scarecrow
– Spinal Cord
u Statue (Bird)
o Statue (Human-like)
o Totem Pole
u Tree
– Turtle
– X-ray

D12

– Arrow
– Burner (Bunsen)
o Canal
o Candle
o Canyon
o Gorge
– Human
u Missile
– Needle
u Pencil
– Penis
– Rectum
o River
u Road
u Rocket
o Shaft (Mine)
u Spear
u Spinal Cord
u Vagina
o Waterway
u Zipper

Dd21

o v Claw
– Hand
– Head (Animal)

o v Head (Bird)
– Head (Human)
o v Head (Reptile)
u v Horn
o v Pincer
o v Tong

Dd22

– Arms
u Birds (2, profile)
u Branch(es)
u <Cactus
o Feathers
u Flames
– Flowers
u Geese (Flock)
– Ice
u Light Rays (Sun)
– Pelt
u Shrub(s)
u <Tree(s)
o Water (Splashing)
o Whiskers

Dd23

– Bug
– Eyes
u Fist
u Hands (Clasped)
– Head (Animal)
u Head (Bird)
– Head (Human)
u Head (Insect)
u Head (Monster)
u Head (Reptile)
– Heads (2)
u Knob (Door)
– Nose

Dd24

u **v** Animal (Sitting)
–   Boot
u **v** Castle
o   Cliff
u **v** Head (Animal, with upper body)
–   Head (Bird)
–   Head (Human)
–   Leg
–   Paw
o   Peninsula
o   Rock
o <Seal
o <Smokestack
u <Statue
u <Walrus
u   Wood

Dd25

u   Cactus
u   Carving
u   Doll
u   Foot (Human)
–   Head
u   Human
u   Mitten
–   Mountain
u   Paw
–   Penis
u   Shoe
u   Statue

Dd26

u   Antennae
–   Reptiles
u   Sticks
u   Whiskers

Dd27

–   Anatomy
–   Buttocks
u **v** Eggs
–   Eyes
–   Heads
–   Humans
–   Pincers
–   Testicles
–   Vagina
u **v** Waterfall

Dd28

u **v** Claws
–   Heads
u   Horns
u **v** Reptiles
–   Rocket(s)
–   Trees

Dd29

u   Coastline
–   Head
–   Human Profile

DdS30

–   Cup
u   Inlet
–   Vase

Dd31

u   Bird
–   Head
–   Human
u   Iceberg
–   Nose
u   Shaker (Salt or pepper)

Dd32

u   Boat
–   Brain
u   Butterfly
u   Clam (Opened)
–   Eggs
–   Eyes
u   Flames
–   Kidney(s)
–   Lung(s)
u   Oyster (Opened)
u   Shell (Opened)
–   Tonsils
u   Water Wings

Dd33

u **v** Canyon (May include waterfall)
–   Crab
u   Inlet
–   Insect
u   Landscape
o **v** Nest
–   Spider
u   Tongs
u   Tweezers
u   Vagina

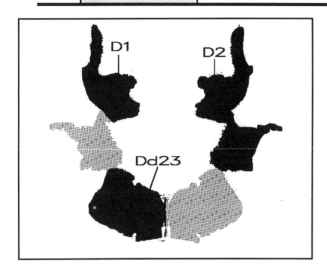

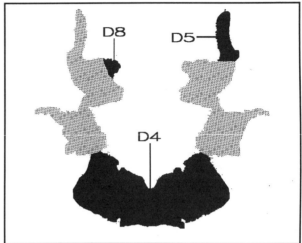

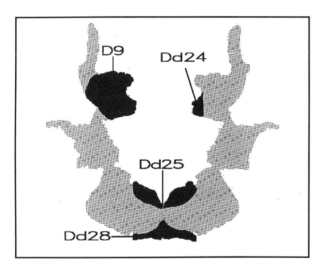

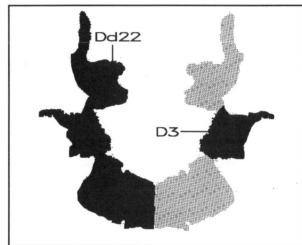

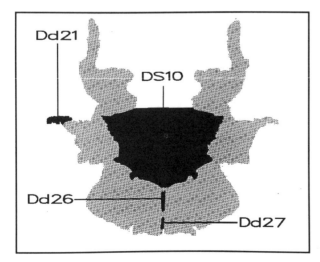

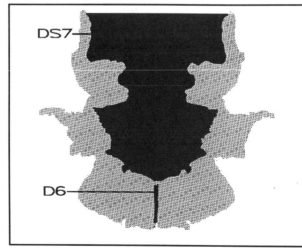

W

u   Abstract
–   Amoeba
–   Anatomy
–   Anchor
u   Animals (2, cartoon with each as one half of the blot)
–   Animals (2, real, with each as one half of the blot)
o   Animals (2, as D2 and identified as cat, cartoon, monkey, or rabbit, with D4 as a separate object)
    NOTE: If the animals reported as D2 are not cat, cartoon, monkey, or rabbit, they should be coded as u if the contours are used in an appropriate way, or - in other cases. Examples of u include flat faced animals such as some dogs. Examples of - include fox, elephant, horse, lion, etc)
u   Antlers
u **v** Arch
–   Beard
–   Bird
–   Body (Lower half)
–   Body (Split)
u   Bones (Unspecified)
u   Boomerang
u   Bowl (Usually involves S)
–   Bug
–   Butterfly
o   Canyon (Usually involves S)
u **v** Cap (With ear flaps)
u   Carving
u **v** Cave (Opening)
o **v** Chair (Includes use of DS7)

o   Children (With D4 as separate object such as cushions, see-saw, etc.)
u   Claw (Crab)
o   Cloud(s)
–   Coat
–   Cookie (Includes broken)
–   Conch Shell
–   Cracker (Includes broken)
u   Crown
o **v** Dancers (2)
–   Dogs
u   Dolls
o   Dolls (As D2 with D4 as separate object)
u **v** Doorframe
o   Elves (As D2 with D4 as separate object)
u **v** Explosion (With D4 as mushroom cloud)
–   Face
u **v** Face (Photo negative and includes use of DS7 or DS10)
o   Food (Breaded or fried)
u   Food (Pieces, usually cut up fish or chicken)
–   Frogs
u   Frog Legs (Food)
o   Genies (D4 usually as lamp)
–   Giant
o **v** Girls
o   Harbor (Includes DS7)
u   Helmet (Ancient)
u   Horseshoe
–   Human
o   Human-Like Figures (Usually angels, snowmen, or spirits, often with D4 as separate object)
o   Humans (2)
o   Humans (As D2 with D4 as separate object)
o **v** Humans (2)
–   Insect

o   Island(s)
–   Keel (Boat)
u **v** Lamp (Ornamental)
u   Landscape (Usually viewed from above, but sometimes when S is used, viewed as a valley between cliffs)
–   Leaf
u   Leaf (Torn)
–   Legs (Animal or human)
u **v** Magnet
–   Map (Specific)
u   Map (Unspecified)
u   Monument
–   Moth
–   Mouth
–   Neck
–   Neckbone
u   Necklace
–   Plant
u   Puzzle
u   Reef
u   Rocks
u   Rocking Horse
u   Sculpture
–   Sea Animal
–   Shrimp (2, natural form)
u   Shrimp (4, Usually breaded or fried)
–   Shrub(s)
–   Skull
u   Smoke
u   Snowmen
u   Spaceship
o   Statues (As D2 with D4 as base)
u   Stool
u   Swing
–   Table
u **v** Trellis
u   "U"
–   Vagina
u   Vase
u **v** Wig
–   X-ray (Specific)
u   X-ray (Unspecified)

D1

-   Anatomy
-   Animal
- u **v** Animal (Small, long tail with nose at Dd24)
- u **<** Animal (Cartoon with D5 as long nose or beak)
- u   Art (Abstract)
-   Bird
- u   Cactus
- u **v** Cap (Coonskin)
-   Cat
- u   Chair
-   Chicken
- u   Chicken leg (Cooked)
- o   Cliff
- o   Cloud(s)
- u   Commode
-   Eagle
- u   Earrings
-   Fish
- u   Fist (With finger pointing upward)
- u   Foliage
- o   Head (Animal, as cat, cartoon, monkey, or rabbit)
  (Note: If animal head reported is not cat, cartoon, monkey or rabbit, it should be coded as u if the contours are used appropriately as for some dogs heads, or - if that is not the case)
- u **v** Head (Animal, with D5 as trunk)
- o   Head (Human, as child, Indian, female or unspecified)
- u   Head (Human, adult male)
- o   Head (Human-like)
-   Horse
-   Insect
- u   Ladle
- u   Landscape
-   Map (Specific)
- u   Map (Unspecified)
- u   Mask
-   Mountain

- o   Rabbit (With nose as D8)
- u **v** Rudder
-   Sea Animal
- o   Shrimp (Breaded or fried)
- o   Statue
-   Tree
-   X-ray

D2

- o   Angel
- o   Animal (Small, with D5 as ear, and Dd21 as tail, such as cat, dog, monkey, rabbit)
- o   Animal (Cartoon)
-   Animal (Large)
- **v** Animal
- u **v** Animal (Cartoon)
-   Bird
- u   Bush(es)
- o   Cherub
-   Chicken
- u   Chicken Wings (Breaded or fried)
- o   Cloud(s)
-   Cow
- o **<** Dog
-   Donkey
-   Dragon
- o   Dwarf
- o **v** Elephant (Cartoon or toy)
-   Fish
- u   Food (Breaded or fried)
-   Fox
-   Frog
-   Head
- u   Hill
-   Horse
- o   Human (Child, Indian, female or unspecified may be whole human or head and upper body)
- u   Human (Adult, male)
- o   Human-like Figure
- o   Island(s)
-   Knife
- u **<** Lamb
- u   Landscape

- o   Map (Specific)
-   Meat
- u   Mountains
- o   Rabbit
- u   Shrimp (2, Breaded or fried)
- o   Snowman
- o   Statue
-   Tiger
- o   Toy (Human or animal)
-   Tree(s)
-   X-ray

D3

-   Animal
-   Beard
- u   Candy (Cotton)
-   Cap
- u   Cleaver
- u   Cliff
- u   Cloud
-   Cup
-   Dog
- u   Fish (Tail as Dd21)
- u   Fist (Thumb as Dd21)
-   Hairpiece
-   Ham
-   Hand
- o   Head (Animal, with Dd21 as ear or horn)
- u **v** Head (Animal, with Dd21 as nose or trunk)
- o   Head (Animal, cartoon or toy)
- u **v** Head (Bird, with Dd21 as beak)
- u   Head (Statue, usually gargoyle)
-   Head (Human)
- u   Head (Human-like)
- u   Head, Monster
-   Head (Reptile)
-   Insect
- u   Island
- u   Kite (With Dd21 as tail)
- u   Landscape
-   Map

D3 (Continued)

- o   Mask
- –   Nest
- u   Peninsula
- u   Rock
- –   Sack
- u   Shrimp (Breaded or fried)
- –   Shrub
- u   Statue
- –   Tree
- –   X-ray

D4

- –   Anatomy
- –   Animal(s)
- u   Basket
- o v Bat
- o   Bird
- u   Book (Open)
- u   Bookends
- –   Boots
- o   Bow
- –   Bowl
- u   Bowtie
- –   Bridge (Man made)
- u   Bridge (Natural)
- –   Bug (Not winged)
- u   Bug (Winged)
- o   Butterfly
- –   Buttocks
- –   Carcass
- –   Chest
- o   Cloud(s)
- u   Cradle
- u   Cushion(s)
- u   Doors (Swinging)
- –   Emblem
- –   Fly
- u   Gate
- u   Hang Glider (May include D6 as person)
- –   Head
- –   Human
- –   Insect (Not winged)
- u   Insect (Winged)
- u   Kite

- u   Landscape
- –   Lung(s)
- –   Map (Specific)
- u   Map (Unspecified)
- –   Mountain(s)
- u   Paper (Torn)
- o   Pelvis
- u   Plateau (Aerial view)
- –   Rib Cage
- o   Rock(s)
- –   Sea Animal
- –   Shell
- –   Shoes
- –   Shrub(s)
- –   Skull
- –   Tent
- –   Vagina
- u v Wig
- u   Wings
- o   X-ray (Pelvis)
- –   X-ray (Specific, other than pelvis)
- u   X-ray (Unspecified)

D5

- –   Animal
- –   Arrow
- u   Arrowhead
- –   Bird
- o   Blade (Knife)
- u   <Boat
- u   Bone
- u   <Canoe
- u   Caterpillar
- u   Claw
- u   Comb (Decorative)
- –   Drill
- u   Ears (Long as in rabbit)
- –   Eel
- o   Feather
- u   Finger
- –   Gun
- u   Hair (Groomed or styled as in hairpiece or pony tail)
- –   Head (Animal or human)
- u   Head (Rabbit with nose on outside)

- u   Headdress
- u   Horn
- –   Human
- u v Icicle
- –   Insect
- u   Leg
- –   Log
- –   Penis
- u   Pick (Guitar)
- u   Plant
- –   Rifle
- u   Sabre
- –   Sausage
- u   Saw
- –   Smoke
- u   Stalagmite
- u   Sword
- u   Tail (Long such as racoon)
- u   Thumb
- u   Totem
- –   Tree
- u   Wing
- –   Worm

D6

- –   Animal
- u   Anus
- –   Bone
- –   Bug
- o   Canal
- o   Canyon
- –   Caterpillar
- u   Clitoris
- u   Crack
- u   Dam
- u   Doll
- –   Drill
- –   Fish
- o   Gorge
- –   Head
- o   Hinge (Door)
- o   Human
- o   Human-Like Figure
- –   Insect
- u   Missile (Often with Dd28 as pad or smoke)
- u   Monster (Animal)
- –   Penis

D6 (Continued)

o River
u Rocket (Often with Dd28 as pad or smoke)
− Spine
u Stick
− Tower
− Tree
o Vagina
o Waterway

DS7

− Anatomy
u Arrowhead
− Bell
o Bowl
− Cloud
u Entrance
− Face
o Harbor
u **v** Hat (Historical)
− Head
u **v** Head (Negative as in photo)
u **v** Helmet
u Lake
o **v** Lamp
o **v** Mushroom
u **v** Pagoda
u Pot
o **v** Sphinx
o **v** Statue
u **v** Temple with dome
− Tree
u Vase

D8

u City (In distance)
u Cliff(s)
− Dragon
o Forest
− Head

u Humans (Several on cliff or hill)
u **v** Icicles
o Landscape
u Nest
u Sea Animal
u Snail
u Snail (Cartoon)
u Stalagmites
u Towers (Electric)
u Trees
o Village
u Whale

D9

u Cliff
u Cloud
o Head (Animal, small such as cat, dog, monkey, etc.)
− Head (Animal, large)
u **v** Head (Animal)
− Head (Bird)
o Head (Human)
o Head (Human-Like)
− Insect
u Landscape
− Sea Animal
o Statue (Bust)

DS10

o Bowl
u Doorknob
u Entrance
− Face
o Harbor
o **v** Hat (Historical)
− Head
o Helmet
u Hole
u Lake
o Lampshade
u **v** Mushroom (Cap)

− Penis
u Tent

Dd21

− Ant
u Arm
− Bird
u Caterpillar
− Face
o Finger
u Hand
− Head
u Horn
u Paw
u Peninsula
− Penis
− Rifle
u Tail
u Thumb
u Trunk (Elephant)

Dd22

− Animal
u Animal (Cartoon or toy)
− Bones
u **v** Doll
o Human
o Human-like Figure
u **v** Human
u Puppet
u Statue

Dd23

-   Animal
- u Brick
- u Cloud
- u Hat (Fur)
-   Head (Animal except bear or dog)
- o Head (Animal, bear or dog)
-   Head (Human)
- u Hill
- u Pillow
- u Rock
-   Shoe

Dd24

- u Cave
-   Cloud
- u Dirt
-   Head

Dd25

- u Bird
- u Landscape
- u Mountains
- u Seagull
-   Vagina
- u Waterfall

Dd26

- o Canyon
- o Gorge
- u Human
- u Human-Like Figure
- o River
- o Statue
- o Vagina

Dd27

-   Animal
- u Anus
-   Human
-   Lock
-   Teeth
-   Vagina
-   Window

Dd28

-   Animal
-   Bird
-   Buttocks
- u Face (Animal)
-   Face (Human)
- u Face (Monster)
- u Humans (2)
- u **v** Parachute (With D6 or Dd26 as person)
-   Plant
- u Statue(s)
- u Water
- o **v** Waterfall
- u **v** Waves

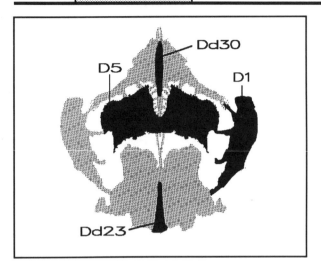

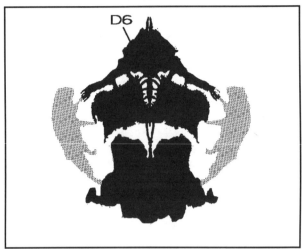

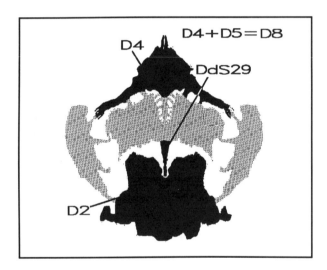

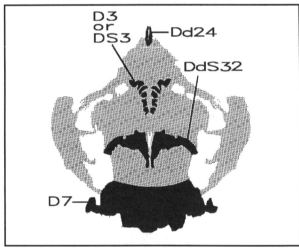

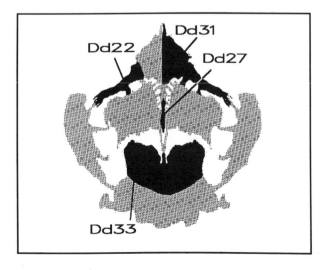

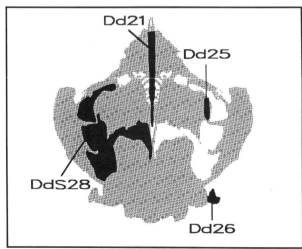

CARD VIII

Popular is to D1: WHOLE ANIMAL FIGURE

Z Values: W = 4.5   ADJACENT = 3.0   DISTANT = 3.0   SPACE = 4.0

W

- – Airplane
- – Anatomy (Specific)
- o Anatomy (Unspecified)
- – Animal
- o Animals (As D1 with other areas identified as object(s) that are consistent with contours)
- o Art (Abstract)
- u Badge
- – Bat
- – Bird
- o Boat (With sails, front view)
- – Bones (Skeletal)
- o Bowl (Ornamental)
- – Brain
- – Butterfly
- u Cage (Bird)
- – Cake
- o Carousel
- o Chandelier
- o Christmas Tree
- u Circus Tent
- – Cloud(s)
- o Coat-of-Arms
- u Coral
- – Crab
- u Crown
- o Design (Abstract)
- o Emblem
- – Explosion
- – Face
- u Face (Clown)
- u Face (Monster)
- – Fish
- u Flag
- o Floral Design
- o Flower
- u Foliage
- o Fountain
- – Frog

- u Garden
- u Gazebo
- – Head (Animal)
- – Head (Bird)
- – Head (Human)
- – Head (Insect)
- u Head (Monster)
- u Headdress (Ornamental)
- u Helmet (Science fiction)
- – Human
- u **v** Ice Cream (Melting)
- – Insect
- – Intestines
- u Island(s)
- – Jacket
- – Jellyfish
- u Jewelry
- – Kidney(s)
- u Kite
- u Lamp (Decorative)
- o Landscape (Often an aerial view)
- u Lantern (Oriental)
- u Leaf
- u Lights (Colored as created by strobes)
- – Lobster
- – Lung(s)
- – Machine
- – Map (Specific)
- u Map (Unspecified)
- u Mask
- – Meat
- o Medical Illustration (Parts are representative rather than real)
- u Monster
- u Monument
- – Moth
- u Mountain
- u Mountain and Forest (Distant view)
- o Ornament
- u Pagoda
- – Pelvis
- o Plant (Often in pot)

- o Poster (Abstract)
- o Poster (Nature)
- – Pyramid
- u Robot
- u Rocket
- u Rocks (Colored)
- u Rubbish
- u Rug (Oriental)
- u Scarab (Beetle pin)
- – Sea Animal
- u Sea Shell
- o Ship (With sails, view from end)
- – Skeleton
- – Skull
- – Snowflake
- u Spaceship (Usually with flames)
- – Spider
- u Statue
- – Stomach
- u **v** Top
- u **v** Torch
- u Totem Pole
- – Tree
- u Tree (Abstract or cartoon)
- u Trophy
- u Vase
- u Vegetation (Tropical)
- u Vegetation (Underwater)
- u Volcano (Erupting)
- – X-ray

D1

- Anatomy
- o Animal (Four legged, and appropriate to contours. This class of response includes a wide variety of animals, including some considered to be pre-historic. The most commonly reported include the badger, bear, cat, dog, gopher, lion, mouse, opossum, rat, and wolf. Four legged animals that are not appropriate for the contours should be coded as -, such as elephant, giraffe, horse, kangaroo, etc.)
- u Animal (Prehistoric)
- Bird
- u Blood
- Camel
- u Chameleon
- u Demon
- Dolphin
- Fish
- Flower
- Frog
- Human
- u Iguana
- Insect
- u Lizard
- Lung
- Parrot
- u Petal (Flower)
- Porpoise
- Reptile (Other than chameleon, iguana or lizard)
- Scorpion
- Seal
- Shrimp
- Tree
- Turtle
- X-ray

D2

- Anatomy
- Animal
- Bat
- u Blood
- u Bowl (Decorative)
- Brain
- u Bug
- o Butterfly
- Buttocks
- u Cake
- u Canyon
- u v Cape
- Chest
- u v Coat
- u Coral
- Crab
- Crown
- Disc (Spinal)
- Dog
- Emblem
- u Fire
- Flesh
- o Flower
- Frog
- Hat
- u v Head (Animal, short eared or horned)
- Head (Animal, not short eared or horned)
- Head (Bird)
- Head (Human)
- Head (Insect)
- u v Head (Monster)
- o Ice Cream
- Insect
- u v Jacket
- u Jello
- u Kite
- u Landscape
- o Lava
- u Leaf
- u Map (Unspecified)
- u v Mask
- Meat
- u Mountain(s)
- u Painted Desert
- Pelvis
- u Pot
- u Rock(s)

- u Rug
- u Scab
- Skull
- u Slide (Biological)
- Stomach
- Vagina
- Vertebrae (Cross section)
- u Volcano

D3/DS3

- u <Animal (Reflected)
- Badge
- o Bone Structure
- Cave
- u Corset
- Door
- Face
- Head
- u Ice
- o Mask
- Net
- o Rib Cage
- o Skeleton (Partial)
- o Skull (Animal)
- Skull (Human)
- u Snow
- u v Spaceship
- u v Tent
- u v Tepee
- u v Tree (Fir)
- o Vertebrae
- Web

D4

(Note: D4+D5 = D8)

- u Airplane (Jet, front view)
- Animal
- u Animal (Prehistoric)
- u v Antlers
- Bat
- u v Boomerang
- Bridge (Man made)

D4 (Continued)

u v Bridge (Natural)
- Butterfly
u Castle (On mountain)
u Cliff(s)
- Cloud
u Crab
- Crawfish
- Crown
u Dragon
- Face
u Face (Science fiction)
- Fish
o Frog
- Hat
- Head (Animal or human)
u Head (Science fiction)
- House
- Human(s)
u Ice
u Iceberg
u Insect
- Jellyfish
u Lichen (On rock)
u Lizard (Front view)
- Lobster
u Mask (Science fiction)
o Monster
o Mountain
- Octopus
u v Pelvis
u Robot
u Rock
u Rocket
o Roots
- Scorpion
u Sea Animal
u Shrub(s)
- Skull
o Spaceship
u Spider
u Stump (Tree)
u Temple
u Tent
u Tree
u Vine
u Waterfall

D5

(Note: D4+D5 = D8)

- Animal
u Bat
u Bird
o Bird (Prehistoric or science fiction)
- Bone
o Butterfly
u Cliff(s)
o Cloth
u Cloud(s)
u Corset
- Face
o Flags
- Flower
- Head(s)
o Ice
- Kidney(s)
o Lake
o Landscape (Often as aerial view)
- Leaves
- Lung(s)
u Paper (Torn)
- Pelvis
u Pillow(s)
- Rib Cage
u Rocks
u Sails
u Shrubs
- Skull
- Sky
o Water
- X-Ray

D6

- Anatomy (Specific)
o Anatomy (Unspecified)
u Art (Abstract)
- Bird
- Bones
- Brain
o Bush
u Chandelier

o Christmas Tree
- Crab
- Face
o Flower
u Glacier
- Head
u Helmet (Science fiction)
- House
- Human
u Insect
u Island(s)
u Kite
u Lamp (Oriental)
o Landscape (Often aerial view)
- Lobster
u Mask
o Mountain
u Ornament
u Pagoda
o Plant
u Rocks
u Sea Shells
u Ship (With sails, view from end)
u Spaceship
u Statue
o Tree
u Vegetation
u Waterfall (As center with vegetation around)

D7

- Animal
- Bird
o Blood (Usually dried)
u Butterfly
- Buttocks
u Canyon
- Chest
- Face
- Head
u Horns (Rams)
o Ice Cream
u v Jacket
u Jello
u Landscape
u Leaf (Autumn)

D7 (Continued)

-   Mountain
- u Painted Desert
- o Rocks
- u **v** Vest

D8

(Note: D4+D5 = D8)

-   Anatomy
- u Bird
-   Butterfly
- u **v** Chandelier
-   Crab
-   Face
- u Floral Display
-   Flower
- u Glacier
-   Head
- u Helmet (Science fiction)
- u Landscape
- u Mask
- u Pagoda
- o Plant
- u Rocket
- u Shack (House)
-   Shell
- o Spaceship
- u Tent
- u Tree

Dd21

-   Animal
- o Bone (Skeletal)
-   Esophagus
-   Human
- u Knife (And case)
- u **v** Missile Launch
- o River
- u Rockets (Separating stages)

-   Spear
- o Spinal cord
- u Stick(s)
- u Waterfall
- o Waterway

Dd22

-   Animal
- o Arm (Human)
- u Branch
- u Claw
- u Feet (Animal)
- u Glove
- u Hand
- u Horn (Animal)
- u Root

Dd23

- u Anus
- u Candle (Altar)
- u Canyon
-   Face
- u Flask
-   Head
-   Human(s)
- u Vagina
- u Vase
- u Waterfall

Dd24

- u Antennae
- u Arrow
-   Birds
- u Beak (Bird)
- u Feelers
- u Fingers
- u Horns
-   Human(s)
- u **v** Legs (Human)

- u Pincers
- u Roots
-   Teeth
- o Trees

Dd25

- u Alligator
-   Animal
-   Bird
-   Fish
- u Island
-   Penis
- u Spaceship
- u Statue

Dd26

- u **v** Cliff
- u <Dog
- u <Head (Animal)
-   Head (Bird)
-   Head (Human)
- u Horns
- u Rock
- u <Statue

Dd27

- u Alligator
- u Bone
- u Drill Bit
- u Hypodermic
- u Knife
- u Missile
-   Needle
- u Pen
- u Rocket
- u Spear
-   Worm

DdS28

u   Cloud(s)
u   Snow
u   Water

DdS29

u **v** Bottle (Milk)
u **v** Bowling Pin
–   Ghost
u **v** Salt Shaker
–   Statue
–   Tooth
u **v** Triangle (Music)
u **<** Whale

Dd30

u **v** Cane
u   Gorge
u   River
u   Snake
o   Spinal Cord
o   Stick
–   Sword
u   Waterfall

Dd31

–   Animal
–   Crab
–   Insect
u   Monster (Animal-like)
–   Reptile
u   Root(s)
–   Wing

DdS32

u   Albatross
o   Bird
u   Butterfly
o   Gull
o   Snow
u   Water

Dd33

–   Anatomy
u   Butterfly
–   Face
u   Flower(s)
u   Head (Animal)
–   Head (Bird)
–   Head (Human)
u   Ice Cream
–   Lung(s)
u   Rock(s)

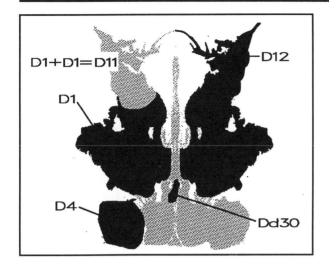

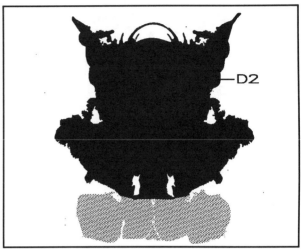

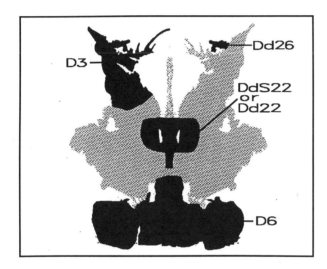

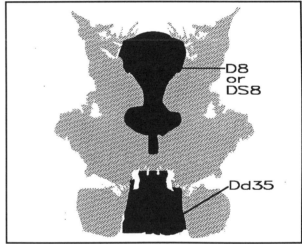

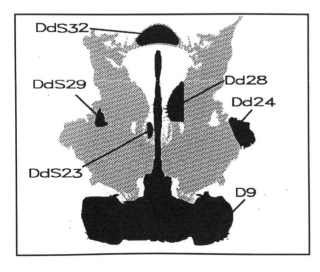

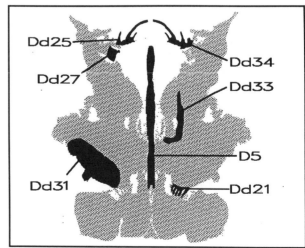

Popular is to D3: HUMAN OR HUMAN-LIKE FIGURES

Z Values: W = 5.5   ADJACENT = 2.5   DISTANT = 4.5   SPACE = 5.0

W

- Anatomy
- u Anchor
- Ant
- o Art (Abstract)
- u Badge
- Bird
- o **v** Birds (As D3 under tree)
- o Bowl (Ornamental)
- u Bridge (Top area over forest)
- Butterfly
- u Cactus
- u Cake (With D3 as candles)
- o Canyon (As D8 with other areas as foliage and/or landscape)
- u **v** Cape (Theatrical)
- u Chair (Winged with D6 as base or swivel)
- u **v** Clothing (Woman's)
- Cloud(s)
- Cocoon
- o Coral
- Crab
- u Crater (As D8 with other areas as foliage and/or landscape)
- u Decoration
- u **v** Doll
- u **v** Dummy (Dressmaker's)
- u **v** Elephant (Cartoon)
- u Emblem
- o Explosion
- Face
- u Face (Clown)
- u Face (Monster)
- o Fire (Usually with D1 as smoke)
- o Floral Arrangement
- o Flower (Often with D6 as pot)
- Fly
- o Foliage

- o Forest Fire
- o Fountain
- o Garden
- u Hat
- Head (Animal)
- Head (Human)
- Head (Insect)
- u Head (Monster)
- o Headdress (Ceremonial)
- u Helmet (Science fiction)
- Human
- u **v** Human (In costume)
- u **v** Human-like Figure
- o Illustration (Medical)
- Insect
- u Island
- u **v** Jellyfish
- u Lamp (Kerosene)
- u **v** Lamp (Ornamental)
- o Landscape
- o <Landscape (Reflected)
- Leaf
- Lung(s)
- Machine
- Map (Specific)
- u Map (Unspecified)
- o Mask
- u Monster
- u Ornament
- o Paint
- o Palette (Artist's)
- o Plant (Sometimes with D6 as pot)
- u **v** Robot
- u Rocket (As D5, with smoke and flames)
- Rug
- u Salad (Usually in bowl)
- Sea Animal
- u Seaweed
- Seed
- Skull
- u **v** Spaceship
- Throat
- u Throne
- u **v** Tree

- Vagina
- o Vase
- o Vegetables (D3 as carrots, D1 as lettuce, D6 as tomatoes)
- u Volcano
- o Waterfall (As D5 with other areas as foliage and/or landscape)
- u **v** Wizard
- X-ray

D1

(Note: D1+D1 = D11)

- Anatomy
- Animal
- u <Animal (Unspecified)
- o <Ape
- o <Bear
- Bird
- Bone
- Bug
- Butterfly
- Cat
- Chair
- u Cloud
- u Coral
- u <Dog
- Elephant
- u Fern
- Fish
- o Foliage
- u Forest (Usually aerial view)
- Frog
- o <Giant
- u <Gorilla
- o Grass
- Hat
- u Head (Animal, with snout at the D5 centerline)

o Head (Animal, with snout at Dd24, often with DdS29 as eye)
o **v** Head (Animal, with snout at D5 centerline or at Dd24)
– Head (Bird)
u **<**Head (Human or human-like with chin at Dd24)
– Head (Insect)
– Heart
– Human
o **<**Human (With Dd24 as head)
– Insect
– Ireland
u Lake
o Landscape
u Leaf
u Lettuce
– Lion
– Lung
– Map
u **<**Monkey
u **<**Monster
– Mushroom
u **v** Pig
u Plant
u **<**Rabbit
u Rock
– Sea Animal
u Seaweed
o Shrub
u Smoke
u Sponge
u **<**Statue
– Tree
– Wing
– X-ray

D2

– Anatomy
o Anchor
u Art (Abstract)
u Badge
– Bird
o **v** Birds (As D3 under bush)

o Bowl
– Bug
– Butterfly
o Canyon (As D8 with other areas as foliage and/or landscape)
u Chair (Wing)
– Clothing
– Cloud(s)
u Clouds and Lightning
u Coral
– Crab
o Crater (As D8 with other areas as foliage and/or landscape)
u Dragon
u Emblem
u Explosion
– Face
o Face (Clown)
u Face (Monster)
o Fire (As D3 with other areas as smoke)
o Flower
– Fly
o Foliage
u Fountain
u Garden
– Head (Animal)
– Head (Human)
u Head (Human-like)
– Head (Insect)
o Headdress (Ceremonial)
u Helmet
– Human
u Illustration (Medical)
– Insect
u **v** Jellyfish
o Landscape
o **<**Landscape (Reflected)
u Leaf (Autumn)
u Lobster & Seaweed
– Map
o Mask
u Ornament
u Painting (Abstract)
o Plant
– Sea Animal
– Skull
o **v** Tree
u Vagina
o Vase
u **v** Waterfall (As D5 with

other areas as foliage and/or landscape)

D3

– Anatomy
o Animal (Antlered or horned)
– Animal (Not antlered or horned)
u Bird
o **v** Bird
u Blood
– Bone
– Bug
u Carrot
o Cliff
u Cloud
o Clown
– Club
u Crab
o Dancer (In costume)
o **<**Deer
o Demon
– Dog
u Dragon
– Face
o Fire
– Fish
o Flower
o Ghost
o **v** Gnome
o Head (Animal, antlered or horned)
– Head (Animal, not antlered or horned)
u Head (Human)
o Head (Human-like)
– Head (Insect)
o Hill
u Horns
o Human
o Human Like-Figure
– Insect
o Landscape
o Lava
– Leg
u Lobster

D3 (Continued)

-   Lung
- u Map (Unspecified)
-   Meat
- u **v** Owl
- o **v** Parrot
- u Plant
-   Rodent
- u **v** Roots
- o Sand
-   Sea Animal
- u Sea Horse
-   Shrimp
- u Statue
- u Sun Spot
- u Torch
- o Toy (For punching)
-   Tree
- u Wing
- o Witch

D4

-   Anatomy
- o Apple
- o Ball
- u Blood
-   Bug
- o Candy (Cotton)
-   Cocoon
-   Eye
-   Fish
- u Flower
- u Head (Animal)
- o <Head (Human)
- u Ice cream
- u Mask
-   Meat
-   Pot
- o Raspberry
- u Rock
- u Roses
- u Sea Shell
-   Sperm
- u Sponge
- u Strawberry
-   Turtle

D5

- u Alligator
-   Anatomy
-   Animal
- u Arrow
- o Bone
- o Candle
- u Cane
- u Drill Bit
-   Esophagus
- u Flame
- u Geyser
- u Gorge
-   Head
-   Human
-   Insect
- o Landscape
- o Match
- u Missile
-   Peninsula
-   Penis
- u Reptile
- u River
- u Road
- u Sand Bar
- o <Shoreline
- o Skewer
- o Spinal Cord
- u Stalagmite
- u Stem
- u Sword
-   Tree
- o Waterfall (With D8 as background)
- u Waterway

D6

-   Anatomy
-   Animal(s)
- o Apples (4)
- o Babies (2)
- o Balloons
-   Bird
- o Blood
- u Bubblegum

- u **v** Butterfly
-   Buttocks
- o Candy (Cotton)
- o Cloud (Including mushroom cloud)
- o Embryos (2)
-   Face
- u **v** Face (Insect)
- u **v** Face (Science Fiction)
- u Fire
- u Flower(s)
-   Head (Animal)
- u Head (Cartoon)
- u **v** Head (Elephant or rodent)
- u **v** Head (Insect)
- o <Head (Human, reflected)
-   Human
- o <Human (Sitting, reflected)
-   Insect
-   Island
- u Marshmallows
-   Meat
- u **v** Mushroom
-   Pot(s)
- u Powder Puff
- u Radishes
- u Raspberries
- u Rocks
- u Rosebuds
- o Sherbet
- u **v** Shoulders (Human)
- u **v** Shoulder Pads
-   Skin
- u Smoke
- u Strawberries
-   Vagina
-   Wing

D8/DS8

-   Anatomy
-   Animal
- u Blender
- o Bottle
- u Bubble
- o Canyon
- o Cave
- u Chandelier
-   Chest

D8/DS8 (Continued)

u   Cloud
u **v** Dress
u **v** Dummy (Dressmaker's)
-   Face (Animal)
u   Face (Dragon)
-   Face (Human)
u **v** Face (Monster)
u **v** Flask
o **v** Ghost
u **v** Glass
-   Head (Animal)
-   Head (Human)
u **v** Head (Monster)
o   Hourglass
-   Human
u **v** Human-Like Figure
u   Keyhole
u **v** Lamp
o   Light Bulb
u **v** Mask
u **v** Monster
u   Nose (Cow or horse)
u   Parking Meter
u **v** Robot
o **v** Salt Shaker
-   Skull
u   Sky
u   Tornado
-   Tree
-   Vagina
o   Vase
u   Violin
o   Water
o   Waterfall
-   Womb

D9

-   Animal
u   Chandelier
o **v** Cloud (Mushroom)
u **v** Corkscrew
-   Drill
u **v** Hammer (Ball peen)
-   Head (Animal other than elephant)

u **v** Head (Elephant)
-   Head (Human)
-   Head (Insect)
u **v** Heron (On one leg)
-   Human
o **v** Flower
o   Fountain
u **v** Lamp
o   Spindle (Office)
u **v** Tree
o **v** Umbrella
u **v** Valve

D11

-   Anatomy
u   Bat
u   Bird
u   Bookends
o   Butterfly
-   Ear Muffs
-   Earphones
o   Foliage
-   Head
-   Human
-   Insect
u   Insect (Winged)
-   Lungs
o   Pelvis
u   Plant
u   Shrubs

D12

-   Animal
u   <Dragon
o   Fire (Forest)
o   <Human (As D1 with D3 as other object such as hill, sand, etc.)
o   <Landscape
u   Leaves
-   Monster
-   Tree

Dd21

o   Claws
o   Fingers
u **v** Fins
u **v** Horns
-   Humans
u   Icicles
-   Rake
u **v** Rockets (Group)
-   Spears
u   Stalagmites
-   Trees

Dd22
DdS22

u   Bowl
-   Candles
u   Cavern
-   Cup
-   Door(s)
-   Eyes
-   Face (Animal)
-   Face (Human)
-   Face (Insect)
o   Face (Monster)
-   Head
-   Jar
-   Jellyfish
u   Lake(s)
o   Mask
u   Nose (Animal)
o   Pumpkin (Halloween)
-   Skull

DdS23

- u   Caves
- u   Eyes
- o   Holes
- u   Islands
- u   Lakes
- u   Nostrils (Animal)
- –   Pillows
- –   Shells

Dd24

- u   Cliff
- u   Head (Animal)
- u   <Head (Human)

Dd25

- u   Branches
- u   Claws
- u   Feelers
- –   Fingers
- u   Roots
- u   Tentacles
- –   Trees
- u   Weeds

Dd26

- –   Animal
- u   Claw
- o   Finger
- –   Foot
- u   Gun (Often science fiction)
- u   Hose (Nozzle)
- –   Human
- u   Key

- –   Nose
- u   <Person
- u   <Scarecrow
- u   <Statue
- u   Trumpet

Dd27

- –   Animal
- –   Face
- –   Head
- –   Human
- u   <Tent
- u   <Top

Dd28

- –   Blood
- u   Breast
- u   Egg
- –   Head
- u   Insect (Hard shelled)
- –   Scab
- u   Shell
- –   Stomach

DdS29

- o   Bell
- –   Bug
- u   Eye
- –   Face
- o   Ghost
- –   Human
- u   Human-Like Figure
- u   Lake

Dd30

- u   Candlewax
- u   Caterpillar
- –   Intestine
- –   Penis
- –   Reptile

Dd31

- u   Breast
- u v Cover (Pot)
- u   <Face (Animal)
- u   <Face (Human)
- u   Foliage
- –   Tree(s)

DdS32

- u v Bowl
- u   Dome
- –   Helmet
- u   Moon (Upper half)
- u   Shell
- u   Sun (Upper half)
- u   Sunspot
- u   Tent

Dd33

- o < Alligator
- o < Crocodile
- u   Foliage
- u < Head (Animal other than deer)
- o < Head (Deer)
- –   Head (Human)
- u < Head (Reptile)
- u   Lizard
- u   Log
- –   Mountain(s)
- –   Tree

Dd34

- –   Animal
- u   Antlers
- u   Branches
- u   Bridge (Natural)
- u   Cannon (Usually science fiction)
- u   Claw(s)
- o   Drawbridge (Often opening)
- –   Hands
- u   Horns
- u   Hose
- –   Human(s)
- u   Lightning Flash
- u   Roots
- –   Skeletal
- u   Thorns
- –   Trees
- u   Vines

Dd35

- –   Animal
- u   Bathysphere
- –   Bird
- u   Buttocks
- u   Furnace
- –   Head
- –   Lung(s)
- –   Mask
- u   Pot
- u   Rock(s)
- u   Stove (Iron)
- u   Vaginal area

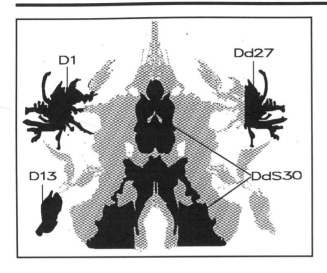

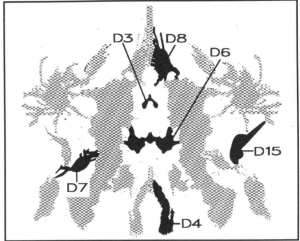

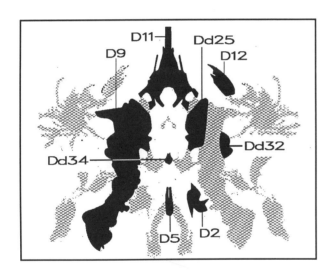

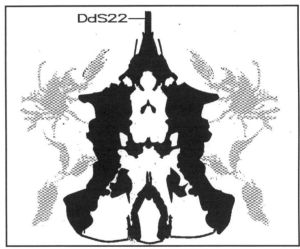

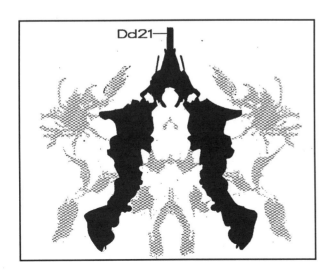

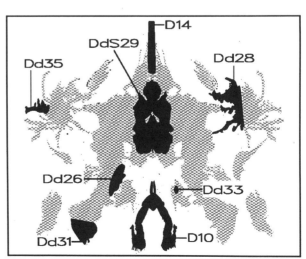

W

-   Anatomy
- o   Animals (Marine, unspecified, or if specified, meeting appropriate contour requirements)
- u   Animals (Not marine but meeting contour requirements)
- o   Aquarium
- o   Art (Abstract)
- u **v** Aviary
- u   Bacteria
- –   Birds
- –   Bones
- –   Bug (Squashed)
- u   Chandelier
- u   Children's Play Park (With all areas included as play equipment)
- –   Christmas Tree
- –   Clouds
- u   Costume (Theatrical, hanging on wall)
- u   Design (Abstract)
- u **v** Explosion
- –   Face
- o   Fireworks Display
- o   Floral Display
- o   Flower Garden
- o **v** Flowers (Bouquet)
- o   Garden Scene (With some areas as flowers or shrubbery and areas such as D11 and/or D6 as sculpture or architecture)
- –   Headdress
- –   Human
- o   Insects (Unspecified, or if specified, meeting appropriate contour requirements)
- u   Islands
- u   Junk Yard
- u   Kaleidoscope

- u   Lights (Created by strobe)
- –   Map (Specific)
- u   Map (Unspecified)
- –   Mask
- u   Mobile (Abstract)
- –   Pagoda
- o   Painting (Modern)
- u   Painting (Finger)
- u   Palette (Artist's)
- u   Plants
- o   Poster (Abstract)
- u   Puzzle (Pieces)
- u   Rug (Design)
- –   Sea Animal
- u   Science fiction scene (Usually includes aliens, creatures, monsters, but may involve space battle such as from Star Wars)
- o   Underwater Scene
- o   Walkway (As center space and other areas as flowers and/or shrubbery)

- u   Insect
- u   Island
- –   Jellyfish
- u   Landscape
- –   Leaf
- u   Lobster
- –   Map
- –   Mask
- u   Monster
- o   Octopus
- u   Orchid
- u   Paint (Splash)
- u   Pom Pom
- –   Reindeer
- u   Roots
- o   Scorpion
- –   Sea Shell
- u   Seaweed
- u   Snowflake
- o   Spider
- –   Spider Web
- u   Star
- o   Water (Drop)
- –   Web
- u   Weed

D1

- o   Amoeba
- –   Animal
- u   Bug
- u   Cell (Biological)
- –   Cockroach
- u   Coral
- o   Crab
- u   Dragon
- u   Earring
- –   Face
- u   Fern
- u   Fireworks
- –   Fish
- u   Flower
- u   Germ
- –   Hat
- –   Head

D2

- u   Amoeba
- u   Anemone
- u   Animal (Unspecified)
- –   Bee
- u **v** Bird
- u   Bug
- u   Cat
- o   Cell (Biological)
- –   Chicken
- o   Dog
- u   Duck
- o   Egg (Broken or fried)

D2 (Continued)

-    Eye
-    Face
- u **v** Fish
- o   Flower
- u   Frog
-    Head
- u   Insect
- u   Island
- u   Leaf
- o   Lion
-    Monkey
-    Monster
- u   Plant
-    Sea Animal
- u   Sea Shell
- u   Seal
-    Sperm

D3

-    Airplane
- o **v** Antennae (Radar or TV)
- u   Antennae (Insect)
- o **v** Balloons (Weather)
-    Bird
- u   Buds
-    Bug
- o   Cherry Pits
-    Crab
- u   Ear Muffs
- u   Earphones
-    Eye
-    Flower(s)
- o   Governor (On motor)
-    Head
- u   Headset
-    Human
- o   Instrument (Weather, for wind velocity)
- u   Instrument (Medical)
- u   Knocker (Door)
- u   Lights (Electric)
-    Lungs
- u **v** Necklace
-    Notes (Musical)
-    Ovaries

-    Parachutist
- o   Pawnbroker Symbol
-    Rower (In boat)
-    Scissors
- o   Seed Pod (Maple)
- u **v** Slingshot
- u   Spaceship (Science fiction)
-    Stethoscope
-    Testicles
- u   Tongs (Ice)
- u   Twig
- u   Water Wings
- o   Wishbone
- u **v** "V" (Peace sign)

D4

-    Anatomy
-    Animal
- u **v** Animal (Prehistoric)
-    Arm
- u   Boot (Jester)
-    Bug
- o   Caterpillar
-    Cucumber
- u **v** Dragon
- o   Eel
-    Fish
-    Head (Animal)
- u **v** Head (Animal, prehistoric)
-    Head (Bird, except Peacock or swan)
-    Head (Human)
- u **v** Head (Peacock)
- u **v** Head (Swan)
- u   Horn
-    Insect
- u   Plant
- u **v** Saxophone
- o **v** Sea Horse
- u   Smoke
- u   Snail
- o   Snake
- u   Tail (Bird)
-    Tree
-    Wing

D5

- o **v** Angel
-    Bug
- u   Clothespin
- u **v** Crucifix
- u **v** Devil
-    Face
- o   Head (Animal, long eared)
-    Head (Animal, not long eared)
-    Head (Human)
- u   Head (Insect, with antennae)
- o **v** Human
- u **v** Human-Like Figure
-    Insect
- o   Mask
- u **v** Tack
- u **v** Tooth
- u   Tweezers

D6

-    Anatomy
-    Animal
- o **v** Anthropoids
- u   Bagpipes
-    Bat(s)
- u   Birds
- u   Brassiere
-    Breasts
- o   Bridge (Natural)
-    Cloud(s)
- u   Coral
- u **v** Dolls
- u   Ducks
-    Eyeglasses
-    Face(s)
- u **v** Flowers
- o **v** Ghosts
- o **v** Gorillas
-    Hands
- u **v** Heads (Animal)
- u   Heads (Bird)
-    Heads (Human)
- o **v** Humans

D6 (Continued)

o **v** Human-Like Figures
- Insect(s)
- Jaw
- Lungs
o **v** Monster
u Nest
- Nose
- Ovaries
u Pipes (Smoker's)
u Sea Shells
u Skeletal
u Water

D7

o Animal (Leaping)
o Ant
- Bird
u Branch
- Clam
u Claw
o Cockroach
u Cocoon
o Crab
o Crayfish
o Deer
- Dog
- Face
- Fish
- Frog
o Grasshopper
- Human
- Kidney
u Lobster
o Nest
u Praying Mantis
u Rodent (With head toward D9)
o Roots
u Salamander
u Scorpion
- Sea Animal
u Seed Pod
u Spider
u Tick
u Weed

D8

- Animal (Unspecified)
u Animal (Cartoon or prehistoric)
o Ant
u Bee
o Beetle
u Buffalo
o Bug
u Bull
- Cat
- Chicken
u Chipmunk
u Crab
o Creature (Beast, monster)
u Cricket
o Dragon
u Dwarf
u Elf
u Emblem
- Face
- Fish
u Frog
u Gnome
- Goat
- Head (Animal)
o Head (Animal-like creature)
- Head (Human)
u Head (Human-Like creature)
o Head (Insect)
- Human
o Insect
- Lizard
u Mask
- Monkey
o Monster (Animal)
o Monster (Human-like)
u Parrot
u Porcupine
u Rodent
u Roots
- Sea Animal
- Shrimp
- Skeletal
- Spider
u Troll
u Unicorn
- Witch

D9

- Anatomy (Except intestine)
- Animal
u Animal-Like Creature
u Bacon
o Blood
u Bone
- Bug
o Caterpillar
u Cloud
u Coastline (California)
o Coral
- Dolphin
u Eel
o Elf
o Fire
- Hair
- Head
o Human (With mention that lower body is not distinct)
u Human (With no mention about lower body being indistinct)
o Human-Like Figure
u Insect
u Intestine
u Island
- Italy
- Map
u Map (Topographic)
o Mermaid
o Microorganism
u Mountain Range (Often as aerial view)
o Mummy
- Porpoise
u Sea Horse
u Snail
u Sponge
o Worm

D10

- Anatomy
u v Angel
- Animal
o Arbor
o Arch
u v Bird
u Butterfly
u Caterpillars
u v Comb (Ornamental)
o v Door Knocker
- Flower
u Fountain
- Funnel
u v Head (Animal, horned)
- Head
o v Horns
o v Human (As D5 with other areas as flags, smoke, streamers, swing, etc.)
- Insect
u Lyre
u Mustache
u Necklace
o v Parachutist
u v Pelvis
u Seaweed
o Shrub(s)
u v "U"
o Wishbone
u Worms

D11

u Airplane
- Animal
- Broom
u Building (With chimney or tower)
o Candle (With holder)
u Castle
- Centipede
o Eiffel Tower
- Face
u Face (Monster)
u v Flower

u v Funnel
o Helmet (Science fiction)
- Human
o Insects (As D8 and D14 as another object)
- Intestines
- Lungs
u Mask
o Missile (With smoke or on pad)
u Mistletoe
- Nervous System
u Plant
o Rocket (With smoke or on pad)
o Roots
u Skeletal
- Skull
o Spaceship
u Statue
o v Torch
u v Tree
- X-ray (Specific)
u X-ray (Unspecified)

D12

u Bean
- Bird
o Buffalo
o Bug
o Bull
u Claw
o Cow
u Dog
- Fish
u Goat
u Grasshopper
o Insect
u Lamb
o Leaf
- Plant
u Pickle
o Ram
- Rodent
u Seed Pod
o Unicorn
u Whale

D13

o <Animal (Usually lying or jumping and includes a wide variety such as bear, buffalo, cat, dog, lion, rabbit, etc.)
- Ant
- Bird
u Bug
u Cloud
- Face
u Fish
- Flower
u Fungus
- Head
- Human
u Insect
u Leaf
u Mat
u Oyster
o Potato Chip
u Rock
- Sea Shell
u Sea Urchin
u Sponge
- Tree
u Whale

D14

- Animal
u Artery
u Baton
u Bird Feeder
o Bone
o Candle
o Chimney
u Crowbar
- Face
- Finger
u Flute
u Handle
- Head
- Human
- Knife
u Log
o Missile

D14 (Continued)

u   Pencil (Not sharpened)
u   Penis
o   Post
o   Rocket
u   Root
u   Ruler
u   Shotgun
o   Spinal Cord
u   Statue
u   Stick
o   Stove Pipe
u   Sword
u   Telescope
u   Test Tube
u   Tire Pump
u   Vase

D15

–   Animal
o   Bird
o   Bud (Flower)
u   Butterfly
–   Cloud
u   Fish
o   Flower
–   Head
–   Insect
–   Jellyfish
u   Leaf
o   Rose
–   Seal
–   Smoke
–   Walrus
u   Wing

Dd21

–   Animal(s)
u **v** Antennae
u   Arch
u **v** Bird (Flying)

–   Boomerang
o **v** Butterfly (Front view)
u **v** Canyon
u **v** Chevron
o **v** Flower (Sometimes including D6)
–   Human(s)
–   Insect
u **v** Keel (Boat)
u   Landscape
u **v** Ornament
u   Pliers (Cutting)
u   Reef
–   Tuning Fork
u   Tweezers
u **v** Wishbone

DdS22

–   Anatomy
u   Design (Abstract)
–   Face
–   Head
u   Islands
–   Map (Specific)
u   Map (Unspecified)
–   Mask
u   Underwater Scene

Dd25

u   Coastline
–   Head (Animal)
o   Head (Human)
o   Head (Human-like)

Dd26

–   Breast
–   Face (Animal)
u   Face (Human, Profile)
u   Face (Human-like, profile)

Dd27

–   Face
u   Insect
–   Seaweed
–   Trees

Dd28

–   Clown
u   Insect
u   Puppet
u   Roots

DdS29

o   Buddha
o   Child (With hands up)
–   Face
o   Fan (With D11 as handle)
o   Human (Sitting or squatting)
u   Lantern (Sometimes with D11 as handle)
u   Paddle (With D11 as handle)

DdS30

- – Skeleton
- u Water

Dd31

- u **v** Head (Animal)
- u **v** Head (Caterpillar)
- – Head (Human)
- u **v** Head (Human-like)

Dd32

- – Animal
- u Head (Animal)
- – Head (Human)

Dd33

- o Acorn
- u Ball
- u Cookie
- – Eye
- – Head
- u Orange
- u Sun
- o Walnut

Dd34

- u Basket
- u Bottle
- – Bullet
- – Head
- – Skull
- u Tooth

Dd35

- – Animal
- u People (On a cliff)
- – Reptile
- u Trees (On a cliff)

TABLE B. ILLUSTRATIONS OF RESPONSES THAT SHOULD BE CODED FQ+

CARD	RESPONSE	INQUIRY
I	Ths ll one of thos bf's, it has the **irregulr edges** & the **markgs** & the littl **antennae**	E: (Rpts Ss resp) S: Yes, well most bf's have wings that r straighter, but som of the one's tht r rare hav a mor **irreg structure** lik ths. And there r the triangular **white markings** & here r the very small **antennae** & the little round **nobs** at the head & the **tail** is here
I	There is s.o. **standg** in the cntr & **people dancing arnd** her with large **flowg capes** on, thy hav little **caps** on too	E: (Rpts Ss resp) S: Ths is the person, the **legs**, the **waist** & up here r her **hands**, her head is not apparent, mayb she's dancg too & her head is back & on each side there r **other dancers** E: Other dancers? S: Thy hav thes long **flowing capes** out here & their **heads** r here & it almost ll thy all hav their **feet** down here, together, mayb its a balancing act or dance, thy seem to hav little **caps** on too, c up here
II	There r 2 witches, thy hav red **hats** on, thyr **leaning** inward w their **hands** togethr	E: (Rpts Ss resp) S: Thy look **huddled** togethr, as if castg a spell. Their **hands** r togethr here & there is a **fire** in frnt of them. Thy hav **peaked red hats** on, ths cb their **nose** & **hands** & thy hav **capes** on, c blk capes tht cling lik to their **bodies** & there is a fire blazing dwn here, c the flames **shootg** outward
II	A **rocketship**, the **wgspread**, the **blast** out of the bttm, a command **capsule** up here, the narrow escape **pod** toward the top	E: (Rpts Ss resp) S: Sort of lik a Buck Rogers space ship, the **rounded** command **capsule**, an escape **pod** & the flames shootg **out the back** lik a launch, c the redness lik exhaust flames & the whole thg is highlited against the dark background, lik it is at nite
III	Two native **wm**, the **busts** here, a **cauldron** in the middl, thy hav **aprons** on & **rings** arnd their necks	E: (Rpts Ss resp) S: The **cauldron** here, here r their **heads, jaw, nose**, the **forehead**, thes r **neck rings**, their **busts, arms** & **legs** & this is lik an **apron**. Thyr leaning ovr the cauldron
IV	Ths ll a **fellow** like sorta **hunched** over riding a **bike** or a motorcycle, he has a litl **helmet** on & he's stickg his **feet** out	E: (Rpts Ss resp) S: Here r his **big legs**, comg out this way & the cntr is lik the **tire** of the motorcycle & thes r the **handlebars** c how thy come to **points** as thy r bent **downwrd** & ths is his **body** & up here is lik his **head** prob bent forwrd u can c the **helmet** & here r his big **feet**
IV	It ll a critter or monster lik u c on a kids show, littl **arms**, a weird **head**, big **feet**, a silly monster lik on TV	E: (Rpts Ss resp) S: **Arms, head, nose, eyes**, its lik ur lookg up at a 45 degree **angle**, big **feet, bigger at the heels** & a big **toe** & a very large **tail structure**

TABLE B. (Continued)

CARD	RESPONSE	INQUIRY

V   Ths ll 2 **people, sittg** on the ground resting **back to back**, lik maybe thy hav ski **caps** on & thyr covrd w blankets

E: (Rpts Ss resp)
S: Thy r **back to back**, here is their **heads** & thes ll tassled **caps** lik skiers wear sometimes & their **legs** r out here, c the **outline** of them but the **bodies** look too full, lik theyr covered lik w a blanket, u can c the **bulges** lik where their **arms** and **knees** might be

V   It ll a vulture

E: (Rpts Ss resp)
S: Well it has its **legs** out in front & a split **tail** & thes huge **jagged wings**, thy **slant** backward & thyr very **irregular**, the contours r irregular, & thy hav **talon** lik ends, I thk vultures hav wgs lik tht

VI< Ths ll a **submarine** in a **battl** u can c the **conning tower** & the bomb **blasts** out in frnt of it

E: (Rpts Ss resp)
S: Here is the **conning tower** & the **bow** & ths is the **wtrlin** & the **hull**, here is the **stern** & out here is a blast lik effect, lik it was being shelled, c the **splash effect**

VII Ths is lik 2 littl **childrn** on a **see-saw**, littl girls w their **pony tails** bouncing up

E: (Rpts Ss resp)
S: Yes, one here & here, c the **head**, the littl **nose** & **mouth** & ths is the **pony tail** & ths is lik a **bar** that thy lean against & thy r lik **squatting** & down here is the base of the thg sorta **curved upward** lik the see-saw

VIII Ths is a **carousel**, mayb a painting of one, lik an elaborate painting w **each prt detailed by a diff color**

E: (Rpts Ss resp)
S: Well it has the two **animals** on the sides, lik **standg** on their **hind legs** & this blue square prt wb the **machinery** & the top has a **tent** lik effect & the **round base** dwn here

VIII< Ths ll an **animal** is walkg ovr som **rocks** & thgs stickg up from the watr to get fr ths rock to ths **stump** dwn here & its all **reflctd** dwn here

E: (Rpts Ss resp)
S: Here, the pink, c the **head** & the **legs** and the **tail**, c the tail, c the pointed **nose** & ths orange is lik a big **boulder** & he's stepping on thes smallr **rocks** & his front **paw** is on ths **stump** tht is **sticking up** here & the blue is the water and all of the **details r reflected** dwn here

VIII Let's c, two mice

E: (Rpts Ss resp)
S: There r **two** of thm, one here & here (points), thy hav **four legs**, the **tail**, the **head**, torso, ear, nose, eyes & tiny **frnt feet**

TABLE B. (Continued)

CARD	RESPONSE	INQUIRY

IX< Ths ll a **heavy set person** chasing a **littl kid** up ths **hill** here

E: (Rpts Ss resp)
S: Well here is the person, it ll a **woman**, sorta **bulky**, c the **head** & the **body** & ths is her **arm** & out in front of her is the kid, c the **head** & her **body**, her **hair is lik flyg** in the breeze & this is lik a hill, going up, mayb a sand **dune** caus its got the orange color, lik mayb thy r running in the sand

IX A very colorful **headdress** of ss lik u mite c in s.e. asia

E: (Rpts Ss resp)
S: It has large orange **pointed parts** at the **top on each side** & then an **arch** connectg the two. Dwn below r the **heads** of two animals, one on each side (D1), c the **nose** & **chin** & ths wb the **eye** & the cntr has an **hourglass shape** & then the pink down here is the **band** that fits on the head

X It ll the inside of an **aquarium**

E: (Rpts Ss resp)
S: There r alot of undersea creatures. The blue & ths brwn both ll **crabs**, thy hav a lot of **legs sticking out**, & the green ll **vegetation** & the pink is lik **logs or coral** & ths green dwn here is lik two **seahorses**, c the curved **heads** & the yellow r lik **amoeba** but bigger with the **rounded cntr** & ths brown cb sk of **shell**

X It cb the garden in front of the **Eiffel Tower**, as if ur **looking across** the garden toward it

E: (Rpts Ss resp)
S: Well ths is the Eiffel **Tower** (D11) in the backgrnd. The **tall** structur, & the white is the **walkway** leadg to it & it is lined with **beds of pink flwrs** (D9) & there r 2 small **pools** (D6) of water on the walkway & some **statues**, an **arch** here at the beginning (D10) & the statues of 2 **lions** (D2), c the **legs** & **heads**, lik **sitting** on their haunches & then a small **triangular statue** further dwn the walkway, c here (D3), I'm not countg the stuff outside of the pink areas

11 ❖ Descriptive Statistics

This chapter contains several reference tables of nonpatient and patient data that can be helpful in understanding and utilizing the test. The bulk of the data presented in this chapter are not extraordinarily different from reference data that have been published previous editions of this *Workbook*, or in the various editions of the three volumes series, *The Rorschach: A Comprehensive System*, but some are presented in a different format.

Historically, most group reference data have been presented in single tables that afford no consideration to distinctive subgroups within a sample. Although data presented in such a format can be useful when interpreting the test, they also can be misleading. This is because the distributions for some variables tend to be bimodal, or even trimodal. These unusual distributions generally are created because of differences in response styles such as are represented by the *EB* (introversive, extratensive, ambient), or by *Lambda* (avoidant).

For instance, by definition, introversives give more human movement answers than chromatic color responses while extratensives do the reverse. When the data for *M* and *WSumC* for these subgroups are merged in a composite data set, the resulting descriptive statistics for both variables tend to be spurious. They do not adequately represent either introversives or extratensives. This matter would not be important if only two variables were involved and were relevant to only two response styles. However, introversives and extratensives differ substantially in the frequencies by which they report more than 20 determinants, contents, and Special Scores. These differences often become more clouded when data for ambients are added into a matrix, and the matter become even more complex because of the *Lambda* variable.

Lambda represents the proportion of Pure *F* answers in a protocol. Pure *F* responses are economical, and some are found in almost every record. When the frequency of Pure *F* answers is substantial, yielding *Lambda* values of 1.0 or greater, the frequency of other determinants and some additional test variables is typically lowered. At times, a high *Lambda* value will simply represent a form of test taking defensiveness, but many high *Lambda* records represent a response style that is as potent, or even moreso, than the introversive or extratensive response styles identified by the *EB*. When data from high *Lambda* records are merged with those for introversives, ambients, and extratensives the likelihood of misleading descriptive statistics increases. While the data set reflects the findings for the total group, it provides only hints about features common to each of the subgroups.

The main purpose of reference data is to provide some aids to those responsible for the interpretation of test results. In that the differing response styles noted above seem to promote substantially different approaches to the test, it seem most appropriate to present data in the context of those styles, when practical. Some of the tables in this chapter are formatted in that framework.

There are ten tables (13 to 22) of data that have been generated from the protocols of 600 nonpatient adults, partially stratified for geographic distribution and socioeconomic level. The group contains 300 males and 300 females, 50 fewer of each than in the tables of nonpatient data presented in the previous edition of this *Workbook*. The reduced number results from the fact that when the sample of 700 nonpatients was selected, using stratification criteria, more than 200 duplicate records were included. Once detected, those records were deleted from the sample and most have been replaced to constitute the sample used here.

The first two tables concerning nonpatients contain the mixture of data for the entire sample. They have been included primarily for those with research interests. The remaining eight tables contain data for the subgroups, differentiated by the response styles, introversive, ambitent, extratensive, and avoidant (high *Lambda*). They should be the most useful to interpreters of the test.

Tables 23 and 24 contain reference data concerning 1390 nonpatient children, subdivided by ages, from five to 16. These groups are *not* subdivided by response styles, because to do so would yield samples for which the size would be much smaller than necessary to provide meaningful data. In fact, these data should be used very cautiously for two reasons. First, the number of subjects included for any given age group is not substantial. Second, these are children who have been volunteered by parents to participate in the nonpatient project. Logically, parents usually might not volunteer a child for participation unless they have a sense of confidence about the performance of the youngster. Thus, children who are functioning very well may be overly representative in the various age groups.

Tables 25 through 34 include data for a group of 535 adult outpatients that present a broad variety of symptoms. Like the format for the nonpatients adults, two tables include data for the total group, and eight additional tables contain data for the subgroups, differentiated by response styles. The remaining tables (35 through 42) present data for 279 inpatients diagnosed as having a major depressive disorder, and 328 first admission schizophrenics. These groups are subdivided using the *Lambda* variable ($L < 1.0$ & $L > 0.99$). A further differentiation by responses styles would result in some subgroups being too small to be meaningful.

When reviewing a table, it is important to consider *all* of the data concerning a variable. Means and standard deviations, considered alone, can be misleading for many Rorschach variables, especially those with distributions that fall on a J-curve. The values for medians and modes are been included in each table because they often provide more realistic information about a variable. This is particularly true for those variables that have standard deviations in brackets. The bracketing of the *SD* signifies that the use of the standard deviation to establish an expected or "normal" range can be very misleading and, generally, should not be used in the interpretive framework.

TABLE 13. DESCRIPTIVE STATISTICS FOR NONPATIENT ADULTS (N = 600)

VARIABLE	MEAN	SD	MIN	MAX	FREQ	MEDIAN	MODE	SK	KU
AGE	31.73	10.69	19.00	69.00	600	30.00	22.00	1.34	1.65
Years Educ	13.43	1.58	8.00	19.00	600	13.00	12.00	0.33	0.22
R	22.32	4.40	14.00	43.00	600	22.00	23.00	0.86	1.90
W	8.28	2.36	3.00	24.00	600	8.00	9.00	1.67	7.82
D	12.88	3.77	0.00	32.00	598	13.00	14.00	-0.14	1.72
Dd	1.16	[1.67]	0.00	15.00	370	1.00	0.00	4.00	24.01
S	1.57	[1.28]	0.00	10.00	514	1.00	1.00	1.99	7.61
DQ+	7.36	2.23	1.00	19.00	600	7.00	6.00	0.53	1.24
DQo	13.58	3.67	5.00	36.00	600	14.00	15.00	1.26	5.69
DQv	0.98	[1.26]	0.00	6.00	306	1.00	0.00	1.35	1.30
DQv/+	0.39	[0.61]	0.00	2.00	193	0.00	0.00	1.32	0.65
FQx+	0.71	0.88	0.00	5.00	290	0.00	0.00	1.33	2.19
FQxo	16.44	3.34	7.00	29.00	600	17.00	17.00	0.25	0.59
FQxu	3.49	2.03	0.00	16.00	580	3.00	3.00	1.50	5.33
FQx-	1.56	1.20	0.00	8.00	513	1.00	1.00	1.25	2.58
FQxNone	0.11	[0.37]	0.00	3.00	60	0.00	0.00	3.80	17.53
MQ+	0.44	0.68	0.00	3.00	210	0.00	0.00	1.52	1.98
MQo	3.57	1.84	0.00	8.00	595	3.00	3.00	0.42	-0.62
MQu	0.21	0.51	0.00	5.00	104	0.00	0.00	3.24	16.14
MQ-	0.07	[0.27]	0.00	2.00	35	0.00	0.00	4.48	21.40
MQNone	0.01	[0.08]	0.00	1.00	4	0.00	0.00	12.15	146.23
S-	0.25	[0.56]	0.00	3.00	117	0.00	0.00	2.71	8.25
M	4.30	1.95	1.00	10.00	600	4.00	3.00	0.48	-0.55
FM	3.74	1.31	0.00	9.00	598	4.00	4.00	0.15	0.58
m	1.28	0.99	0.00	6.00	458	1.00	1.00	0.62	0.61
FM+m	5.01	1.70	0.00	12.00	599	5.00	5.00	0.20	0.25
FC	3.56	1.88	0.00	9.00	580	3.00	3.00	0.38	-0.24
CF	2.41	1.31	0.00	7.00	564	2.00	3.00	0.29	-0.17
C	0.12	[0.37]	0.00	3.00	61	0.00	0.00	3.76	17.14
Cn	0.01	[0.08]	0.00	1.00	4	0.00	0.00	12.15	146.23
Sum Color	6.09	2.44	0.00	12.00	599	6.00	5.00	0.11	-0.66
WSumC	4.36	1.78	0.00	9.50	599	4.00	3.50	0.11	-0.54
Sum C'	1.49	[1.16]	0.00	10.00	490	1.00	1.00	1.41	5.96
Sum T	0.95	[0.61]	0.00	4.00	490	1.00	1.00	0.83	3.33
Sum V	0.28	[0.61]	0.00	5.00	124	0.00	0.00	2.71	9.58
Sum Y	0.61	[0.96]	0.00	10.00	262	0.00	0.00	3.53	23.46
Sum Shading	3.32	2.09	0.00	23.00	588	3.00	3.00	2.54	15.45
Fr+rF	0.11	[0.43]	0.00	4.00	48	0.00	0.00	4.98	30.45
FD	1.18	[0.94]	0.00	5.00	456	1.00	1.00	0.84	1.35
F	7.95	2.83	2.00	23.00	600	8.00	7.00	0.92	2.04
(2)	8.52	2.18	1.00	21.00	600	8.00	8.00	0.29	2.11
3r+(2)/R	0.40	0.09	0.03	0.87	600	0.39	0.33	0.47	3.86
Lambda	0.60	0.31	0.11	2.33	600	0.53	0.50	2.27	8.01
EA	8.66	2.38	2.00	18.00	600	9.00	9.50	-0.04	0.42
es	8.34	2.99	3.00	31.00	600	8.00	7.00	1.43	6.58
D Score	-0.03	0.97	-10.00	3.00	600	0.00	0.00	-3.06	24.34
AdjD	0.15	0.82	-5.00	3.00	600	0.00	0.00	-0.88	5.89
a (active)	6.44	2.23	0.00	14.00	599	6.00	6.00	0.32	0.01
p (passive)	2.90	1.64	0.00	9.00	572	3.00	2.00	0.57	0.03
Ma	2.90	1.57	0.00	8.00	583	3.00	2.00	0.52	-0.26
Mp	1.42	1.03	0.00	5.00	493	1.00	1.00	0.53	-0.13
Intellect	1.57	1.48	0.00	9.00	449	1.00	1.00	1.27	2.16
Zf	11.84	2.78	5.00	27.00	600	12.00	12.00	0.87	3.44
Zd	0.57	2.98	-11.50	9.50	560	0.50	-1.00	0.31	0.48
Blends	5.15	2.08	0.00	12.00	598	5.00	5.00	0.00	-0.26
Blends/R	0.24	0.10	0.00	0.67	598	0.24	0.26	0.35	0.65
Col-Shd Blends	0.45	[0.68]	0.00	5.00	215	0.00	0.00	1.70	4.12
Afr	0.67	0.16	0.23	1.29	600	0.67	0.67	0.35	0.65

TABLE 13. NONPATIENT ADULTS (N = 600) (Continued)

VARIABLE	MEAN	SD	MIN	MAX	FREQ	MEDIAN	MODE	SK	KU
Populars	6.58	1.39	3.00	10.00	600	6.00	6.00	-0.09	-0.47
XA%	0.92	0.06	0.57	1.00	600	0.94	0.96	-1.34	3.68
WDA%	0.94	0.06	0.54	1.00	600	0.95	1.00	-1.42	4.93
X+%	0.77	0.09	0.35	1.00	600	0.78	0.80	-0.86	2.33
X-%	0.07	0.05	0.00	0.43	513	0.05	0.04	1.41	4.56
Xu%	0.15	0.07	0.00	0.45	580	0.15	0.13	0.54	0.86
Isolate/R	0.19	0.09	0.00	0.60	588	0.18	0.16	0.51	0.41
H	3.21	1.71	0.00	9.00	595	3.00	2.00	0.97	0.84
(H)	1.22	1.02	0.00	6.00	432	1.00	1.00	0.65	0.48
HD	0.84	1.02	0.00	7.00	336	1.00	0.00	1.98	6.60
(Hd)	0.21	0.50	0.00	4.00	109	0.00	0.00	2.90	11.25
Hx	0.03	[0.23]	0.00	4.00	14	0.00	0.00	11.29	164.54
All H Cont	5.49	1.75	1.00	15.00	600	5.00	5.00	0.59	1.24
A	7.96	2.25	3.00	25.00	600	8.00	7.00	1.06	5.03
(A)	0.27	[0.54]	0.00	3.00	137	0.00	0.00	2.31	6.38
Ad	2.30	[1.20]	0.00	9.00	571	2.00	2.00	0.79	2.85
(Ad)	0.10	[0.34]	0.00	2.00	53	0.00	0.00	3.57	13.07
An	0.54	[0.77]	0.00	4.00	243	0.00	0.00	1.59	2.81
Art	0.90	0.91	0.00	5.00	363	1.00	0.00	0.98	1.20
Ay	0.35	[0.52]	0.00	3.00	198	0.00	0.00	1.23	1.38
Bl	0.20	[0.46]	0.00	3.00	104	0.00	0.00	2.40	5.80
Bt	2.37	1.32	0.00	6.00	551	2.00	3.00	0.17	-0.29
Cg	1.41	1.09	0.00	5.00	482	1.00	1.00	0.73	0.29
Cl	0.14	[0.38]	0.00	2.00	78	0.00	0.00	2.67	6.76
Ex	0.20	[0.40]	0.00	2.00	119	0.00	0.00	1.57	0.74
Fi	0.56	[0.77]	0.00	4.00	240	0.00	0.00	1.09	0.22
Food	0.21	[0.47]	0.00	3.00	112	0.00	0.00	2.26	5.03
Ge	0.05	[0.24]	0.00	2.00	27	0.00	0.00	5.18	28.97
Hh	0.99	0.90	0.00	4.00	407	1.00	1.00	0.85	0.57
Ls	0.86	0.79	0.00	3.00	382	1.00	1.00	0.60	-0.23
Na	0.36	[0.63]	0.00	6.00	178	0.00	0.00	2.35	11.12
Sc	1.12	[1.15]	0.00	6.00	388	1.00	0.00	1.22	1.96
Sx	0.11	[0.47]	0.00	5.00	46	0.00	0.00	6.16	48.09
Xy	0.05	[0.24]	0.00	2.00	29	0.00	0.00	4.80	24.46
Idio	1.36	1.32	0.00	7.00	404	1.00	0.00	1.03	1.43
DV	0.59	[0.78]	0.00	4.00	266	0.00	0.00	1.36	1.77
INCOM	0.56	[0.78]	0.00	4.00	263	0.00	0.00	1.74	3.91
DR	0.39	[0.69]	0.00	4.00	175	0.00	0.00	1.97	4.15
FABCOM	0.27	[0.52]	0.00	3.00	141	0.00	0.00	1.85	3.02
DV2	0.00	[0.06]	0.00	1.00	2	0.00	0.00	17.27	297.49
INC2	0.02	[0.13]	0.00	1.00	10	0.00	0.00	7.57	55.49
DR2	0.01	[0.11]	0.00	1.00	8	0.00	0.00	8.50	70.61
FAB2	0.03	[0.16]	0.00	1.00	16	0.00	0.00	5.89	32.81
ALOG	0.04	[0.20]	0.00	2.00	21	0.00	0.00	5.58	33.07
CONTAM	0.00	0.00	0.00	0.00	0	0.00	0.00	----	----
Sum 6 Sp Sc	1.91	1.47	0.00	7.00	496	2.00	1.00	0.80	0.56
Lvl 2 Sp Sc	0.06	[0.25]	0.00	2.00	34	0.00	0.00	4.33	19.52
WSum6	4.48	4.08	0.00	28.00	496	4.00	0.00	1.42	3.25
AB	0.16	[0.43]	0.00	3.00	84	0.00	0.00	2.82	8.39
AG	1.11	1.15	0.00	5.00	380	1.00	0.00	1.02	0.60
COP	2.00	1.38	0.00	6.00	498	2.00	2.00	0.25	-0.63
CP	0.01	[0.09]	0.00	1.00	5	0.00	0.00	10.84	115.98
GOODHR	4.93	1.78	0.00	10.00	598	5.00	5.00	0.36	0.02
POORHR	1.53	1.46	0.00	8.00	431	1.00	1.00	1.25	2.30
MOR	0.79	[0.89]	0.00	4.00	321	1.00	0.00	1.01	0.60
PER	0.92	0.91	0.00	5.00	385	1.00	1.00	1.33	3.39
PSV	0.07	[0.25]	0.00	2.00	38	0.00	0.00	3.84	14.28

NOTE: Standard Deviations shown in brackets indicate that the value is probably unreliable and/or misleading and should not be used to estimate expected ranges. Ordinarily these variables should not be included in most parametric analyses.

TABLE 14. FREQUENCIES FOR 36 VARIABLES FOR NONPATIENT ADULTS
(N = 600)

DEMOGRAPHY VARIABLES

MARITAL STATUS			AGE			RACE		
Single	165	28%	18-25	195	33%	White	493	82%
Lives w/S.O.	49	8%	26-35	240	40%	Black	60	10%
Married	270	45%	36-45	102	17%	Hispanic	36	6%
Separated	32	5%	46-55	32	5%	Asian	11	2%
Divorced	72	12%	56-65	23	4%			
Widowed	12	2%	OVER 65	8	1%			
						EDUCATION		
SEX						UNDER 12	32	5%
Male	300	50%				12 Years	163	27%
Female	300	50%				13-15 Yrs	318	53%
						16+ Yrs	87	15%

RATIOS, PERCENTAGES AND SPECIAL INDICES

STYLES			FORM QUALITY DEVIATIONS		
Introversive	199	33%	XA% > .89	443	74%
Pervasive	52	9%	XA% < .70	2	0%
Ambitent	116	19%	WDA% < .85	29	5%
Extratensive	227	38%	WDA% < .75	3	1%
Pervasive	59	10%	X+% < .55	9	2%
Avoidant	58	10%	Xu% > .20	129	22%
			X-% > .20	15	3%
D-SCORES			X-% > .30	2	0%
D Score > 0	100	17%			
D Score = 0	420	70%			
D Score < 0	80	13%	FC:CF+C RATIO		
D Score < -1	29	5%	FC > (CF+C) + 2	151	25%
			FC > (CF+C) + 1	245	41%
Adj D Score > 0	151	25%	(CF+C) > FC+1	70	12%
Adj D Score = 0	389	65%	(CF+C) > FC+2	24	4%
Adj D Score < 0	60	10%			
Adj D Score < -1	21	4%			
			S-Constellation Positive	0	0%
Zd > +3.0 (Overincorp)	100	17%	HVI Positive	18	3%
Zd < -3.0 (Underincorp)	39	7%	OBS Positive	8	1%

PTI = 5	0	0%	DEPI = 7	2	0%	CDI = 5	2	0%
PTI = 4	0	0%	DEPI = 6	4	1%	CDI = 4	21	4%
PTI = 3	1	0%	DEPI = 5	24	4%			

MISCELLANEOUS VARIABLES

R < 17	58	10%	(2AB+Art+Ay) > 5	12	2%
R > 27	55	9%	Populars < 4	7	1%
DQv > 2	73	12%	Populars > 7	184	31%
S > 2	86	14%	COP = 0	102	17%
Sum T = 0	110	18%	COP > 2	213	36%
Sum T >1	65	11%	AG = 0	220	37%
3r+(2)/R < .33	80	13%	AG > 2	74	12%
3r+(2)/R > .44	140	23%	MOR > 2	26	4%
Fr + rF > 0	48	8%	Level 2 Sp.Sc. > 0	34	6%
PureC > 0	61	10%	GHR > PHR	526	88%
PureC > 1	7	1%	Pure H < 2	71	12%
Afr < .40	18	3%	Pure H = 0	5	1%
Afr < .50	66	11%	p > a+1	11	2%
(FM+m) < Sum Shading	87	15%	Mp > Ma	82	14%

TABLE 15. DESCRIPTIVE STATISTICS FOR ADULT INTROVERSIVES (N = 199)

VARIABLE	MEAN	SD	MIN	MAX	FREQ	MEDIAN	MODE	SK	KU
AGE	33.23	11.39	19.00	69.00	199	31.00	26.00	1.26	1.30
Years Educ	13.69	1.52	8.00	18.00	199	14.00	14.00	0.08	0.05
R	22.90	4.84	14.00	38.00	199	23.00	20.00	0.63	0.56
W	8.62	2.59	3.00	20.00	199	8.00	8.00	1.58	6.26
D	13.01	3.88	0.00	22.00	198	13.00	14.00	-0.06	0.96
Dd	1.27	[1.34]	0.00	9.00	137	1.00	1.00	1.97	7.36
S	1.51	[1.24]	0.00	7.00	165	1.00	1.00	1.35	2.48
DQ+	8.54	2.31	4.00	19.00	199	9.00	9.00	0.15	1.12
DQo	12.77	3.61	5.00	26.00	199	12.00	11.00	0.68	0.40
DQv	1.20	[1.41]	0.00	5.00	111	1.00	0.00	0.97	-0.27
DQv/+	0.39	[0.61]	0.00	2.00	65	0.00	0.00	1.30	0.63
FQx+	0.79	0.99	0.00	5.00	99	0.00	0.00	1.46	2.71
FQxo	17.00	3.68	8.00	27.00	199	17.00	18.00	0.36	0.52
FQxu	3.64	1.94	0.00	14.00	196	4.00	4.00	1.50	5.39
FQx-	1.45	1.17	0.00	6.00	163	1.00	1.00	0.98	0.85
FQxNone	0.02	[0.14]	0.00	1.00	4	0.00	0.00	6.89	45.95
MQ+	0.52	0.76	0.00	3.00	78	0.00	0.00	1.47	1.77
MQo	5.41	1.36	1.00	8.00	199	5.00	6.00	-0.33	0.12
MQu	0.39	0.69	0.00	5.00	62	0.00	0.00	2.52	10.38
MQ-	0.09	[0.35]	0.00	2.00	13	0.00	0.00	4.33	19.06
MQNone	0.01	[0.10]	0.00	1.00	2	0.00	0.00	9.89	96.96
S-	0.20	[0.48]	0.00	3.00	34	0.00	0.00	3.01	11.58
M	6.42	1.26	2.00	10.00	199	7.00	7.00	-0.02	0.27
FM	3.72	1.21	1.00	6.00	199	4.00	4.00	0.07	-0.31
m	1.47	0.94	0.00	4.00	164	2.00	2.00	0.06	-0.40
FM+m	5.20	1.49	1.00	9.00	199	5.00	5.00	0.17	-0.32
FC	3.03	1.49	0.00	7.00	193	3.00	3.00	0.31	-0.13
CF	1.65	0.82	0.00	5.00	185	2.00	2.00	0.17	0.66
C	0.02	[0.12]	0.00	1.00	3	0.00	0.00	8.02	62.95
Cn	0.00	[0.00]	0.00	0.00	0	0.00	0.00	----	----
Sum Color	4.70	1.65	0.00	9.00	198	5.00	5.00	0.08	0.39
WSumC	3.19	1.07	0.00	6.00	198	3.50	3.50	-0.18	0.36
Sum C'	1.33	[1.13]	0.00	8.00	146	1.00	2.00	1.21	4.89
Sum T	0.93	[0.54]	0.00	3.00	164	1.00	1.00	0.32	2.08
Sum V	0.31	[0.53]	0.00	2.00	54	0.00	0.00	1.53	1.44
Sum Y	0.45	[0.83]	0.00	6.00	65	0.00	0.00	3.06	13.94
Sum Shading	3.01	1.88	0.00	13.00	194	3.00	3.00	1.50	4.30
Fr+rF	0.11	[0.49]	0.00	4.00	14	0.00	0.00	5.97	41.10
FD	1.30	[0.95]	0.00	4.00	154	1.00	1.00	0.31	-0.31
F	7.46	2.56	2.00	15.00	199	7.00	7.00	0.48	-0.39
(2)	8.99	2.06	3.00	14.00	199	9.00	8.00	0.38	0.28
3r+(2)/R	0.41	0.09	0.25	0.87	199	0.40	0.38	1.81	6.56
Lambda	0.50	0.17	0.11	0.92	199	0.50	0.33	0.40	-0.17
EA	9.61	2.17	2.00	16.00	199	9.50	9.50	-0.05	0.47
es	8.21	2.72	3.00	21.00	199	8.00	7.00	0.96	2.39
D Score	0.17	0.74	-3.00	2.00	199	0.00	0.00	-0.57	4.25
AdjD	0.41	0.73	-3.00	2.00	199	0.00	0.00	-0.25	2.31
a (active)	7.84	2.09	2.00	14.00	199	8.00	6.00	0.29	-0.30
p (passive)	3.79	1.72	0.00	9.00	192	4.00	5.00	-0.08	-0.29
Ma	4.41	1.27	1.00	8.00	199	4.00	4.00	-0.13	0.08
Mp	2.03	1.12	0.00	5.00	181	2.00	3.00	-0.01	-0.50
Intellect	1.35	1.47	0.00	9.00	136	1.00	1.00	1.67	4.02
Zf	12.80	2.98	6.00	25.00	199	13.00	13.00	0.42	2.52
Zd	-0.12	3.08	-6.50	8.50	190	-0.50	-3.00	0.39	-0.28
Blends	4.83	2.11	0.00	11.00	198	5.00	5.00	0.24	-0.27
Blends/R	0.22	0.10	0.00	0.57	198	0.20	0.25	0.63	0.24
Col-Shd Blends	0.29	[0.52]	0.00	2.00	52	0.00	0.00	1.56	1.57
Afr	0.64	0.15	0.23	1.14	199	0.67	0.67	0.33	1.03

TABLE 15. ADULT NONPATIENT INTROVERSIVES (N = 199) (Continued)

VARIABLE	MEAN	SD	MIN	MAX	FREQ	MEDIAN	MODE	SK	KU
Populars	6.54	1.36	3.00	10.00	199	6.00	6.00	0.07	-0.11
XA%	0.94	0.05	0.69	1.00	199	0.95	0.95	-1.39	4.25
WDA%	0.95	0.05	0.69	1.00	199	0.96	1.00	-1.50	3.83
X+%	0.78	0.09	0.35	1.00	199	0.79	0.80	-1.36	4.66
X-%	0.06	0.05	0.00	0.31	163	0.05	0.05	1.43	4.47
Xu%	0.16	0.07	0.00	0.45	196	0.15	0.15	0.87	1.92
Isolate/R	0.19	0.10	0.00	0.60	193	0.17	0.13	0.69	1.00
H	4.79	1.71	1.00	9.00	199	5.00	5.00	0.30	-0.09
(H)	1.27	1.19	0.00	4.00	134	1.00	0.00	0.66	-0.46
HD	0.48	0.85	0.00	5.00	65	0.00	0.00	2.25	5.99
(Hd)	0.15	0.40	0.00	2.00	27	0.00	0.00	2.66	6.77
Hx	0.03	[0.16]	0.00	1.00	5	0.00	0.00	6.11	35.75
All H Cont	6.69	1.51	2.00	15.00	199	7.00	7.00	0.72	4.14
A	7.91	2.07	3.00	14.00	199	8.00	8.00	0.22	0.07
(A)	0.29	[0.56]	0.00	3.00	48	0.00	0.00	2.19	5.43
Ad	2.34	[1.07]	0.00	5.00	189	2.00	2.00	-0.13	-0.17
(Ad)	0.08	[0.29]	0.00	2.00	15	0.00	0.00	3.71	14.19
An	0.59	[0.79]	0.00	4.00	86	0.00	0.00	1.31	1.60
Art	0.72	0.84	0.00	4.00	103	1.00	0.00	1.12	1.28
Ay	0.38	[0.53]	0.00	3.00	73	0.00	0.00	1.11	1.47
Bl	0.06	[0.27]	0.00	2.00	9	0.00	0.00	5.35	30.64
Bt	2.03	1.25	0.00	5.00	177	2.00	3.00	0.09	-0.73
Cg	1.73	1.27	0.00	5.00	163	1.00	1.00	0.32	-0.79
Cl	0.18	[0.45]	0.00	2.00	31	0.00	0.00	2.48	5.68
Ex	0.31	[0.46]	0.00	1.00	61	0.00	0.00	0.84	-1.30
Fi	0.46	[0.66]	0.00	2.00	72	0.00	0.00	1.15	0.10
Food	0.10	[0.30]	0.00	1.00	20	0.00	0.00	2.67	5.22
Ge	0.03	[0.16]	0.00	1.00	5	0.00	0.00	6.11	35.75
Hh	1.24	1.00	0.00	4.00	151	1.00	1.00	0.70	0.35
Ls	1.14	0.85	0.00	3.00	148	1.00	1.00	0.13	-0.86
Na	0.41	[0.75]	0.00	6.00	60	0.00	0.00	2.88	14.66
Sc	1.09	[1.09]	0.00	6.00	136	1.00	1.00	1.44	2.92
Sx	0.10	[0.49]	0.00	5.00	12	0.00	0.00	6.89	57.06
Xy	0.03	[0.16]	0.00	1.00	5	0.00	0.00	6.11	35.75
Idio	1.42	1.22	0.00	7.00	141	1.00	0.00	0.71	0.97
DV	0.70	[0.89]	0.00	4.00	94	0.00	0.00	1.18	0.78
INCOM	0.51	[0.77]	0.00	4.00	76	0.00	0.00	1.77	3.46
DR	0.30	[0.61]	0.00	3.00	45	0.00	0.00	2.17	4.52
FABCOM	0.27	[0.50]	0.00	3.00	49	0.00	0.00	1.92	4.47
DV2	0.01	[0.07]	0.00	1.00	1	0.00	0.00	14.10	199.00
INC2	0.01	[0.10]	0.00	1.00	2	0.00	0.00	9.89	96.96
DR2	0.03	[0.17]	0.00	1.00	6	0.00	0.00	5.53	28.95
FAB2	0.05	[0.21]	0.00	1.00	9	0.00	0.00	4.41	17.63
ALOG	0.02	[0.16]	0.00	2.00	2	0.00	0.00	11.30	133.83
CONTAM	0.00	0.00	0.00	0.00	0	0.00	0.00	----	----
Sum 6 Sp Sc	1.88	1.54	0.00	7.00	155	2.00	2.00	0.70	0.10
Lvl 2 Sp Sc	0.09	[0.32]	0.00	2.00	16	0.00	0.00	3.76	14.75
WSum6	4.30	4.09	0.00	28.00	155	4.00	0.00	1.56	4.97
AB	0.12	[0.42]	0.00	2.00	17	0.00	0.00	3.61	12.41
AG	1.16	1.17	0.00	5.00	132	1.00	1.00	1.09	0.81
COP	2.45	1.54	0.00	6.00	170	2.00	2.00	0.04	-0.76
CP	0.00	[0.00]	0.00	0.00	0	0.00	0.00	----	----
GOODHR	6.24	1.69	2.00	10.00	199	6.00	5.00	-0.04	-0.49
POORHR	1.35	1.45	0.00	7.00	126	1.00	0.00	1.15	1.12
MOR	0.93	[0.98]	0.00	4.00	114	1.00	0.00	0.75	-0.23
PER	0.98	0.87	0.00	5.00	133	1.00	1.00	0.80	1.51
PSV	0.04	[0.19]	0.00	1.00	7	0.00	0.00	5.08	24.10

NOTE: Standard Deviations shown in brackets indicate that the value is probably unreliable and/or misleading and should not be used to estimate expected ranges. Ordinarily these variables should not be included in most parametric analyses.

TABLE 16. FREQUENCIES FOR 36 VARIABLES FOR ADULT INTROVERSIVES
(N = 199)

DEMOGRAPHY VARIABLES

MARITAL STATUS			AGE			RACE		
Single	47	24%	18-25	56	28%	White	172	86%
Lives w/S.O.	13	7%	26-35	75	38%	Black	16	8%
Married	99	50%	36-45	43	22%	Hispanic	5	3%
Separated	14	7%	46-55	11	6%	Asian	6	3%
Divorced	21	11%	56-65	10	5%			
Widowed	5	3%	OVER 65	4	2%			
						EDUCATION		
SEX						UNDER 12	4	2%
Male	104	52%				12 Years	47	24%
Female	95	48%				13-15 Yrs	112	56%
						16+ Yrs	36	18%

RATIOS, PERCENTAGES AND SPECIAL INDICES

STYLES			FORM QUALITY DEVIATIONS		
Introversive	199	100%	XA% > .89	167	84%
Pervasive	52	26%	XA% < .70	1	1%
Ambitent	0	0%	WDA% < .85	6	3%
Extratensive	0	0%	WDA% < .75	1	1%
Pervasive	0	0%	X+% < .55	3	2%
Avoidant	0	0%	Xu% > .20	40	20%
			X-% > .20	4	2%
D-SCORES			X-% > .30	1	1%
D Score > 0	47	24%			
D Score = 0	138	69%	FC:CF+C RATIO		
D Score < 0	14	7%	FC > (CF+C) + 2	53	27%
D Score < -1	6	3%	FC > (CF+C) + 1	89	45%
			(CF+C) > FC+1	9	5%
Adj D Score > 0	82	41%	(CF+C) > FC+2	4	2%
Adj D Score = 0	108	54%			
Adj D Score < 0	9	5%			
Adj D Score < -1	2	1%	S-Constellation Positive	0	0%
			HVI Positive	6	3%
Zd > +3.0 (Overincorp)	33	17%	OBS Positive	5	3%
Zd < -3.0 (Underincorp)	22	11%			

PTI = 5	0	0%	DEPI = 7	0	0%	CDI = 5	0	0%
PTI = 4	0	0%	DEPI = 6	1	1%	CDI = 4	1	1%
PTI = 3	1	1%	DEPI = 5	9	5%			

MISCELLANEOUS VARIABLES

R < 17	18	9%	(2AB+Art+Ay) > 5	2	1%
R > 27	25	13%	Populars < 4	3	2%
DQv > 2	40	20%	Populars > 7	58	29%
S > 2	28	14%	COP = 0	29	15%
Sum T = 0	35	18%	COP > 2	97	49%
Sum T > 1	18	9%	AG = 0	67	34%
3r+(2)/R < .33	20	10%	AG > 2	25	13%
3r+(2)/R > .44	52	26%	MOR > 2	13	7%
Fr + rF > 0	14	7%	Level 2 Sp.Sc. > 0	16	8%
PureC > 0	3	2%	GHR > PHR	187	94%
PureC > 1	0	0%	Pure H < 2	3	2%
Afr < .40	9	5%	Pure H = 0	0	0%
Afr < .50	25	13%	p > a+1	3	2%
(FM+m) < Sum Shading	17	9%	Mp > Ma	16	8%

TABLE 17. DESCRIPTIVE STATISTICS FOR ADULT EXTRATENSIVES (N = 227)

VARIABLE	MEAN	SD	MIN	MAX	FREQ	MEDIAN	MODE	SK	KU
AGE	31.25	11.06	19.00	67.00	227	29.00	22.00	1.38	1.53
Years Educ	13.41	1.61	9.00	19.00	227	13.00	12.00	0.40	0.22
R	22.43	3.09	15.00	32.00	227	22.00	21.00	0.06	0.61
W	8.68	2.11	5.00	24.00	227	9.00	9.00	2.80	15.52
D	12.92	3.26	1.00	23.00	227	13.00	13.00	-0.59	1.50
Dd	0.82	[0.84]	0.00	3.00	130	1.00	0.00	0.65	-0.50
S	1.45	[0.87]	0.00	4.00	205	1.00	1.00	0.62	0.45
DQ+	7.11	1.91	3.00	17.00	227	7.00	6.00	1.21	3.33
DQo	14.00	2.44	7.00	22.00	227	14.00	15.00	-0.19	0.87
DQv	0.87	[1.00]	0.00	5.00	123	1.00	0.00	1.17	1.36
DQv/+	0.44	[0.61]	0.00	2.00	86	0.00	0.00	1.05	0.09
FQx+	0.86	0.83	0.00	4.00	138	1.00	0.00	0.65	-0.04
FQxo	16.70	2.74	10.00	23.00	227	17.00	17.00	-0.08	-0.15
FQxu	3.22	1.73	0.00	9.00	216	3.00	3.00	0.48	0.25
FQx-	1.49	1.09	0.00	7.00	198	1.00	1.00	1.49	4.28
FQxNone	0.17	[0.42]	0.00	3.00	35	0.00	0.00	2.85	10.50
MQ+	0.57	0.67	0.00	3.00	107	0.00	0.00	0.85	-0.02
MQo	2.36	1.02	0.00	5.00	226	2.00	3.00	0.18	-0.69
MQu	0.04	0.21	0.00	1.00	10	0.00	0.00	4.47	18.17
MQ-	0.02	[0.13]	0.00	1.00	4	0.00	0.00	7.38	52.95
MQNone	0.00	[0.00]	0.00	0.00	0	0.00	0.00	----	----
S	-0.19	[0.45]	0.00	3.00	40	0.00	0.00	2.56	8.09
M	2.99	0.92	1.00	6.00	227	3.00	3.00	0.12	0.52
FM	3.94	1.17	0.00	8.00	226	4.00	4.00	-0.08	0.52
m	1.13	0.96	0.00	6.00	172	1.00	1.00	1.27	3.31
FM+m	5.07	1.59	1.00	9.00	227	5.00	5.00	0.19	-0.15
FC	4.65	1.80	0.00	9.00	224	5.00	5.00	0.04	-0.11
CF	3.45	1.07	0.00	7.00	226	3.00	3.00	0.18	0.59
C	0.19	[0.47]	0.00	3.00	37	0.00	0.00	3.03	11.39
Cn	0.00	[0.00]	0.00	0.00	0	0.00	0.00	----	----
Sum Color	8.28	1.65	3.00	12.00	227	8.00	8.00	-0.14	0.03
WSumC	6.05	1.09	4.00	9.50	227	6.00	6.00	0.26	0.09
Sum C'	1.47	[1.04]	0.00	5.00	194	1.00	1.00	0.83	0.93
Sum T	1.04	[0.59]	0.00	4.00	201	1.00	1.00	1.27	4.75
Sum V	0.23	[0.61]	0.00	5.00	38	0.00	0.00	3.59	18.47
Sum Y	0.71	[0.77]	0.00	3.00	124	1.00	0.00	0.96	0.58
Sum Shading	3.46	1.61	0.00	10.00	225	3.00	3.00	1.03	1.56
Fr+rF	0.08	[0.37]	0.00	3.00	12	0.00	0.00	5.25	29.80
FD	1.18	[0.79]	0.00	5.00	191	1.00	1.00	0.92	2.44
F	7.66	1.87	3.00	12.00	227	8.00	8.00	-0.10	-0.35
(2)	8.46	1.67	5.00	12.00	227	8.00	8.00	0.20	-0.65
3r+(2)/R	0.39	0.07	0.27	0.61	227	0.38	0.33	0.90	0.55
Lambda	0.54	0.17	0.19	0.91	227	0.53	0.53	0.10	-0.51
EA	9.04	1.82	5.50	15.50	227	9.00	8.50	0.26	0.49
es	8.53	2.48	4.00	18.00	227	8.00	7.00	0.59	0.83
D Score	0.07	0.69	-3.00	2.00	227	0.00	0.00	-0.08	3.88
AdjD	0.15	0.68	-2.00	3.00	227	0.00	0.00	0.59	3.48
a (active)	5.73	1.81	0.00	11.00	226	6.00	5.00	0.21	-0.20
p (passive)	2.37	1.31	0.00	8.00	221	2.00	2.00	1.31	2.99
Ma	1.95	0.99	0.00	6.00	214	2.00	2.00	0.29	0.47
Mp	1.07	0.78	0.00	4.00	179	1.00	1.00	0.65	0.70
Intellect	1.96	1.44	0.00	7.00	201	2.00	1.00	1.12	1.42
Zf	11.83	2.31	8.00	27.00	227	11.00	11.00	1.92	9.10
Zd	1.57	2.74	-3.50	9.50	210	1.00	2.00	0.73	0.49
Blends	5.86	1.75	0.00	12.00	226	6.00	6.00	-0.02	0.87
Blends/R	0.26	0.08	0.00	0.57	226	0.26	0.26	0.01	2.22
Col-Shd Blends	0.70	[0.83]	0.00	5.00	116	1.00	0.00	1.33	2.75
Afr	0.71	0.16	0.27	1.09	227	0.71	0.91	0.18	-0.15

TABLE 17. ADULT NONPATIENT EXTRATENSIVES (N = 227) (Continued)

VARIABLE	MEAN	SD	MIN	MAX	FREQ	MEDIAN	MODE	SK	KU
Populars	6.77	1.36	4.00	9.00	227	7.00	8.00	-0.36	-0.63
XA%	0.93	0.05	0.72	1.00	227	0.94	0.96	-1.01	1.99
WDA%	0.93	0.05	0.72	1.00	227	0.95	0.96	-1.00	2.12
X+%	0.78	0.09	0.38	1.00	227	0.79	0.86	-0.74	2.16
X-%	0.07	0.05	0.00	0.24	198	0.05	0.04	0.88	1.32
Xu%	0.14	0.07	0.00	0.35	216	0.14	0.14	0.22	0.18
Isolate/R	0.21	0.09	0.05	0.45	227	0.19	0.16	0.57	-0.37
H	2.41	0.90	1.00	6.00	227	2.00	2.00	0.47	0.75
(H)	1.18	0.90	0.00	6.00	170	1.00	1.00	0.69	2.50
HD	0.93	0.84	0.00	4.00	153	1.00	1.00	0.81	0.78
(Hd)	0.24	0.49	0.00	3.00	49	0.00	0.00	2.42	7.80
Hx	0.01	[0.13]	0.00	2.00	1	0.00	0.00	15.06	227.00
All H Cont	4.76	1.43	2.00	12.00	227	5.00	4.00	0.95	2.79
A	8.14	2.08	4.00	14.00	227	8.00	7.00	0.75	-0.17
(A)	0.21	[0.49]	0.00	3.00	42	0.00	0.00	2.75	9.48
Ad	2.21	[0.98]	0.00	5.00	219	2.00	2.00	0.02	-0.19
(Ad)	0.12	[0.40]	0.00	2.00	21	0.00	0.00	3.53	12.22
An	0.44	[0.67]	0.00	4.00	82	0.00	0.00	1.96	5.93
Art	1.15	0.87	0.00	5.00	176	1.00	1.00	0.76	1.69
Ay	0.34	[0.51]	0.00	2.00	72	0.00	0.00	1.10	0.08
Bl	0.35	[0.58]	0.00	3.00	68	0.00	0.00	1.58	2.22
Bt	2.97	1.30	0.00	6.00	220	3.00	3.00	0.09	-0.15
Cg	1.17	0.86	0.00	5.00	181	1.00	1.00	0.86	1.87
Cl	0.11	[0.32]	0.00	2.00	23	0.00	0.00	2.97	8.33
Ex	0.10	[0.30]	0.00	1.00	23	0.00	0.00	2.66	5.12
Fi	0.75	[0.88]	0.00	4.00	110	0.00	0.00	0.74	-0.51
Food	0.36	[0.58]	0.00	3.00	71	0.00	0.00	1.51	1.98
Ge	0.08	[0.28]	0.00	2.00	16	0.00	0.00	3.84	15.22
Hh	0.88	0.75	0.00	3.00	157	1.00	1.00	0.76	0.70
Ls	0.76	0.72	0.00	3.00	138	1.00	1.00	0.68	0.19
Na	0.37	[0.56]	0.00	2.00	74	0.00	0.00	1.23	0.56
Sc	1.12	[1.07]	0.00	6.00	150	1.00	0.00	1.08	2.29
Sx	0.05	[0.24]	0.00	2.00	11	0.00	0.00	4.91	26.09
Xy	0.04	[0.21]	0.00	1.00	10	0.00	0.00	4.47	18.17
Idio	1.53	1.28	0.00	5.00	170	1.00	1.00	0.59	-0.30
DV	0.53	[0.65]	0.00	3.00	102	0.00	0.00	0.93	0.20
INCOM	0.61	[0.76]	0.00	4.00	112	0.00	0.00	1.58	3.63
DR	0.37	[0.73]	0.00	4.00	60	0.00	0.00	2.29	6.03
FABCOM	0.23	[0.47]	0.00	2.00	47	0.00	0.00	1.91	2.93
DV2	0.00	[0.00]	0.00	0.00	0	0.00	0.00	----	----
INC2	0.00	[0.07]	0.00	1.00	1	0.00	0.00	15.06	227.00
DR2	0.00	[0.00]	0.00	0.00	0	0.00	0.00	----	----
FAB2	0.02	[0.15]	0.00	1.00	5	0.00	0.00	6.55	41.35
ALOG	0.05	[0.22]	0.00	1.00	11	0.00	0.00	4.23	16.06
CONTAM	0.00	0.00	0.00	0.00	0	0.00	0.00	----	----
Sum 6 Sp Sc	1.82	1.46	0.00	7.00	190	2.00	1.00	1.09	1.34
Lvl 2 Sp Sc	0.03	[0.16]	0.00	1.00	6	0.00	0.00	5.94	33.62
WSum6	4.21	4.23	0.00	22.00	190	3.00	2.00	1.80	4.08
AB	0.23	[0.47]	0.00	2.00	48	0.00	0.00	1.88	2.76
AG	1.15	1.19	0.00	5.00	145	1.00	0.00	1.00	0.46
COP	1.83	1.23	0.00	4.00	189	2.00	2.00	0.14	-0.91
CP	0.02	[0.15]	0.00	1.00	5	0.00	0.00	6.55	41.35
GOODHR	4.32	1.33	1.00	8.00	227	4.00	4.00	0.27	0.50
POORHR	1.51	1.33	0.00	8.00	168	1.00	1.00	1.02	1.89
MOR	0.71	[0.78]	0.00	4.00	121	1.00	0.00	1.01	0.97
PER	0.99	0.94	0.00	5.00	158	1.00	1.00	1.57	4.24
PSV	0.07	[0.27]	0.00	2.00	15	0.00	0.00	4.01	16.78

NOTE: Standard Deviations shown in brackets indicate that the value is probably unreliable and/or misleading and should not be used to estimate expected ranges. Ordinarily these variables should not be included in most parametric analyses.

TABLE 18. FREQUENCIES FOR 36 VARIABLES FOR ADULT EXTRATENSIVES
(N = 227)

DEMOGRAPHY VARIABLES

MARITAL STATUS			AGE			RACE		
Single	73	32%	18-25	82	36%	White	176	78%
Lives w/S.O.	14	6%	26-35	90	40%	Black	27	12%
Married	99	44%	36-45	26	11%	Hispanic	19	8%
Separated	13	6%	46-55	18	8%	Asian	5	2%
Divorced	24	11%	56-65	7	3%			
Widowed	4	2%	OVER 65	4	2%			

SEX						EDUCATION		
						UNDER 12	13	6%
Male	118	52%				12 Years	65	29%
Female	109	48%				13-15 Yrs	115	51%
						16+ Yrs	34	15%

RATIOS, PERCENTAGES AND SPECIAL INDICES

STYLES			FORM QUALITY DEVIATIONS		
Introversive	0	0%	XA% > .89	168	74%
Pervasive	0	0%	XA% < .70	0	0%
Ambitent	0	0%	WDA% < .85	7	3%
Extratensive	227	100%	WDA% < .75	1	0%
Pervasive	59	26%	X+% < .55	2	1%
Avoidant	0	0%	Xu% > .20	41	18%
			X-% > .20	3	1%
D-SCORES			X-% > .30	0	0%
D Score > 0	36	16%			
D Score = 0	168	74%			
D Score < 0	23	10%	FC:CF+C RATIO		
D Score < -1	6	3%	FC > (CF+C) + 2	67	30%
			FC > (CF+C) + 1	102	45%
Adj D Score > 0	44	19%	(CF+C) > FC+1	36	16%
Adj D Score = 0	166	73%	(CF+C) > FC+2	11	5%
Adj D Score < 0	17	7%			
Adj D Score < -1	4	2%			
			S-Constellation Positive	0	0%
Zd > +3.0 (Overincorp)	45	20%	HVI Positive	3	1%
Zd < -3.0 (Underincorp)	3	1%	OBS Positive	1	0%

PTI = 5	0	0%	DEPI = 7	1	0%	CDI = 5	0	0%
PTI = 4	0	0%	DEPI = 6	0	0%	CDI = 4	6	3%
PTI = 3	0	0%	DEPI = 5	7	3%			

MISCELLANEOUS VARIABLES

R < 17	14	6%	(2AB+Art+Ay) > 5	8	4%
R > 27	17	7%	Populars < 4	0	0%
DQv > 2	13	6%	Populars > 7	81	36%
S > 2	25	11%	COP = 0	38	17%
Sum T = 0	26	11%	COP > 2	68	30%
Sum T > 1	28	12%	AG = 0	82	36%
3r+(2)/R < .33	36	16%	AG > 2	36	16%
3r+(2)/R > .44	39	17%	MOR > 2	5	2%
Fr + rF > 0	12	5%	Level 2 Sp.Sc. > 0	6	3%
PureC > 0	37	16%	GHR > PHR	195	86%
PureC > 1	4	2%	Pure H < 2	34	15%
Afr < .40	2	1%	Pure H = 0	0	0%
Afr < .50	14	6%	p > a+1	7	3%
(FM+m) < Sum Shading	30	13%	Mp > Ma	47	21%

TABLE 19. DESCRIPTIVE STATISTICS FOR ADULT AMBITENTS (N = 116)

VARIABLE	MEAN	SD	MIN	MAX	FREQ	MEDIAN	MODE	SK	KU
AGE	31.13	9.36	19.00	62.00	116	30.00	30.00	1.30	2.14
Years Educ	13.09	1.54	9.00	18.00	116	13.00	12.00	0.33	0.76
R	20.84	4.99	14.00	38.00	116	20.00	20.00	1.21	1.96
W	7.86	2.17	3.00	18.00	116	8.00	7.00	0.95	3.74
D	11.53	3.82	0.00	20.00	115	12.00	14.00	-0.37	0.15
Dd	1.45	[2.49]	0.00	15.00	70	1.00	0.00	3.75	16.62
S	1.90	[1.65]	0.00	9.00	98	2.00	2.00	1.89	5.21
DQ+	6.73	1.87	2.00	13.00	116	7.00	8.00	-0.15	0.56
DQo	12.82	4.58	5.00	34.00	116	12.00	14.00	2.18	7.93
DQv	0.88	[1.25]	0.00	5.00	50	0.00	0.00	1.50	1.85
DQv/+	0.41	[0.70]	0.00	2.00	33	0.00	0.00	1.44	0.60
FQx+	0.57	0.83	0.00	4.00	47	0.00	0.00	1.70	3.61
FQxo	15.27	3.54	7.00	29.00	116	15.00	13.00	0.55	0.95
FQxu	3.16	2.10	0.00	13.00	110	3.00	2.00	1.93	6.78
FQx-	1.68	1.26	0.00	6.00	101	1.00	1.00	1.07	1.16
FQxNone	0.16	[0.47]	0.00	3.00	14	0.00	0.00	3.60	14.91
MQ+	0.26	0.59	0.00	3.00	23	0.00	0.00	2.68	7.87
MQo	3.28	1.44	0.00	8.00	114	3.00	3.00	0.54	0.86
MQu	0.25	0.51	0.00	2.00	25	0.00	0.00	1.94	3.01
MQ-	0.15	[0.36]	0.00	1.00	17	0.00	0.00	2.02	2.14
MQNone	0.01	[0.09]	0.00	1.00	1	0.00	0.00	10.77	116.00
S-	0.41	[0.82]	0.00	3.00	29	0.00	0.00	2.03	3.21
M	3.95	1.36	1.00	10.00	116	4.00	3.00	1.08	2.65
FM	3.85	1.33	1.00	9.00	116	4.00	4.00	0.43	1.22
m	1.48	1.08	0.00	4.00	90	2.00	2.00	0.31	-0.29
FM+m	5.34	1.69	2.00	10.00	116	5.00	5.00	0.19	0.18
FC	3.12	1.77	0.00	8.00	111	3.00	2.00	0.53	0.05
CF	1.91	1.13	0.00	5.00	105	2.00	1.00	0.20	-0.54
C	0.15	[0.40]	0.00	2.00	15	0.00	0.00	2.80	7.72
Cn	0.02	[0.13]	0.00	1.00	2	0.00	0.00	7.51	55.43
Sum Color	5.20	2.02	1.00	9.00	116	5.00	4.00	0.11	-0.59
WSumC	3.69	1.40	0.50	8.00	116	3.50	3.50	0.02	0.01
Sum C'	1.97	[1.38]	0.00	10.00	107	2.00	1.00	1.97	8.83
Sum T	0.94	[0.64]	0.00	4.00	92	1.00	1.00	0.87	3.85
Sum V	0.38	[0.77]	0.00	3.00	28	0.00	0.00	2.07	3.55
Sum Y	0.80	[1.42]	0.00	10.00	55	0.00	0.00	3.92	20.18
Sum Shading	4.09	2.95	1.00	23.00	116	3.00	3.00	3.16	15.33
Fr+rF	0.10	[0.35]	0.00	2.00	9	0.00	0.00	3.96	16.24
FD	1.29	[1.17]	0.00	5.00	84	1.00	1.00	1.08	1.39
F	6.96	2.56	2.00	17.00	116	7.00	7.00	0.91	2.36
(2)	7.89	2.76	1.00	13.00	116	8.00	7.00	-0.07	0.22
3r+(2)/R	0.40	0.11	0.03	0.63	116	0.40	0.50	-0.91	2.43
Lambda	0.52	0.19	0.13	0.92	116	0.50	0.50	0.11	-0.25
EA	7.64	2.53	2.00	18.00	116	7.50	7.50	0.51	1.52
es	9.42	3.65	4.00	31.00	116	9.00	9.00	2.60	11.17
D Score	-0.53	1.51	-10.00	2.00	116	0.00	0.00	-3.24	15.20
AdjD	-0.25	1.05	-5.00	2.00	116	0.00	0.00	-1.75	5.49
a (active)	6.37	1.87	2.00	12.00	116	6.00	6.00	0.55	0.58
p (passive)	2.93	1.48	0.00	6.00	109	3.00	2.00	0.28	-0.12
Ma	2.60	1.08	1.00	7.00	116	2.00	2.00	1.29	2.78
Mp	1.37	0.87	0.00	3.00	98	1.00	1.00	0.16	-0.61
Intellect	1.27	1.37	0.00	6.00	72	1.00	0.00	1.04	0.47
Zf	11.29	2.66	5.00	24.00	116	11.00	10.00	0.78	3.71
Zd	0.64	2.69	-6.50	8.00	108	0.50	1.00	0.38	0.16
Blends	5.34	2.01	1.00	10.00	116	5.00	5.00	-0.03	-0.55
Blends/R	0.26	0.11	0.05	0.67	116	0.26	0.26	0.69	1.14
Col-Shd Blends	0.33	[0.54]	0.00	2.00	34	0.00	0.00	1.40	1.05
Afr	0.63	0.16	0.27	1.29	116	0.60	0.60	0.54	1.83

TABLE 19. ADULT NONPATIENT AMBITENTS (N = 116) (Continued)

VARIABLE	MEAN	SD	MIN	MAX	FREQ	MEDIAN	MODE	SK	KU
Populars	6.43	1.53	3.00	10.00	116	6.00	8.00	-0.02	-0.37
XA%	0.91	0.07	0.57	1.00	116	0.93	0.95	-1.53	4.07
WDA%	0.92	0.07	0.54	1.00	116	0.94	1.00	-1.81	7.49
X+%	0.76	0.09	0.50	1.00	116	0.78	0.75	-0.46	1.02
X-%	0.08	0.07	0.00	0.43	101	0.06	0.04	1.76	5.67
Xu%	0.15	0.08	0.00	0.39	110	0.15	0.16	0.50	0.75
Isolate/R	0.18	0.09	0.00	0.47	111	0.17	0.13	0.25	0.07
H	2.55	1.23	0.00	7.00	113	3.00	3.00	0.85	2.25
(H)	1.32	0.99	0.00	4.00	87	1.00	2.00	0.29	-0.24
HD	0.97	1.19	0.00	7.00	71	1.00	1.00	2.61	10.41
(Hd)	0.26	0.63	0.00	4.00	22	0.00	0.00	3.26	13.10
Hx	0.02	[0.13]	0.00	1.00	2	0.00	0.00	7.51	55.43
All H Cont	5.09	1.75	1.00	10.00	116	5.00	5.00	0.60	0.91
A	7.65	2.31	3.00	14.00	116	7.00	6.00	0.24	-0.51
(A)	0.27	[0.53]	0.00	3.00	27	0.00	0.00	2.24	6.11
Ad	2.10	[1.55]	0.00	9.00	107	2.00	2.00	1.83	5.45
(Ad)	0.11	[0.34]	0.00	2.00	12	0.00	0.00	3.12	9.84
An	0.57	[0.87]	0.00	4.00	45	0.00	0.00	1.69	2.68
Art	0.76	0.98	0.00	5.00	55	0.00	0.00	1.39	2.17
Ay	0.30	[0.48]	0.00	2.00	34	0.00	0.00	1.11	-0.16
Bl	0.18	[0.43]	0.00	2.00	19	0.00	0.00	2.32	4.91
Bt	1.94	1.14	0.00	4.00	100	2.00	2.00	-0.12	-0.72
Cg	1.43	0.93	0.00	4.00	98	1.00	1.00	0.33	-0.19
Cl	0.20	[0.42]	0.00	2.00	22	0.00	0.00	1.88	2.53
Ex	0.23	[0.44]	0.00	2.00	26	0.00	0.00	1.58	1.31
Fi	0.48	[0.70]	0.00	3.00	43	0.00	0.00	1.28	0.83
Food	0.16	[0.44]	0.00	2.00	16	0.00	0.00	2.74	7.17
Ge	0.03	[0.18]	0.00	1.00	4	0.00	0.00	5.17	25.16
Hh	0.76	0.87	0.00	3.00	61	1.00	0.00	0.97	0.19
Ls	0.72	0.79	0.00	3.00	65	1.00	0.00	1.07	1.04
Na	0.29	[0.56]	0.00	2.00	28	0.00	0.00	1.78	2.25
Sc	1.05	[1.28]	0.00	5.00	63	1.00	0.00	1.37	1.70
Sx	0.17	[0.58]	0.00	3.00	12	0.00	0.00	3.80	14.65
Xy	0.11	[0.37]	0.00	2.00	11	0.00	0.00	3.49	12.48
Idio	1.09	1.19	0.00	5.00	67	1.00	0.00	0.96	0.50
DV	0.61	[0.88]	0.00	4.00	49	0.00	0.00	1.62	2.41
INCOM	0.51	[0.75]	0.00	4.00	46	0.00	0.00	1.84	4.44
DR	0.46	[0.75]	0.00	3.00	39	0.00	0.00	1.78	2.90
FABCOM	0.37	[0.65]	0.00	2.00	32	0.00	0.00	1.54	1.07
DV2	0.01	[0.09]	0.00	1.00	1	0.00	0.00	10.77	116.00
INC2	0.03	[0.18]	0.00	1.00	4	0.00	0.00	5.17	25.16
DR2	0.02	[0.13]	0.00	1.00	2	0.00	0.00	7.51	55.43
FAB2	0.01	[0.09]	0.00	1.00	1	0.00	0.00	10.77	116.00
ALOG	0.03	[0.18]	0.00	1.00	4	0.00	0.00	5.17	25.16
CONTAM	0.00	0.00	0.00	0.00	0	0.00	0.00	----	----
Sum 6 Sp Sc	2.05	1.48	0.00	6.00	96	2.00	2.00	0.45	-0.31
Lvl 2 Sp Sc	0.07	[0.25]	0.00	1.00	8	0.00	0.00	3.44	10.05
WSum6	4.97	4.06	0.00	17.00	96	4.00	0.00	0.83	0.33
AB	0.10	[0.31]	0.00	1.00	12	0.00	0.00	2.63	5.05
AG	1.15	1.05	0.00	4.00	79	1.00	1.00	0.77	0.34
COP	1.82	1.25	0.00	4.00	94	2.00	2.00	0.08	-0.98
CP	0.00	[0.00]	0.00	0.00	0	0.00	0.00	----	----
GOODHR	4.37	1.65	0.00	10.00	115	4.00	4.00	0.32	0.92
POORHR	1.69	1.53	0.00	7.00	90	1.00	1.00	1.37	2.54
MOR	0.78	[0.99]	0.00	4.00	55	0.00	0.00	1.18	0.80
PER	0.94	0.88	0.00	5.00	77	1.00	1.00	1.14	2.85
PSV	0.04	[0.20]	0.00	1.00	5	0.00	0.00	4.55	19.11

NOTE: Standard Deviations shown in brackets indicate that the value is probably unreliable and/or misleading and should not be used to estimate expected ranges. Ordinarily these variables should not be included in most parametric analyses.

TABLE 20. FREQUENCIES FOR 36 VARIABLES FOR ADULT AMBITENTS
(N = 116)

DEMOGRAPHY VARIABLES

MARITAL STATUS			AGE			RACE		
Single	30	26%	18-25	35	30%	White	98	84%
Lives w/S.O.	12	10%	26-35	53	46%	Black	7	6%
Married	45	39%	36-45	21	18%	Hispanic	11	9%
Separated	4	3%	46-55	2	2%	Asian	0	0%
Divorced	22	19%	56-65	5	4%			
Widowed	3	3%	OVER 65	0	0%			
						EDUCATION		
SEX						UNDER 12	10	9%
Male	52	45%				12 Years	36	31%
Female	64	55%				13-15 Yrs	61	53%
						16+ Yrs	9	8%

RATIOS, PERCENTAGES AND SPECIAL INDICES

STYLES			FORM QUALITY DEVIATIONS		
Introversive	0	0%	XA% > .89	76	66%
Pervasive	0	0%	XA% < .70	1	1%
Ambitent	116	100%	WDA% < .85	10	9%
Extratensive	0	0%	WDA% < .75	1	1%
Pervasive	0	0%	X+% < .55	2	2%
Avoidant	0	0%	Xu% > .20	21	18%
			X-% > .20	8	7%
D-SCORES			X-% > .30	1	1%
D Score > 0	10	9%			
D Score = 0	69	59%	FC:CF+C RATIO		
D Score < 0	37	32%	FC > (CF+C) + 2	23	20%
D Score < -1	12	10%	FC > (CF+C) + 1	42	36%
			(CF+C) > FC+1	13	11%
Adj D Score > 0	16	14%	(CF+C) > FC+2	4	3%
Adj D Score = 0	72	62%			
Adj D Score < 0	28	24%			
Adj D Score < -1	11	9%	S-Constellation Positive	0	0%
			HVI Positive	8	7%
Zd > +3.0 (Overincorp) 20 17%			OBS Positive	2	2%
Zd < -3.0 (Underincorp) 6 5%					

PTI = 5	0	0%	DEPI = 7	1	1%	CDI = 5	2	2%
PTI = 4	0	0%	DEPI = 6	2	2%	CDI = 4	8	7%
PTI = 3	0	0%	DEPI = 5	6	5%			

MISCELLANEOUS VARIABLES

R < 17	23	20%	(2AB+Art+Ay) > 5	1	1%
R > 27	8	7%	Populars < 4	4	3%
DQv > 2	11	9%	Populars > 7	35	30%
S > 2	24	21%	COP = 0	22	19%
Sum T = 0	24	21%	COP > 2	36	31%
Sum T > 1	15	13%	AG = 0	37	32%
3r+(2)/R < .33	17	15%	AG > 2	9	8%
3r+(2)/R > .44	35	30%	MOR > 2	7	6%
Fr + rF > 0	9	8%	Level 2 Sp.Sc. > 0	8	7%
PureC > 0	15	13%	GHR > PHR	95	82%
PureC > 1	2	2%	Pure H < 2	20	17%
Afr < .40	5	4%	Pure H = 0	3	3%
Afr < .50	18	16%	p > a+1	1	1%
(FM+m) < Sum Shading	24	21%	Mp > Ma	14	12%

TABLE 21. DESCRIPTIVE STATISTICS FOR ADULTS HIGH LAMBDA (N = 58)

VARIABLE	MEAN	SD	MIN	MAX	FREQ	MEDIAN	MODE	SK	KU
AGE	29.64	8.66	19.00	61.00	58	28.50	24.00	1.21	1.90
Years Educ	13.28	1.66	10.00	18.00	58	13.00	13.00	0.91	0.94
R	22.83	5.34	14.00	43.00	58	21.50	23.00	1.68	3.83
W	6.36	1.72	4.00	12.00	58	6.00	5.00	0.85	0.61
D	14.91	4.19	2.00	32.00	58	15.00	16.00	0.47	5.28
Dd	1.55	[2.65]	0.00	11.00	33	1.00	0.00	2.54	6.11
S	1.65	[1.72]	0.00	10.00	46	1.00	1.00	2.45	8.98
DQ+	5.55	1.72	1.00	10.00	58	6.00	6.00	0.07	0.53
DQo	16.21	4.34	6.00	36.00	58	16.00	16.00	1.90	7.78
DQv	0.91	[1.57]	0.00	6.00	22	0.00	0.00	1.89	2.79
DQv/+	0.16	[0.37]	0.00	1.00	9	0.00	0.00	1.95	1.89
FQx+	0.12	0.38	0.00	2.00	6	0.00	0.00	3.33	11.57
FQxo	15.88	3.24	8.00	24.00	58	16.00	16.00	0.13	0.71
FQxu	4.72	2.67	1.00	16.00	58	4.00	3.00	1.78	4.95
FQx-	1.95	1.47	0.00	8.00	51	2.00	1.00	1.29	3.53
FQxNone	0.16	[0.45]	0.00	2.00	7	0.00	0.00	3.04	8.94
MQ+	0.05	0.29	0.00	2.00	2	0.00	0.00	6.04	37.89
MQo	2.59	1.44	0.00	7.00	56	2.00	2.00	0.80	0.74
MQu	0.16	0.45	0.00	2.00	7	0.00	0.00	3.04	8.94
MQ-	0.02	[0.13]	0.00	1.00	1	0.00	0.00	7.61	58.00
MQNone	0.02	[0.13]	0.00	1.00	1	0.00	0.00	7.61	58.00
S-	0.28	[0.52]	0.00	2.00	14	0.00	0.00	1.76	2.37
M	2.83	1.49	1.00	7.00	58	3.00	2.00	0.80	0.18
FM	2.78	1.64	0.00	9.00	57	3.00	3.00	1.37	3.22
m	0.76	0.82	0.00	3.00	32	1.00	0.00	0.87	0.15
FM+m	3.53	2.06	0.00	12.00	57	3.00	3.00	1.67	4.75
FC	1.95	1.22	0.00	5.00	52	2.00	2.00	0.70	0.87
CF	1.95	1.29	0.00	4.00	48	2.00	3.00	-0.05	-1.08
C	0.12	[0.38]	0.00	2.00	6	0.00	0.00	3.33	11.57
Cn	0.03	[0.18]	0.00	1.00	2	0.00	0.00	5.23	26.35
Sum Color	4.05	1.63	1.00	7.00	58	4.00	3.00	0.16	-0.64
WSumC	3.10	1.36	0.50	5.50	58	2.75	4.00	0.06	-0.94
Sum C'	1.12	[0.94]	0.00	3.00	43	1.00	1.00	0.67	-0.25
Sum T	0.67	[0.71]	0.00	3.00	33	1.00	1.00	1.18	2.22
Sum V	0.12	[0.50]	0.00	3.00	4	0.00	0.00	4.66	22.88
Sum Y	0.41	[0.73]	0.00	3.00	18	0.00	0.00	2.01	4.19
Sum Shading	2.33	1.78	0.00	9.00	53	2.00	2.00	1.43	2.70
Fr+rF	0.28	[0.56]	0.00	2.00	13	0.00	0.00	1.93	2.88
FD	0.57	[0.68]	0.00	2.00	27	0.00	0.00	0.78	-0.48
F	12.72	2.80	7.00	23.00	58	12.00	11.00	1.24	3.08
(2)	8.38	2.71	3.00	21.00	58	8.00	8.00	1.74	7.27
3r+(2)/R	0.40	0.08	0.21	0.61	58	0.40	0.35	0.27	0.16
Lambda	1.33	0.38	1.00	2.33	58	1.16	1.00	1.53	1.29
EA	5.93	1.92	2.00	11.00	58	6.00	6.00	0.12	0.11
es	5.86	2.87	3.00	14.00	58	5.00	3.00	1.40	1.62
D Score	-0.07	0.90	-3.00	3.00	58	0.00	0.00	-0.92	5.52
AdjD	0.02	0.78	-2.00	3.00	58	0.00	0.00	-0.03	4.86
a (active)	4.57	2.15	1.00	10.00	58	4.50	5.00	0.72	0.63
p (passive)	1.79	1.32	0.00	7.00	50	2.00	1.00	1.10	2.75
Ma	2.02	1.28	0.00	6.00	54	2.00	2.00	1.11	2.02
Mp	0.81	0.81	0.00	3.00	35	1.00	1.00	0.78	0.18
Intellect	1.45	1.53	0.00	8.00	40	1.00	1.00	1.66	4.53
Zf	9.62	2.42	5.00	19.00	58	9.00	9.00	1.14	2.75
Zd	-1.12	2.66	-11.50	4.50	52	-1.25	-3.00	-0.78	2.95
Blends	3.07	1.68	1.00	7.00	58	3.00	2.00	0.48	-0.66
Blends/R	0.14	0.07	0.04	0.36	58	0.13	0.05	0.74	0.26
Col-Shd Blends	0.24	[0.47]	0.00	2.00	13	0.00	0.00	1.75	2.28
Afr	0.56	0.18	0.27	1.26	58	0.54	0.67	0.80	1.61

TABLE 21. ADULT NONPATIENTS HIGH LAMBDA (N = 58) (Continued)

VARIABLE	MEAN	SD	MIN	MAX	FREQ	MEDIAN	MODE	SK	KU
Populars	6.31	1.22	4.00	9.00	58	6.00	5.00	0.27	-0.87
XA%	0.91	0.06	0.76	1.00	58	0.90	0.96	-0.39	-0.55
WDA%	0.92	0.06	0.78	1.00	58	0.94	0.96	-0.62	-0.36
X+%	0.71	0.09	0.40	0.85	58	0.71	0.65	-0.99	2.41
X-%	0.09	0.06	0.00	0.19	51	0.07	0.04	0.23	-1.03
Xu%	0.20	0.08	0.05	0.40	58	0.19	0.15	0.51	-0.17
Isolate/R	0.15	0.08	0.00	0.35	57	0.16	0.17	0.27	-0.30
H	2.29	1.18	0.00	5.00	56	2.00	2.00	0.58	0.21
(H)	0.98	0.83	0.00	3.00	41	1.00	1.00	0.61	0.01
HD	1.47	1.38	0.00	6.00	47	1.00	1.00	1.59	2.68
(Hd)	0.22	0.50	0.00	2.00	11	0.00	0.00	2.20	4.26
Hx	0.16	[0.59]	0.00	4.00	6	0.00	0.00	5.37	33.27
All H Cont	4.97	1.52	2.00	9.00	58	5.00	4.00	0.89	0.94
A	8.07	3.14	3.00	25.00	58	8.00	6.00	2.90	14.31
(A)	0.40	[0.62]	0.00	3.00	20	0.00	0.00	1.78	4.23
Ad	2.95	[1.43]	0.00	7.00	56	3.00	3.00	0.24	0.41
(Ad)	0.09	[0.28]	0.00	1.00	5	0.00	0.00	3.02	7.42
An	0.72	[0.85]	0.00	3.00	30	1.00	0.00	1.09	0.65
Art	0.76	0.96	0.00	3.00	29	0.50	0.00	1.24	0.68
Ay	0.38	[0.62]	0.00	3.00	19	0.00	0.00	1.87	4.59
Bl	0.14	[0.35]	0.00	1.00	8	0.00	0.00	2.15	2.74
Bt	1.97	1.14	0.00	5.00	54	2.00	2.00	0.43	-0.17
Cg	1.24	1.26	0.00	5.00	40	1.00	1.00	1.26	1.46
Cl	0.03	[0.18]	0.00	1.00	2	0.00	0.00	5.23	26.35
Ex	0.16	[0.37]	0.00	1.00	9	0.00	0.00	1.95	1.89
Fi	0.31	[0.57]	0.00	2.00	15	0.00	0.00	1.69	1.98
Food	0.12	[0.42]	0.00	2.00	5	0.00	0.00	3.67	13.26
Ge	0.07	[0.37]	0.00	2.00	2	0.00	0.00	5.23	26.35
Hh	1.00	0.97	0.00	3.00	38	1.00	1.00	0.82	-0.17
Ls	0.57	0.57	0.00	2.00	31	1.00	1.00	0.32	-0.84
Na	0.29	[0.50]	0.00	2.00	16	0.00	0.00	1.37	0.88
Sc	1.38	[1.30]	0.00	5.00	39	1.00	0.00	0.75	0.18
Sx	0.26	[0.74]	0.00	5.00	11	0.00	0.00	4.94	30.09
Xy	0.05	[0.22]	0.00	1.00	3	0.00	0.00	4.15	15.82
Idio	1.05	1.85	0.00	7.00	26	0.00	0.00	2.26	4.49
DV	0.38	[0.52]	0.00	2.00	21	0.00	0.00	0.88	-0.42
INCOM	0.67	[0.91]	0.00	4.00	29	0.50	0.00	2.02	5.14
DR	0.64	[0.67]	0.00	2.00	31	1.00	0.00	0.57	-0.66
FABCOM	0.22	[0.42]	0.00	1.00	13	0.00	0.00	1.35	-0.16
DV2	0.00	[0.00]	0.00	0.00	0	0.00	0.00	----	----
INC2	0.05	[0.22]	0.00	1.00	3	0.00	0.00	4.15	15.82
DR2	0.00	[0.00]	0.00	0.00	0	0.00	0.00	----	----
FAB2	0.02	[0.13]	0.00	1.00	1	0.00	0.00	7.61	58.00
ALOG	0.07	[0.26]	0.00	1.00	4	0.00	0.00	3.49	10.57
CONTAM	0.00	0.00	0.00	0.00	0	0.00	0.00	----	----
Sum 6 Sp Sc	2.05	1.26	0.00	7.00	55	2.00	1.00	1.20	3.02
Lvl 2 Sp Sc	0.07	[0.26]	0.00	1.00	4	0.00	0.00	3.49	10.57
WSum6	5.21	3.30	0.00	15.00	55	4.50	2.00	0.45	-0.16
AB	0.16	[0.49]	0.00	3.00	7	0.00	0.00	4.12	20.31
AG	0.71	1.01	0.00	4.00	24	0.00	0.00	1.37	1.19
COP	1.47	1.13	0.00	4.00	45	1.00	1.00	0.35	-0.75
CP	0.00	[0.00]	0.00	0.00	0	0.00	0.00	----	----
GOODHR	4.00	1.34	0.00	7.00	57	4.00	3.00	-0.13	0.74
POORHR	1.85	1.72	0.00	8.00	47	1.00	1.00	1.67	3.98
MOR	0.62	[0.67]	0.00	3.00	31	1.00	0.00	0.98	1.40
PER	0.40	0.82	0.00	5.00	17	0.00	0.00	3.56	17.37
PSV	0.19	[0.40]	0.00	1.00	11	0.00	0.00	1.62	0.66

NOTE: Standard Deviations shown in brackets indicate that the value is probably unreliable and/or misleading and should not be used to estimate expected ranges. Ordinarily these variables should not be included in most parametric analyses.

TABLE 22. FREQUENCIES FOR 36 VARIABLES FOR ADULTS HIGH LAMBDA
(N = 58)

DEMOGRAPHY VARIABLES

MARITAL STATUS			AGE			RACE		
Single	15	26%	18-25	22	38%	White	47	81%
Lives w/S.O.	10	17%	26-35	22	38%	Black	10	17%
Married	27	47%	36-45	12	21%	Hispanic	1	2%
Separated	1	2%	46-55	1	2%	Asian	0	0%
Divorced	5	9%	56-65	1	2%			
Widowed	0	0%	OVER 65	0	0%			
						EDUCATION		
SEX						UNDER 12	5	9%
Male	26	45%				12 Years	15	26%
Female	32	55%				13-15 Yrs	30	52%
						16+ Yrs	8	14%

RATIOS, PERCENTAGES AND SPECIAL INDICES

STYLES			FORM QUALITY DEVIATIONS		
Introversive	0	0%	XA% > .89	32	55%
Pervasive	0	0%	XA% < .70	0	0%
Ambitent	0	0%	WDA% < .85	6	10%
Extratensive	0	0%	WDA% < .75	0	0%
Pervasive	0	0%	X+% < .55	2	3%
Avoidant	58	100%	Xu% > .20	27	47%
			X-% > .20	0	0%
D-SCORES			X-% > .30	0	0%
D Score > 0	7	12%			
D Score = 0	45	78%			
D Score < 0	6	10%	FC:CF+C RATIO		
D Score < -1	5	9%	FC > (CF+C) + 2	8	14%
			FC > (CF+C) + 1	12	21%
Adj D Score > 0	9	16%	(CF+C) > FC+1	12	21%
Adj D Score = 0	43	74%	(CF+C) > FC+2	5	9%
Adj D Score < 0	6	10%			
Adj D Score < -1	4	7%			
			S-Constellation Positive	0	0%
Zd > +3.0 (Overincorp)	2	3%	HVI Positive	1	2%
Zd < -3.0 (Underincorp)	8	14%	OBS Positive	0	0%

PTI = 5	0	0%	DEPI = 7	0	0%	CDI = 5	0	0%
PTI = 4	0	0%	DEPI = 6	1	2%	CDI = 4	6	10%
PTI = 3	0	0%	DEPI = 5	2	3%			

MISCELLANEOUS VARIABLES

R < 17	3	5%	(2AB+Art+Ay) > 5	1	2%
R > 27	5	9%	Populars < 4	0	0%
DQv > 2	9	16%	Populars > 7	10	17%
S > 2	9	16%	COP = 0	13	22%
Sum T = 0	25	43%	COP > 2	12	21%
Sum T > 1	4	7%	AG = 0	34	59%
3r+(2)/R < .33	7	12%	AG > 2	4	7%
3r+(2)/R > .44	14	24%	MOR > 2	1	2%
Fr + rF > 0	13	22%	Level 2 Sp.Sc. > 0	4	7%
PureC > 0	6	10%	GHR > PHR	49	84%
PureC > 1	1	2%	Pure H < 2	14	24%
Afr < .40	2	3%	Pure H = 0	2	3%
Afr < .50	9	16%	p > a+1	0	0%
(FM+m) < Sum Shading	16	28%	Mp > Ma	5	9%

TABLE 23. DESCRIPTIVE STATISTICS FOR 1390 NONPATIENT CHILDREN AND ADOLESCENTS BY AGE   5 YEAR OLDS (N = 90)

VARIABLE	MEAN	SD	MIN	MAX	FREQ	MEDIAN	MODE	SK	KU
R	17.64	1.44	14.00	20.00	90	18.00	18.00	–0.83	–0.25
W	9.97	1.65	7.00	12.00	90	9.00	11.00	0.24	–1.35
D	7.10	2.61	3.00	12.00	90	8.00	6.00	–0.83	–0.24
Dd	0.58	[0.65]	0.00	2.00	44	0.00	0.00	0.70	–0.53
S	1.40	[1.14]	0.00	3.00	64	1.00	0.00	0.14	–1.39
DQ+	5.47	1.43	2.00	8.00	90	5.50	4.00	0.35	–1.29
DQo	10.72	2.07	7.00	13.00	90	12.00	13.00	–1.25	0.05
DQv	1.37	[0.62]	0.00	4.00	83	1.00	1.00	0.36	–0.63
DQv/+	0.09	[0.29]	0.00	1.00	8	0.00	0.00	2.94	6.78
FQX+	0.00	0.00	0.00	0.00	0	0.00	0.00	----	----
FQXo	11.54	2.50	6.00	15.00	90	13.00	13.00	–0.70	–0.52
FQXu	3.59	1.96	1.00	7.00	90	4.00	1.00	0.13	–1.19
FQX–	1.46	0.64	0.00	3.00	86	1.00	1.00	0.04	–0.19
FQXNone	0.87	[0.62]	0.00	2.00	63	1.00	1.00	0.36	–0.63
MQ+	0.00	0.00	0.00	0.00	0	0.00	0.00	----	----
MQo	1.13	0.34	1.00	2.00	90	1.00	1.00	2.19	2.88
MQu	0.38	0.66	0.00	2.00	25	0.00	0.00	1.53	1.00
MQ–	0.19	[0.39]	0.00	1.00	17	0.00	0.00	1.62	0.63
MQNone	0.00	[0.00]	0.00	0.00	0	0.00	0.00	----	----
S–	0.91	[0.69]	0.00	3.00	62	1.00	1.00	0.45	–0.83
M	1.70	1.00	1.00	4.00	90	1.00	1.00	1.26	0.36
FM	5.00	0.95	4.00	7.00	90	5.00	4.00	0.32	–1.20
m	0.78	0.80	0.00	3.00	49	1.00	0.00	0.43	–1.32
FM+m	5.78	1.19	4.00	9.00	90	6.00	5.00	0.65	0.50
FC	0.71	0.46	0.00	1.00	64	1.00	1.00	–0.95	–1.13
CF	3.02	1.41	1.00	6.00	90	3.00	3.00	0.53	–0.20
C	0.67	[0.62]	0.00	2.00	63	1.00	1.00	0.36	–0.63
Cn	0.00	[0.00]	0.00	0.00	0	0.00	0.00	----	----
FC+CF+C+Cn	4.40	1.10	2.00	6.00	90	4.00	4.00	–0.39	–0.11
WSum C	4.38	1.09	2.50	6.50	90	4.00	4.00	0.27	–0.73
Sum C'	0.63	[0.48]	0.00	1.00	57	1.00	1.00	–0.56	–1.72
Sum T	0.83	[0.48]	0.00	2.00	57	1.00	1.00	0.42	2.42
Sum V	0.00	[0.00]	0.00	0.00	0	0.00	0.00	----	----
Sum Y	0.36	[0.33]	0.00	2.00	20	0.00	0.00	–0.65	2.71
SumShd	1.77	0.97	0.00	2.00	57	2.00	2.00	–0.56	–1.72
Fr+rF	0.38	[0.45]	0.00	2.00	29	0.00	0.00	1.01	–1.00
FD	0.28	[0.63]	0.00	1.00	16	0.00	0.00	1.77	0.58
F	6.98	1.26	4.00	9.00	90	6.00	6.00	0.19	–0.35
PAIR	9.08	1.96	5.00	11.00	90	9.00	11.00	–0.91	–0.29
3r(2)/R	0.69	0.14	0.33	1.00	90	0.60	0.64	0.28	0.57
LAMBDA	0.86	0.15	0.36	1.25	90	0.75	0.60	0.76	–0.52
EA	5.08	1.34	2.50	8.50	90	5.50	5.00	–0.24	–0.75
es	7.04	1.14	5.00	9.00	90	7.00	7.00	0.10	–0.60
D	–0.24	0.43	–1.00	0.00	90	0.00	0.00	–1.21	–0.55
AdjD	–0.20	0.40	–1.00	0.00	90	0.00	0.00	–1.53	0.33
a (active)	6.28	0.95	5.00	8.00	90	6.00	6.00	0.38	–0.70
p (passive)	1.20	1.37	0.00	4.00	49	1.00	0.00	0.82	–0.60
Ma	1.42	0.67	1.00	3.00	90	1.00	1.00	1.32	0.47
Mp	0.28	0.45	0.00	1.00	25	0.00	0.00	1.01	–1.00
Intellect	0.17	0.38	0.00	1.00	90	0.00	0.00	1.82	1.34
Zf	10.08	2.18	8.00	14.00	90	10.00	14.00	0.15	–1.52
Zd	–1.13	2.60	–5.00	4.50	90	–1.75	–2.50	0.70	0.09
Blends	2.86	1.92	0.00	5.00	77	3.00	5.00	–0.21	–1.56
Col Shd Bl	0.18	[0.56]	0.00	1.00	5	0.00	0.00	1.81	–2.37
Afr	0.88	0.13	0.50	1.00	90	0.90	0.80	–0.65	–0.08
Popular	4.66	1.69	3.00	10.00	90	4.00	4.00	0.55	–0.94

TABLE 23. 5 YEAR OLDS (N = 90)

VARIABLE	MEAN	SD	MIN	MAX	FREQ	MEDIAN	MODE	SK	KU
XA%	0.88	0.05	0.78	1.00	90	0.88	0.83	0.43	-0.34
WDA%	0.91	0.06	0.78	1.00	90	0.91	0.94	-0.08	-0.73
X+%	0.67	0.10	0.47	0.83	90	0.68	0.78	-0.27	-0.68
X-%	0.08	0.04	0.00	0.17	86	0.07	0.11	-0.02	-0.16
Xu%	0.21	0.11	0.06	0.40	90	0.22	0.06	0.09	-1.44
Isolate/R	0.17	0.06	0.11	0.27	90	0.17	0.11	0.57	-0.88
H	2.19	0.50	1.00	3.00	90	2.00	2.00	0.38	0.34
(H)	1.46	0.50	1.00	2.00	90	1.00	1.00	0.18	-2.01
HD	0.36	0.48	0.00	1.00	32	0.00	0.00	0.61	-1.66
(Hd)	0.00	0.00	0.00	0.00	0	0.00	0.00	----	----
Hx	0.00	[0.00]	0.00	0.00	0	0.00	0.00	----	----
All H Cont	4.00	1.15	2.00	6.00	90	4.00	3.00	0.40	-0.90
A	10.69	2.32	6.00	14.00	90	11.00	12.00	-0.87	-0.28
(A)	0.37	[0.48]	0.00	1.00	33	0.00	0.00	0.56	-1.72
Ad	0.71	[0.60]	0.00	2.00	57	1.00	1.00	0.22	-0.57
(Ad)	0.00	[0.00]	0.00	0.00	0	0.00	0.00	----	----
An	0.00	[0.00]	0.00	0.00	0	0.00	0.00	----	----
Art	0.17	0.38	0.00	1.00	15	0.00	0.00	1.81	1.34
Ay	0.00	[0.00]	0.00	0.00	0	0.00	0.00	----	----
Bl	1.13	[0.46]	0.00	2.00	86	1.00	1.00	0.54	1.30
Bt	0.28	0.45	0.00	1.00	25	0.00	0.00	1.00	-1.00
Cg	3.73	1.35	2.00	6.00	90	3.00	3.00	0.61	-0.92
Cl	0.00	[0.00]	0.00	0.00	0	0.00	0.00	----	----
Ex	0.00	[0.00]	0.00	0.00	0	0.00	0.00	----	----
Fi	0.22	[0.51]	0.00	2.00	16	0.00	0.00	2.30	4.54
Food	0.00	[0.00]	0.00	0.00	0	0.00	0.00	----	----
Ge	0.00	[0.00]	0.00	0.00	0	0.00	0.00	----	----
Hh	0.00	0.00	0.00	0.00	0	0.00	0.00	----	----
Ls	2.68	0.63	2.00	4.00	90	3.00	3.00	0.38	-0.65
Na	0.00	[0.00]	0.00	0.00	0	0.00	0.00	----	----
Sc	0.12	[0.33]	0.00	1.00	11	0.00	0.00	2.34	3.58
Sx	0.00	[0.00]	0.00	0.00	0	0.00	0.00	----	----
Xy	0.00	[0.00]	0.00	0.00	0	0.00	0.00	----	----
Idiographic	0.14	0.35	0.00	1.00	13	0.00	0.00	2.05	2.28
DV	0.98	[1.05]	0.00	4.00	53	1.00	0.00	1.00	0.57
INCOM	0.96	[0.70]	0.00	2.00	66	1.00	1.00	0.06	-0.93
DR	0.04	[0.21]	0.00	1.00	4	0.00	0.00	4.49	18.63
FABCOM	0.89	[0.57]	0.00	2.00	70	1.00	1.00	-0.01	0.06
DV2	0.00	[0.00]	0.00	0.00	0	0.00	0.00	----	----
INC2	0.09	[0.29]	0.00	1.00	8	0.00	0.00	2.93	6.78
DR2	0.09	[0.29]	0.00	1.00	8	0.00	0.00	2.93	6.78
FAB2	0.22	[0.42]	0.00	1.00	20	0.00	0.00	1.35	-0.16
ALOG	0.41	[0.50]	0.00	1.00	37	0.00	0.00	0.36	-1.91
CONTAM	0.00	0.00	0.00	0.00	0	0.00	0.00	----	----
Sum 6 Sp Sc	3.68	1.92	1.00	8.00	90	4.00	5.00	0.16	-0.77
Lvl 2 Sp Sc	0.40	[0.58]	0.00	2.00	32	0.00	0.00	1.12	0.30
WSum6	11.08	4.68	4.00	19.00	90	12.00	4.00	-0.10	-1.05
AB	0.00	[0.00]	0.00	0.00	0	0.00	0.00	----	----
AG	1.23	0.67	0.00	3.00	82	1.00	1.00	0.60	0.74
COP	1.08	0.52	0.00	2.00	81	1.00	1.00	0.10	0.67
CP	0.00	[0.00]	0.00	0.00	0	0.00	0.00	----	----
GOODHR	3.59	0.98	1.00	6.00	90	3.50	3.00	0.03	1.46
POORHR	1.50	0.80	0.00	3.00	86	1.00	1.00	0.61	-0.40
MOR	0.78	[0.75]	0.00	2.00	53	1.00	0.00	0.38	-1.10
PER	0.00	0.00	0.00	0.00	0	0.00	0.00	----	----
PSV	0.63	[0.48]	0.00	1.00	57	1.00	1.00	-0.56	-1.72

NOTE: Standard Deviations shown in brackets indicate that the value is probably unreliable and/or misleading and should not be used to estimate expected ranges. Ordinarily these variables should not be included in most parametric analyses.

TABLE 23. 6 YEAR OLDS (N = 80)

VARIABLE	MEAN	SD	MIN	MAX	FREQ	MEDIAN	MODE	SK	KU
R	18.91	0.98	14.00	20.00	80	19.00	20.00	–0.23	–1.25
W	10.79	1.17	7.00	10.00	80	11.00	9.00	–0.56	–1.16
D	7.94	1.01	7.00	11.00	80	7.00	8.00	–1.38	2.27
Dd	0.30	[0.46]	0.00	1.00	24	0.00	0.00	0.89	–1.24
S	0.79	[0.76]	0.00	3.00	51	1.00	1.00	1.09	1.67
DQ+	4.42	0.59	3.00	5.00	80	4.00	4.00	–0.46	–0.66
DQo	11.31	1.35	9.00	13.00	80	11.00	13.00	0.11	–1.45
DQv	2.54	[1.19]	1.00	5.00	80	3.00	3.00	0.14	–0.89
DQv/+	0.45	[0.64]	0.00	1.00	38	1.00	1.00	–1.18	–0.63
FQX+	0.00	0.00	0.00	0.00	0	0.00	0.00	----	----
FQXo	13.39	1.22	12.00	16.00	80	14.00	14.00	0.25	–0.92
FQXu	4.01	1.29	3.00	7.00	80	4.00	4.00	0.75	–0.32
FQX–	0.94	0.50	0.00	6.00	66	0.00	0.00	0.21	–2.01
FQXNone	0.74	[0.48]	0.00	2.00	68	1.00	1.00	–0.58	–1.70
MQ+	0.00	0.00	0.00	0.00	0	0.00	0.00	----	----
MQo	1.96	0.75	1.00	3.00	80	2.00	2.00	0.06	–1.22
MQu	0.00	0.00	0.00	0.00	0	0.00	0.00	----	----
MQ–	0.23	[0.67]	0.00	1.00	6	0.00	0.00	1.24	4.12
MQNone	0.00	[0.00]	0.00	0.00	0	0.00	0.00	----	----
S–	0.42	[0.78]	0.00	0.50	11	0.00	0.00	0.98	3.15
M	1.96	0.75	1.00	3.00	80	2.00	2.00	0.06	–1.22
FM	4.52	0.81	1.00	8.00	80	5.00	4.00	–1.25	2.76
m	1.40	1.48	0.00	4.00	51	1.00	0.00	0.81	–0.72
FM+m	5.92	0.99	2.00	10.00	80	8.00	8.00	1.11	0.35
FC	1.11	1.09	0.00	3.00	42	2.00	0.00	0.07	–1.72
CF	3.51	0.94	1.00	5.00	80	3.00	3.00	–0.36	0.83
C	0.94	[0.48]	0.00	2.00	68	1.00	1.00	–0.58	–1.70
Cn	0.06	[0.09]	0.00	1.00	1	0.00	0.00	4.15	35.81
FC+CF+C+Cn	5.56	1.63	1.00	7.00	80	6.00	6.00	–0.94	0.29
WSum C	5.02	1.42	1.00	6.50	80	5.50	5.50	–1.23	1.26
Sum C'	0.58	[0.50]	0.00	1.00	46	1.00	1.00	–0.31	–1.95
Sum T	0.83	[0.22]	0.00	1.00	69	1.00	1.00	–1.21	6.12
Sum V	0.00	[0.00]	0.00	0.00	0	0.00	0.00	----	----
Sum Y	0.54	[0.48]	0.00	1.00	37	0.00	0.00	0.70	–1.55
SumShd	1.95	0.88	0.00	3.00	76	2.00	2.00	–0.18	–0.89
Fr+rF	0.28	[0.40]	0.00	2.00	17	0.00	0.00	1.83	0.35
FD	0.48	[0.68]	0.00	1.00	29	0.00	0.00	1.49	2.34
F	5.77	1.47	3.00	10.00	80	4.00	4.00	3.10	10.34
PAIR	9.61	1.79	5.00	12.00	80	10.00	11.00	–0.88	0.30
3r(2)/R	0.67	0.15	0.25	0.90	80	0.66	0.60	0.38	0.61
LAMBDA	0.79	0.17	0.18	1.50	80	0.78	0.65	–1.56	0.64
EA	6.98	1.42	2.00	8.50	80	6.00	5.00	0.85	1.77
es	7.87	1.00	8.00	11.00	80	7.00	6.00	0.13	–1.52
D	–0.41	0.59	–2.00	0.00	80	0.00	0.00	–1.11	0.28
AdjD	–0.21	0.41	–2.00	0.00	80	0.00	0.00	–1.43	0.05
a (active)	6.03	1.27	5.00	9.00	80	6.00	5.00	0.43	–1.17
p (passive)	1.85	1.90	1.00	6.00	80	2.00	1.00	0.51	–1.49
Ma	0.98	0.84	0.00	2.00	51	1.00	0.00	0.05	–1.59
Mp	0.99	1.35	0.00	3.00	29	0.00	0.00	0.70	–1.44
Intellect	0.96	0.51	0.00	2.00	80	1.00	1.00	–0.06	0.93
Zf	10.15	1.44	6.00	12.00	80	11.00	9.00	–0.45	–1.21
Zd	–1.38	2.20	–5.00	1.00	80	0.00	0.00	–0.91	–0.93
Blends	2.16	0.49	1.00	3.00	80	2.00	2.00	0.38	0.64
Col Shd Bl	0.44	[0.64]	0.00	1.00	18	0.00	0.00	2.13	4.67
Afr	0.87	0.26	0.25	1.11	80	0.82	0.78	–0.76	–0.36
Popular	5.02	1.43	4.00	9.00	80	5.00	5.00	0.14	–0.70

TABLE 23. 6 YEAR OLDS (N = 80)

VARIABLE	MEAN	SD	MIN	MAX	FREQ	MEDIAN	MODE	SK	KU
XA%	0.93	0.04	0.84	1.00	80	0.95	0.95	0.04	-0.75
WDA%	0.93	0.04	0.84	1.00	80	0.95	0.95	-0.05	-0.82
X+%	0.70	0.06	0.60	0.80	80	0.70	0.60	-0.07	-0.92
X-%	0.03	0.03	0.00	0.13	45	0.05	0.00	0.42	-0.32
Xu%	0.23	0.07	0.07	0.35	80	0.22	0.22	0.43	-0.22
Isolate/R	0.23	0.09	0.06	0.39	80	0.22	0.15	0.22	-1.27
H	2.49	1.18	1.00	4.00	80	3.00	3.00	-0.18	-1.51
(H)	0.66	0.50	0.00	2.00	52	1.00	1.00	-0.38	-1.12
HD	0.58	0.63	0.00	2.00	40	0.50	0.00	0.63	-0.53
(Hd)	0.04	0.19	0.00	1.00	3	0.00	0.00	4.96	23.21
Hx	0.00	[0.00]	0.00	0.00	0	0.00	0.00	----	----
All H Cont	3.76	0.75	2.00	5.00	80	4.00	4.00	0.23	-0.83
A	8.03	1.34	2.00	10.00	80	8.00	8.00	-1.34	4.29
(A)	0.34	[0.48]	0.00	1.00	27	0.00	0.00	0.70	-1.55
Ad	1.11	[0.60]	0.00	3.00	76	1.00	1.00	2.18	5.90
(Ad)	0.01	[0.11]	0.00	1.00	1	0.00	0.00	8.94	80.00
An	0.01	[0.11]	0.00	1.00	1	0.00	0.00	8.94	80.00
Art	0.86	0.41	0.00	2.00	67	1.00	1.00	-0.96	1.83
Ay	0.00	[0.00]	0.00	0.00	0	0.00	0.00	----	----
Bl	0.30	[0.49]	0.00	2.00	23	0.00	0.00	1.22	0.28
Bt	1.52	0.64	0.00	2.00	74	2.00	2.00	-1.00	-0.04
Cg	0.03	0.16	0.00	1.00	2	0.00	0.00	6.20	37.40
Cl	0.14	[0.35]	0.00	1.00	11	0.00	0.00	2.14	2.67
Ex	0.25	[0.44]	0.00	1.00	20	0.00	0.00	1.17	-0.63
Fi	0.61	[0.52]	0.00	2.00	48	1.00	1.00	-0.18	-1.32
Food	0.59	[0.50]	0.00	1.00	47	1.00	1.00	-0.36	-1.92
Ge	0.05	[0.22]	0.00	1.00	4	0.00	0.00	4.20	16.12
Hh	1.17	0.65	0.00	3.00	73	1.00	1.00	0.93	1.71
Ls	0.96	0.19	0.00	1.00	77	1.00	1.00	-4.96	23.21
Na	0.78	[0.78]	0.00	2.00	45	1.00	0.00	0.41	-1.23
Sc	0.71	[0.66]	0.00	3.00	49	1.00	1.00	0.65	0.64
Sx	0.00	[0.00]	0.00	0.00	0	0.00	0.00	----	----
Xy	0.00	[0.00]	0.00	0.00	0	0.00	0.00	----	----
Idiographic	0.15	0.36	0.00	1.00	12	0.00	0.00	1.99	2.04
DV	0.06	[0.24]	0.00	1.00	5	0.00	0.00	3.68	11.87
INCOM	2.35	[0.58]	0.00	3.00	79	2.00	2.00	-0.60	1.86
DR	0.09	[0.33]	0.00	2.00	6	0.00	0.00	4.03	17.30
FABCOM	0.60	[0.49]	0.00	1.00	48	1.00	1.00	-0.41	-1.87
DV2	0.00	[0.00]	0.00	0.00	0	0.00	0.00	----	----
INC2	0.04	[0.19]	0.00	1.00	3	0.00	0.00	4.96	23.21
DR2	0.00	[0.00]	0.00	0.00	0	0.00	0.00	----	----
FAB2	0.00	[0.00]	0.00	0.00	0	0.00	0.00	----	----
ALOG	0.65	[0.48]	0.00	1.00	52	1.00	1.00	-0.64	-1.63
CONTAM	0.00	0.00	0.00	0.00	0	0.00	0.00	----	----
Sum 6 Sp Sc	3.79	1.35	1.00	6.00	80	4.00	5.00	-0.27	-1.21
Lvl 2 Sp Sc	0.04	[0.19]	0.00	1.00	3	0.00	0.00	4.96	23.21
WSum6	10.83	4.72	3.00	18.00	80	13.00	15.00	-0.55	-1.36
AB	0.00	[0.00]	0.00	0.00	0	0.00	0.00	----	----
AG	0.36	0.60	0.00	2.00	24	0.00	0.00	1.45	1.09
COP	1.84	0.56	0.00	3.00	74	2.00	2.00	-2.68	6.69
CP	0.00	[0.00]	0.00	0.00	0	0.00	0.00	----	----
GOODHR	3.68	0.98	2.00	5.00	80	3.00	3.00	0.20	-1.24
POORHR	1.14	0.73	0.00	3.00	69	1.00	1.00	0.80	1.10
MOR	0.08	[0.35]	0.00	2.00	4	0.00	0.00	4.88	23.92
PER	0.08	0.38	0.00	3.00	4	0.00	0.00	6.35	45.06
PSV	0.01	[0.11]	0.00	1.00	1	0.00	0.00	8.94	80.00

NOTE: Standard Deviations shown in brackets indicate that the value is probably unreliable and/or misleading and should not be used to estimate expected ranges. Ordinarily these variables should not be included in most parametric analyses.

TABLE 23. 7 YEAR OLDS (N = 120)

VARIABLE	MEAN	SD	MIN	MAX	FREQ	MEDIAN	MODE	SK	KU
R	19.93	1.25	14.00	24.00	120	19.00	19.00	–0.10	–0.50
W	10.33	2.01	5.00	12.00	120	9.00	9.00	0.02	–1.34
D	9.09	2.86	7.00	15.00	120	9.00	7.00	0.07	–1.77
Dd	0.82	[0.32]	0.00	3.00	74	0.00	0.00	0.42	2.91
S	1.44	[1.06]	0.00	4.00	102	2.00	2.00	–0.49	–0.38
DQ+	6.48	0.80	6.00	9.00	120	6.00	6.00	0.11	–0.41
DQo	11.15	0.98	10.00	13.00	120	11.00	11.00	0.36	–0.92
DQv	1.63	[0.58]	0.00	3.00	89	2.00	1.00	0.28	–0.71
DQv/+	0.28	[0.45]	0.00	1.00	33	0.00	0.00	1.02	–0.98
FQX+	0.00	0.00	0.00	0.00	0	0.00	0.00	----	----
FQXo	14.37	1.46	12.00	18.00	120	15.00	14.00	0.24	–1.28
FQXu	2.08	0.69	1.00	3.00	120	2.00	2.00	–0.10	–0.86
FQX–	1.99	1.27	0.00	4.00	117	2.00	1.00	0.36	–1.18
FQXNone	1.10	[0.30]	0.00	3.00	72	1.00	1.00	2.70	5.38
MQ+	0.00	0.00	0.00	0.00	0	0.00	0.00	----	----
MQo	2.51	1.16	2.00	6.00	120	3.00	2.00	1.25	0.67
MQu	0.56	0.34	0.00	1.00	13	0.00	0.00	2.20	4.96
MQ–	0.45	[0.22]	0.00	2.00	28	0.00	0.00	2.18	11.75
MQNone	0.00	[0.00]	0.00	0.00	0	0.00	0.00	----	----
S–	0.12	[0.32]	0.00	1.00	14	0.00	0.00	2.42	3.91
M	3.02	1.22	2.00	6.00	120	3.00	2.00	1.15	0.12
FM	5.92	1.20	3.00	7.00	120	6.00	6.00	–1.11	0.14
m	1.06	0.40	0.00	2.00	114	1.00	1.00	0.52	3.35
FM+m	6.08	1.14	5.00	8.00	120	7.00	8.00	–0.80	–0.79
FC	2.17	0.93	1.00	4.00	120	2.00	2.00	0.27	–1.82
CF	3.19	0.98	1.00	6.00	120	3.00	3.00	–0.71	0.47
C	0.99	[0.30]	0.00	3.00	72	0.00	0.00	2.70	5.38
Cn	0.00	[0.00]	0.00	0.00	0	0.00	0.00	----	----
FC+CF+C+Cn	6.15	1.39	4.00	10.00	120	5.00	5.00	0.70	–1.11
WSum C	4.97	1.14	3.00	7.00	120	4.00	4.00	0.16	–1.17
Sum C'	1.25	[0.86]	0.00	2.00	87	2.00	2.00	–0.51	–1.47
Sum T	0.93	[0.78]	0.00	2.00	110	1.00	1.00	0.42	4.14
Sum V	0.00	[0.00]	0.00	0.00	0	0.00	0.00	----	----
Sum Y	0.23	[0.42]	0.00	1.00	37	0.00	0.00	1.33	–0.23
SumShd	2.48	1.12	1.00	4.00	120	3.00	3.00	–0.05	–1.37
Fr+rF	0.30	[0.39]	0.00	2.00	22	0.00	0.00	2.70	5.38
FD	0.13	[0.70]	0.00	1.00	14	0.00	0.00	1.31	–2.94
F	7.62	1.60	3.00	10.00	120	7.00	8.00	–0.68	–0.31
PAIR	9.73	1.94	7.00	12.00	120	9.00	8.00	0.03	–1.75
3r(2)/R	0.65	0.12	0.33	0.90	120	0.62	0.60	0.14	0.28
LAMBDA	0.79	0.16	0.20	1.25	120	0.70	0.62	–0.17	–0.32
EA	7.48	1.04	4.00	9.00	120	8.00	7.00	–0.41	–1.07
es	8.56	1.67	4.00	12.00	120	8.00	7.00	0.01	–0.98
D	–0.53	0.67	–2.00	0.00	120	0.00	0.00	–0.92	–0.32
AdjD	–0.47	0.58	–2.00	0.00	120	0.00	0.00	–0.79	–0.35
a (active)	6.97	1.24	4.00	8.00	120	7.00	8.00	–1.00	–0.19
p (passive)	3.03	1.28	2.00	6.00	120	2.00	2.00	0.91	–0.50
Ma	2.82	0.87	2.00	5.00	120	3.00	2.00	0.84	–0.07
Mp	0.20	0.40	0.00	1.00	24	0.00	0.00	1.52	0.31
Intellect	0.27	0.44	0.00	1.00	120	0.00	0.00	1.07	–0.87
Zf	11.51	1.46	10.00	15.00	120	11.00	14.00	–0.08	–1.14
Zd	–1.04	2.41	–3.50	3.00	120	–1.00	–3.50	0.39	–1.46
Blends	5.11	0.65	3.00	7.00	120	4.00	5.00	–0.72	0.74
Col Shd Bl	0.36	[0.64]	0.00	1.00	20	0.00	0.00	2.12	8.35
Afr	0.79	0.09	0.45	0.83	120	0.67	0.75	0.02	–1.21
Popular	4.75	0.79	2.00	8.00	120	6.00	4.00	–0.35	–0.16

TABLE 23. 7 YEAR OLDS (N = 120)

VARIABLE	MEAN	SD	MIN	MAX	FREQ	MEDIAN	MODE	SK	KU
XA%	0.92	0.07	0.79	1.00	120	0.94	1.00	-0.31	-1.26
WDA%	0.92	0.07	0.79	1.00	120	0.94	1.00	-0.52	-0.99
X+%	0.81	0.05	0.70	0.89	120	0.82	0.86	-0.61	-0.33
X-%	0.08	0.07	0.00	0.21	87	0.06	0.00	0.33	-1.09
Xu%	0.11	0.03	0.05	0.15	120	0.11	0.11	-0.67	-0.56
Isolate/R	0.25	0.05	0.17	0.35	120	0.25	0.25	0.41	-1.08
H	1.67	0.79	1.00	3.00	120	1.00	1.00	0.65	-1.10
(H)	1.34	0.88	0.00	3.00	93	2.00	2.00	-0.28	-1.00
HD	0.38	0.49	0.00	1.00	45	0.00	0.00	0.52	-1.76
(Hd)	0.74	0.87	0.00	3.00	63	1.00	0.00	1.14	0.71
Hx	0.00	[0.00]	0.00	0.00	0	0.00	0.00	----	----
All H Cont	4.13	0.89	3.00	6.00	120	4.00	4.00	0.17	-0.94
A	9.26	0.77	8.00	10.00	120	9.00	10.00	-0.48	-1.16
(A)	1.18	[0.81]	0.00	2.00	90	1.00	2.00	-0.34	-1.39
Ad	0.68	[0.79]	0.00	2.00	57	0.00	0.00	0.65	-1.10
(Ad)	0.05	[0.22]	0.00	1.00	6	0.00	0.00	4.18	15.75
An	0.37	[0.48]	0.00	1.00	44	0.00	0.00	0.56	-1.72
Art	0.10	0.30	0.00	1.00	12	0.00	0.00	2.70	5.38
Ay	0.17	[0.37]	0.00	1.00	20	0.00	0.00	1.81	1.30
Bl	0.28	[0.45]	0.00	1.00	33	0.00	0.00	1.02	-0.98
Bt	2.11	0.56	1.00	3.00	120	2.00	2.00	0.03	0.12
Cg	1.15	0.36	1.00	2.00	120	1.00	1.00	1.98	1.97
Cl	0.00	[0.00]	0.00	0.00	0	0.00	0.00	----	----
Ex	0.00	[0.00]	0.00	0.00	0	0.00	0.00	----	----
Fi	0.48	[0.50]	0.00	1.00	57	0.00	0.00	0.10	-2.02
Food	0.20	[0.40]	0.00	1.00	24	0.00	0.00	1.51	0.31
Ge	0.00	[0.00]	0.00	0.00	0	0.00	0.00	----	----
Hh	0.00	0.00	0.00	0.00	0	0.00	0.00	----	----
Ls	1.00	0.00	1.00	1.00	120	1.00	1.00	----	----
Na	0.96	[0.77]	0.00	2.00	82	1.00	1.00	0.07	-1.31
Sc	1.54	[1.14]	0.00	4.00	96	1.00	1.00	0.39	-0.62
Sx	0.00	[0.00]	0.00	0.00	0	0.00	0.00	----	----
Xy	0.00	[0.00]	0.00	0.00	0	0.00	0.00	----	----
Idiographic	0.53	0.59	0.00	2.00	57	0.00	0.00	0.63	-0.53
DV	1.39	[0.49]	1.00	2.00	120	1.00	1.00	0.45	-1.83
INCOM	1.39	[0.58]	0.00	2.00	114	1.00	1.00	-0.33	-0.71
DR	0.46	[0.63]	0.00	2.00	46	0.00	0.00	1.06	0.06
FABCOM	0.29	[0.46]	0.00	1.00	35	0.00	0.00	0.92	-1.16
DV2	0.00	[0.00]	0.00	0.00	0	0.00	0.00	----	----
INC2	0.00	[0.00]	0.00	0.00	0	0.00	0.00	----	----
DR2	0.00	[0.00]	0.00	0.00	0	0.00	0.00	----	----
FAB2	0.08	[0.26]	0.00	1.00	9	0.00	0.00	3.26	8.83
ALOG	0.38	[0.49]	0.00	1.00	45	0.00	0.00	0.52	-1.76
CONTAM	0.01	0.09	0.00	1.00	1	0.00	0.00	10.95	120.00
Sum 6 Sp Sc	3.99	1.40	1.00	8.00	120	4.00	5.00	0.23	0.45
Lvl 2 Sp Sc	0.08	[0.26]	0.00	1.00	9	0.00	0.00	3.26	8.83
WSum6	9.18	5.66	1.00	29.00	120	10.00	4.00	0.85	0.69
AB	0.00	[0.00]	0.00	0.00	0	0.00	0.00	----	----
AG	1.20	0.40	1.00	2.00	120	1.00	1.00	1.51	0.31
COP	1.17	0.59	0.00	2.00	108	1.00	1.00	-0.05	-0.28
CP	0.00	[0.00]	0.00	0.00	0	0.00	0.00	----	----
GOODHR	3.82	1.16	2.00	5.00	120	4.00	5.00	-0.52	-1.19
POORHR	0.99	0.98	0.00	3.00	71	1.00	0.00	0.50	-0.95
MOR	1.64	[0.58]	1.00	3.00	120	2.00	2.00	0.22	-0.70
PER	1.22	0.57	1.00	3.00	120	1.00	1.00	2.51	4.94
PSV	0.54	[0.50]	0.00	1.00	65	1.00	1.00	-0.16	-2.01

NOTE: Standard Deviations shown in brackets indicate that the value is probably unreliable and/or misleading and should not be used to estimate expected ranges. Ordinarily these variables should not be included in most parametric analyses.

TABLE 23. 8 YEAR OLDS (N = 120)

VARIABLE	MEAN	SD	MIN	MAX	FREQ	MEDIAN	MODE	SK	KU
R	18.73	2.46	14.00	23.00	120	18.00	16.00	0.21	−1.57
W	10.03	1.01	6.00	11.00	120	11.00	8.00	0.55	−1.05
D	7.00	1.28	7.00	11.00	120	7.00	7.00	0.41	−1.12
Dd	1.70	[0.84]	0.00	3.00	104	1.00	0.00	0.40	−1.47
S	1.73	[0.58]	1.00	3.00	119	2.00	2.00	0.08	−0.43
DQ+	6.80	1.74	4.00	10.00	120	6.00	6.00	0.64	−0.57
DQo	11.27	1.40	9.00	14.00	120	12.00	12.00	−0.04	−0.68
DQv	0.90	[0.62]	0.00	3.00	99	1.00	1.00	0.50	−0.59
DQv/+	0.17	[0.25]	0.00	1.00	19	0.00	0.00	3.56	11.07
FQX+	0.00	0.00	0.00	0.00	0	0.00	0.00	----	----
FQXo	13.22	1.83	10.00	17.00	120	13.00	12.00	0.44	−0.37
FQXu	3.47	1.37	2.00	6.00	120	4.00	2.00	0.24	−1.34
FQX−	1.72	0.76	1.00	4.00	120	2.00	1.00	0.53	−1.07
FQXNone	0.43	[0.48]	0.00	1.00	43	0.00	0.00	0.73	−1.53
MQ+	0.00	0.00	0.00	0.00	0	0.00	0.00	----	----
MQo	3.12	1.62	1.00	6.00	120	2.00	2.00	0.68	−0.97
MQu	0.20	0.40	0.00	1.00	24	0.00	0.00	1.54	0.38
MQ−	0.07	[0.25]	0.00	1.00	10	0.00	0.00	3.56	11.07
MQNone	0.00	[0.00]	0.00	0.00	0	0.00	0.00	----	----
S−	0.13	[0.34]	0.00	1.00	29	0.00	0.00	2.21	3.00
M	3.38	1.85	1.00	7.00	120	3.00	2.00	0.79	−0.49
FM	4.72	1.37	3.00	8.00	120	4.00	4.00	0.71	−0.30
m	0.57	0.50	0.00	3.00	57	0.00	0.00	0.14	−2.05
FM+m	5.28	1.56	3.00	8.00	120	5.00	4.00	0.20	−1.29
FC	1.80	0.84	1.00	3.00	120	2.00	1.00	0.40	−1.47
CF	2.73	0.78	1.00	4.00	120	3.00	3.00	−0.38	−0.01
C	0.43	[0.48]	0.00	1.00	43	0.00	0.00	0.73	−1.53
Cn	0.00	[0.00]	0.00	0.00	0	0.00	0.00	----	----
FC+CF+C+Cn	4.87	0.72	3.00	6.00	120	5.00	5.00	−0.90	1.37
WSum C	4.13	0.77	3.00	6.00	120	4.00	3.50	0.80	0.22
Sum C'	1.30	[0.89]	0.00	3.00	102	1.00	1.00	0.92	−0.26
Sum T	1.08	[0.60]	0.00	2.00	107	1.00	1.00	0.76	2.58
Sum V	0.00	[0.00]	0.00	0.00	0	0.00	0.00	----	----
Sum Y	0.92	[0.85]	0.00	2.00	68	1.00	0.00	0.37	−1.54
SumShd	2.90	1.47	1.00	5.00	120	2.00	2.00	0.18	−1.46
Fr+rF	0.33	[0.48]	0.00	1.00	33	0.00	0.00	0.73	−1.53
FD	0.53	[0.34]	0.00	2.00	39	0.00	0.00	2.21	3.00
F	6.98	1.64	5.00	10.00	120	7.00	7.00	0.67	−0.58
PAIR	7.97	1.19	6.00	10.00	120	8.00	8.00	0.07	−0.60
3r(2)/R	0.62	0.12	0.30	0.90	120	0.67	0.60	0.28	0.39
LAMBDA	0.77	0.27	0.29	1.35	120	0.65	0.70	0.91	−0.21
EA	7.51	1.45	4.00	11.50	120	7.00	6.50	0.48	−0.31
es	8.18	2.51	4.00	12.00	120	7.00	6.00	0.07	−1.31
D	−0.22	0.64	−2.00	1.00	120	0.00	0.00	−1.38	2.44
AdjD	−0.15	0.61	−2.00	1.00	120	0.00	0.00	−1.82	4.40
a (active)	6.73	1.63	4.00	10.00	120	6.00	6.00	0.15	−0.34
p (passive)	1.93	1.30	0.00	5.00	112	2.00	1.00	0.89	0.20
Ma	3.12	1.66	1.00	6.00	120	3.00	2.00	0.52	−1.01
Mp	0.37	0.45	0.00	2.00	46	0.00	0.00	1.08	−0.86
Intellect	0.46	0.98	0.00	1.50	120	0.00	0.00	2.46	3.15
Zf	11.27	1.49	10.00	15.00	120	12.00	11.00	0.28	−1.27
Zd	−0.70	1.93	−4.50	5.00	120	−1.00	0.00	1.23	3.73
Blends	4.88	1.03	3.00	6.00	120	5.00	5.00	−0.54	−0.82
Col Shd Bl	0.30	[0.40]	0.00	1.00	34	0.00	0.00	1.54	0.38
Afr	0.69	0.09	0.36	0.90	120	0.68	0.63	0.64	0.00
Popular	5.68	0.80	3.00	7.00	120	6.00	6.00	−0.57	−1.22

TABLE 23. 8 YEAR OLDS (N = 120)

VARIABLE	MEAN	SD	MIN	MAX	FREQ	MEDIAN	MODE	SK	KU
XA%	0.89	0.06	0.75	0.95	120	0.89	0.94	-0.79	-0.05
WDA%	0.90	0.06	0.75	0.95	120	0.93	0.95	-1.29	0.86
X+%	0.71	0.07	0.58	0.81	120	0.71	0.63	0.01	-1.33
X-%	0.09	0.04	0.05	0.19	120	0.09	0.06	0.80	-0.29
Xu%	0.18	0.06	0.12	0.32	120	0.18	0.13	0.89	-0.16
Isolate/R	0.23	0.04	0.14	0.27	120	0.24	0.19	-0.64	-0.47
H	1.87	1.03	1.00	4.00	120	1.00	1.00	0.64	-1.07
(H)	1.47	0.62	1.00	3.00	120	1.00	1.00	0.98	-0.05
HD	0.27	0.44	0.00	1.00	32	0.00	0.00	1.06	-0.87
(Hd)	1.20	0.54	1.00	3.00	120	1.00	1.00	2.65	5.75
Hx	0.00	[0.00]	0.00	0.00	0	0.00	0.00	----	----
H+(H)+Hd+(Hd)	4.80	1.91	3.00	9.00	120	4.00	3.00	0.87	-0.45
A	9.27	1.44	7.00	12.00	120	9.00	8.00	0.34	-1.07
(A)	1.73	[0.58]	1.00	3.00	120	2.00	2.00	0.08	-0.46
Ad	0.33	[0.47]	0.00	1.00	40	0.00	0.00	0.71	-1.51
(Ad)	0.13	[0.34]	0.00	1.00	16	0.00	0.00	2.18	2.82
An	0.20	[0.40]	0.00	1.00	24	0.00	0.00	1.51	0.31
Art	0.00	0.00	0.00	0.00	0	0.00	0.00	----	----
Ay	0.00	[0.00]	0.00	0.00	0	0.00	0.00	----	----
Bl	0.33	[0.47]	0.00	1.00	40	0.00	0.00	0.71	-1.51
Bt	1.45	0.65	0.00	3.00	118	1.00	1.00	0.75	0.04
Cg	1.80	1.17	1.00	4.00	120	1.00	1.00	0.90	-0.93
Cl	0.13	[0.34]	0.00	1.00	16	0.00	0.00	2.18	2.82
Ex	0.00	[0.00]	0.00	0.00	0	0.00	0.00	----	----
Fi	0.33	[0.47]	0.00	1.00	40	0.00	0.00	0.71	-1.51
Food	0.20	[0.40]	0.00	1.00	24	0.00	0.00	1.51	0.31
Ge	0.00	[0.00]	0.00	0.00	0	0.00	0.00	----	----
Hh	0.15	0.36	0.00	1.00	18	0.00	0.00	1.98	1.97
Ls	0.93	0.25	0.00	1.00	112	1.00	1.00	-3.51	10.56
Na	0.80	[0.40]	0.00	1.00	96	1.00	1.00	-1.51	0.31
Sc	2.45	[0.62]	1.00	3.00	120	3.00	3.00	-0.66	-0.50
Sx	0.00	[0.00]	0.00	0.00	0	0.00	0.00	----	----
Xy	0.00	[0.00]	0.00	0.00	0	0.00	0.00	----	----
Idiographic	0.53	0.62	0.00	2.00	56	0.00	0.00	0.72	-0.43
DV	1.33	[0.70]	0.00	2.00	104	1.00	2.00	-0.57	-0.82
INCOM	2.07	[0.44]	1.00	3.00	120	2.00	2.00	0.31	2.04
DR	0.47	[0.62]	0.00	2.00	48	0.00	0.00	0.98	-0.05
FABCOM	0.55	[0.89]	0.00	3.00	42	0.00	0.00	1.60	1.65
DV2	0.07	[0.25]	0.00	1.00	8	0.00	0.00	3.51	10.56
INC2	0.13	[0.34]	0.00	1.00	16	0.00	0.00	2.18	2.82
DR2	0.00	[0.00]	0.00	0.00	0	0.00	0.00	----	----
FAB2	0.13	[0.34]	0.00	1.00	16	0.00	0.00	2.18	2.82
ALOG	0.73	[0.44]	0.00	1.00	88	1.00	1.00	-1.06	-0.87
CONTAM	0.00	0.00	0.00	0.00	0	0.00	0.00	----	----
Sum 6 Sp Sc	5.48	1.70	3.00	10.00	120	5.00	5.00	0.95	1.21
Lvl 2 Sp Sc	0.33	[0.47]	0.00	1.00	40	0.00	0.00	0.71	-1.51
WSum6	14.33	5.10	5.00	28.00	120	14.00	14.00	0.71	1.74
AB	0.00	[0.00]	0.00	0.00	0	0.00	0.00	----	----
AG	0.93	0.58	0.00	2.00	96	1.00	1.00	0.00	0.05
COP	1.93	1.00	1.00	4.00	120	2.00	1.00	0.54	-1.06
CP	0.00	[0.00]	0.00	0.00	0	0.00	0.00	----	----
GOODHR	4.98	2.29	1.00	9.00	120	4.00	4.00	0.48	-0.86
POORHR	0.68	0.83	0.00	3.00	56	0.00	0.00	0.83	-0.51
MOR	1.13	[0.34]	1.00	2.00	120	1.00	1.00	2.18	2.82
PER	0.33	0.47	0.00	1.00	40	0.00	0.00	0.71	-1.51
PSV	0.46	[0.78]	0.00	2.00	18	0.00	0.00	2.74	9.86

NOTE: Standard Deviations shown in brackets indicate that the value is probably unreliable and/or misleading and should not be used to estimate expected ranges. Ordinarily these variables should not be included in most parametric analyses.

TABLE 23. 9 YEAR OLDS (N = 140)

VARIABLE	MEAN	SD	MIN	MAX	FREQ	MEDIAN	MODE	SK	KU
R	20.53	2.46	14.00	26.00	140	21.00	19.00	0.41	0.57
W	10.33	1.57	6.00	12.00	140	11.00	9.00	0.55	0.05
D	9.00	1.28	7.00	13.00	140	9.00	8.00	0.41	0.84
Dd	1.20	[0.84]	0.00	4.00	102	1.00	0.00	0.40	3.47
S	1.73	[0.58]	0.00	4.00	108	2.00	1.00	1.78	3.43
DQ+	6.40	1.94	3.00	12.00	138	7.00	6.00	0.64	2.57
DQo	11.67	1.80	7.00	14.00	140	11.00	10.00	-0.04	-0.68
DQv	1.61	[0.65]	0.00	4.00	72	1.00	0.00	0.50	-0.59
DQv/+	0.45	[0.65]	0.00	1.00	23	0.00	0.00	3.56	11.07
FQX+	0.26	0.31	0.00	1.00	5	0.00	0.00	4.18	13.67
FQXo	14.22	1.83	10.00	18.00	140	14.00	12.00	0.44	-0.37
FQXu	3.49	1.37	2.00	6.00	140	4.00	2.00	0.24	-1.34
FQX-	2.04	0.76	1.00	3.00	140	2.00	1.00	0.53	-1.07
FQXNone	0.38	[0.48]	0.00	2.00	31	0.00	0.00	0.73	-1.53
MQ+	0.00	0.00	0.00	0.00	0	0.00	0.00	----	----
MQo	3.12	1.62	1.00	6.00	140	2.00	2.00	0.68	-0.97
MQu	0.20	0.40	0.00	1.00	22	0.00	0.00	1.54	0.38
MQ-	0.37	[0.25]	0.00	2.00	7	0.00	0.00	3.27	10.61
MQNone	0.00	[0.00]	0.00	0.00	0	0.00	0.00	----	----
S-	0.13	[0.34]	0.00	1.00	29	0.00	0.00	2.21	3.00
M	3.12	1.85	1.00	7.00	140	3.00	2.00	0.79	-0.49
FM	4.22	1.47	3.00	9.00	140	4.00	4.00	0.71	0.64
m	0.67	0.58	0.00	3.00	66	0.00	0.00	0.14	3.65
FM+m	5.64	1.86	2.00	9.00	140	6.00	4.00	0.20	0.59
FC	1.89	0.86	0.00	3.00	131	2.00	1.00	0.40	2.47
CF	2.79	0.78	1.00	4.00	140	3.00	2.00	-0.38	2.01
C	0.43	[0.48]	0.00	2.00	22	0.00	0.00	0.73	2.53
Cn	0.00	[0.00]	0.00	0.00	0	0.00	0.00	----	----
FC+CF+C+Cn	4.15	0.72	3.00	9.00	140	6.00	5.00	-0.90	1.37
WSum C	5.13	1.07	2.50	7.50	140	4.00	3.50	0.80	0.22
Sum C'	1.16	[0.79]	0.00	4.00	104	1.00	1.00	0.92	1.66
Sum T	0.97	[0.63]	0.00	2.00	123	1.00	1.00	0.24	3.58
Sum V	0.00	[0.00]	0.00	0.00	0	0.00	0.00	----	----
Sum Y	0.83	[0.85]	0.00	3.00	102	1.00	1.00	0.37	-1.76
SumShd	2.96	1.27	1.00	6.00	140	2.00	2.00	0.18	-1.46
Fr+rF	0.42	[0.43]	0.00	1.00	26	0.00	0.00	0.73	2.53
FD	0.63	[0.34]	0.00	1.00	64	0.00	0.00	2.45	3.13
F	9.14	1.84	5.00	11.00	140	8.00	8.00	0.67	-0.58
PAIR	8.97	1.69	5.00	12.00	140	9.00	8.00	0.07	-0.60
3r(2)/R	0.57	0.12	0.30	0.88	140	0.60	0.55	0.18	0.54
LAMBDA	0.81	0.37	0.29	1.45	140	0.85	0.70	0.91	0.21
EA	8.25	1.95	4.00	11.50	140	8.00	6.50	0.38	0.56
es	8.60	2.59	4.00	13.00	140	7.00	6.00	0.07	1.31
D	-0.18	0.54	-3.00	1.00	140	0.00	0.00	1.18	1.44
AdjD	-0.10	0.41	-2.00	1.00	140	0.00	0.00	-1.32	3.44
a (active)	6.26	1.23	3.00	11.00	140	7.00	6.00	0.12	0.30
p (passive)	2.51	1.40	0.00	5.00	76	2.00	1.00	0.89	0.70
Ma	2.72	1.36	1.00	6.00	134	3.00	2.00	0.52	-1.01
Mp	0.27	0.45	0.00	1.00	61	0.00	0.00	1.28	1.86
Intellect	1.03	0.98	0.00	1.00	140	0.00	0.00	2.68	10.89
Zf	11.16	1.54	7.00	15.00	140	11.00	11.00	0.28	0.47
Zd	0.40	2.03	-4.50	6.00	140	0.00	0.00	0.23	0.73
Blends	4.38	1.23	2.00	7.00	140	5.00	5.00	-0.44	-0.92
Col Shd Bl	0.90	[0.56]	0.00	3.00	59	0.00	0.00	1.04	0.34
Afr	0.79	0.13	0.38	1.05	140	0.76	0.68	-0.44	0.03
Popular	5.78	0.63	4.00	7.00	140	6.00	5.00	-0.52	-1.02

TABLE 23. 9 YEAR OLDS (N = 140)

VARIABLE	MEAN	SD	MIN	MAX	FREQ	MEDIAN	MODE	SK	KU
XA%	0.91	0.07	0.67	1.00	140	0.91	0.95	−2.07	7.52
WDA%	0.92	0.05	0.71	1.00	140	0.91	0.95	−1.80	5.89
X+%	0.74	0.07	0.61	0.85	140	0.77	0.79	−0.90	−0.22
X−%	0.09	0.06	0.05	0.25	140	0.07	0.09	−0.32	0.25
Xu%	0.17	0.07	0.10	0.33	140	0.18	0.15	0.81	−0.15
Isolate	0.16	0.05	0.06	0.32	140	0.14	0.17	−0.67	−0.34
H	2.87	1.03	0.00	6.00	138	2.00	2.00	0.66	−1.06
(H)	1.32	0.61	1.00	3.00	140	1.00	1.00	0.84	1.25
Hd	0.57	0.40	0.00	2.00	46	0.00	0.00	1.58	0.36
(Hd)	0.74	0.58	0.00	2.00	62	0.00	0.00	1.60	4.06
Hx	0.00	[0.00]	0.00	0.00	0	0.00	0.00	----	----
All H Cont	5.50	1.62	2.00	8.00	140	5.00	4.00	0.59	−0.41
A	8.28	1.59	5.00	13.00	140	9.00	8.00	0.35	0.06
(A)	0.73	[0.68]	0.00	3.00	101	1.00	1.00	0.28	1.63
Ad	0.53	[0.98]	0.00	2.00	80	1.00	1.00	−0.63	2.73
(Ad)	0.23	[0.39]	0.00	1.00	13	0.00	0.00	3.27	4.00
An	0.36	[0.60]	0.00	3.00	34	0.00	0.00	2.54	2.38
Art	0.32	0.71	0.00	2.00	31	0.00	0.00	1.38	3.09
Ay	0.13	[0.28]	0.00	1.00	11	0.00	0.00	3.94	8.28
Bl	0.33	[0.48]	0.00	1.00	28	0.00	0.00	1.03	1.33
Bt	1.45	0.65	0.00	3.00	129	1.00	1.00	0.97	1.10
Cg	1.84	1.08	1.00	4.00	133	1.00	1.00	0.92	1.92
Cl	0.16	[0.39]	0.00	1.00	40	0.00	0.00	2.01	3.34
Ex	0.26	[0.54]	0.00	1.00	21	0.00	0.00	1.93	4.06
Fi	0.69	[0.68]	0.00	1.00	68	0.00	0.00	0.33	2.73
Fd	0.18	[0.46]	0.00	1.00	15	0.00	0.00	2.54	4.38
Ge	0.00	[0.00]	0.00	0.00	0	0.00	0.00	----	----
Hh	0.59	0.36	0.00	1.00	49	0.00	0.00	2.11	2.07
Ls	0.93	0.59	0.00	3.00	107	1.00	1.00	−0.28	0.83
Na	0.70	[0.48]	0.00	2.00	96	1.00	1.00	−0.54	1.38
Sc	1.55	[0.72]	0.00	3.00	102	2.00	1.00	0.68	2.46
Sx	0.00	[0.00]	0.00	0.00	0	0.00	0.00	----	----
Xy	0.00	[0.00]	0.00	0.00	0	0.00	0.00	----	----
Idio	0.63	0.42	0.00	1.00	48	0.00	0.00	0.84	1.40
DV	1.01	[0.61]	0.00	2.00	97	1.00	1.00	−0.08	2.80
INCOM	1.37	[0.75]	0.00	3.00	81	1.00	1.00	0.32	2.18
DR	0.67	[0.72]	0.00	2.00	91	1.00	1.00	−0.73	2.00
FABCOM	1.05	[0.89]	0.00	3.00	102	1.00	1.00	0.63	1.68
DV2	0.07	[0.21]	0.00	1.00	6	0.00	0.00	1.56	12.07
INC2	0.11	[0.59]	0.00	1.00	7	0.00	0.00	1.27	11.40
DR2	0.00	[0.00]	0.00	0.00	0	0.00	0.00	----	----
FAB2	0.05	[0.39]	0.00	1.00	3	0.00	0.00	0.68	13.00
ALOG	0.61	[0.49]	0.00	1.00	56	0.00	0.00	1.08	3.86
CONTAM	0.00	0.00	0.00	0.00	0	0.00	0.00	----	----
Sum6 Sp Sc	5.95	2.16	1.00	9.00	140	6.00	6.00	0.74	0.52
Sum6 Sp Sc2	0.27	[0.51]	0.00	2.00	14	0.00	0.00	0.63	6.53
WSum6	13.06	4.72	3.00	26.00	140	12.00	11.00	0.92	0.86
AB	0.00	[0.00]	0.00	0.00	0	0.00	0.00	----	-----
AG	1.37	0.78	0.00	4.00	128	2.00	1.00	0.67	1.11
COP	2.03	1.14	0.00	5.00	136	2.00	2.00	0.18	1.05
CP	0.00	[0.00]	0.00	0.00	0	0.00	0.00	----	----
GOODHR	4.11	1.42	1.00	8.00	140	4.00	4.00	0.17	−0.78
POORHR	1.86	1.02	0.00	5.00	140	1.00	1.00	1.62	6.02
MOR	0.87	[0.64]	0.00	4.00	116	1.00	1.00	−0.41	1.87
PER	1.16	0.78	0.00	6.00	99	1.00	1.00	0.73	−1.53
PSV	0.26	[0.61]	0.00	2.00	29	0.00	0.00	1.04	4.14

NOTE: Standard Deviations shown in brackets indicate that the value is probably unreliable and/or misleading and should not be used to estimate expected ranges. Ordinarily these variables should not be included in most parametric analyses.

TABLE 23. 10 YEAR OLDS (N = 120)

VARIABLE	MEAN	SD	MIN	MAX	FREQ	MEDIAN	MODE	SK	KU
R	20.97	1.92	18.00	25.00	120	19.00	19.00	0.85	-0.39
W	9.52	0.87	9.00	12.00	120	9.00	9.00	1.59	1.46
D	10.10	1.48	8.00	13.00	120	10.00	9.00	0.31	-1.32
Dd	1.35	[0.44]	0.00	3.00	119	0.00	0.00	1.17	-0.64
S	1.48	[0.70]	1.00	3.00	107	1.00	1.00	1.12	-0.08
DQ+	7.68	0.96	3.00	9.00	120	8.00	7.00	-0.48	-0.18
DQo	12.07	1.78	9.00	17.00	120	12.00	11.00	0.08	0.01
DQv	0.53	[0.50]	0.00	2.00	64	1.00	1.00	-0.14	-2.02
DQv/+	0.38	[0.28]	0.00	1.00	36	0.00	0.00	3.05	7.45
FQX+	0.30	0.50	0.00	1.00	11	0.00	0.00	4.04	9.15
FQXo	15.80	1.98	13.00	21.00	120	15.00	15.00	0.81	0.33
FQXu	2.95	0.79	1.00	4.00	120	3.00	3.00	-0.54	0.12
FQX-	1.58	1.03	0.00	6.00	104	2.00	2.00	1.74	6.56
FQXNone	0.13	[0.34]	0.00	1.00	29	0.00	0.00	2.19	2.82
MQ+	0.08	0.21	0.00	1.00	2	0.00	0.00	4.80	13.25
MQo	3.23	1.48	1.00	6.00	120	3.00	3.00	0.22	-0.78
MQu	0.25	0.44	0.00	1.00	30	0.00	0.00	1.17	-0.64
MQ-	0.17	[0.37]	0.00	2.00	21	0.00	0.00	1.81	1.30
MQNone	0.00	[0.00]	0.00	0.00	0	0.00	0.00	----	----
S-	0.12	[0.32]	0.00	1.00	14	0.00	0.00	2.42	3.91
M	3.65	1.63	1.00	7.00	120	4.00	3.00	-0.04	-0.69
FM	5.53	1.46	3.00	7.00	120	6.00	7.00	-0.43	-1.38
m	1.08	0.28	1.00	2.00	120	1.00	1.00	3.05	7.45
FM+m	6.62	1.40	4.00	8.00	120	7.00	8.00	-0.56	-1.06
FC	2.55	0.96	1.00	4.00	120	2.00	2.00	0.44	-1.03
CF	3.68	1.29	2.00	6.00	120	3.50	5.00	0.14	-1.27
C	0.13	[0.34]	0.00	2.00	29	0.00	0.00	2.19	2.82
Cn	0.00	[0.00]	0.00	0.00	0	0.00	0.00	----	----
FC+CF+C+Cn	6.37	1.50	4.00	8.00	120	7.00	8.00	-0.41	-1.30
WSum C	5.16	1.25	3.00	7.00	120	5.00	4.00	-0.23	-1.26
Sum C'	0.79	[0.85]	0.00	4.00	73	1.00	1.00	0.41	0.44
Sum T	0.98	[0.39]	0.00	2.00	106	1.00	1.00	-0.16	3.86
Sum V	0.02	[0.13]	0.00	1.00	2	0.00	0.00	7.65	57.43
Sum Y	0.43	[0.65]	0.00	2.00	34	0.00	0.00	0.82	-0.37
SumShd	1.83	1.32	1.00	6.00	120	3.00	4.00	0.06	-1.16
Fr+rF	0.35	[0.36]	0.00	1.00	36	0.00	0.00	1.98	1.97
FD	0.67	[0.58]	0.00	2.00	78	1.00	1.00	1.33	0.81
F	6.38	2.04	3.00	12.00	120	5.50	5.00	0.57	-0.73
PAIR	9.62	1.36	6.00	12.00	120	9.00	9.00	-0.29	0.09
3r(2)/R	0.54	0.07	0.29	0.68	120	0.52	0.47	-0.71	6.30
LAMBDA	0.49	0.23	0.19	1.11	120	0.36	0.36	0.90	-0.23
EA	8.81	1.36	4.00	11.00	120	9.00	7.00	-0.37	1.09
es	8.45	1.90	5.00	12.00	120	8.00	7.00	-0.33	-0.89
D	-0.15	0.44	-2.00	1.00	120	0.00	0.00	-1.89	5.07
AdjD	-0.12	0.49	-2.00	1.00	120	0.00	0.00	-1.17	3.81
a (active)	7.15	1.37	6.00	11.00	120	8.00	7.00	0.32	-0.74
p (passive)	3.27	0.66	1.00	4.00	120	2.00	2.00	1.46	1.91
Ma	2.82	1.09	1.00	5.00	120	3.00	3.00	-0.10	-0.63
Mp	0.98	0.83	0.00	3.00	88	1.00	1.00	0.93	0.76
Intellect	0.53	0.56	0.00	2.00	120	0.50	0.00	0.44	-0.81
Zf	13.52	1.19	11.00	16.00	120	13.50	13.00	-0.19	-0.27
Zd	-0.13	2.32	-5.00	5.00	120	0.00	-3.00	0.22	-0.35
Blends	5.80	1.05	3.00	7.00	120	6.00	7.00	-0.39	-0.70
Col Shd Blend	0.42	[0.13]	0.00	1.00	22	0.00	0.00	7.65	57.43
Afr	0.63	0.09	0.50	0.85	120	0.58	0.58	0.94	-0.05
Popular	6.07	0.84	3.00	7.00	120	6.00	6.00	-1.01	1.55s

TABLE 23. 10 YEAR OLDS (N = 120)

VARIABLE	MEAN	SD	MIN	MAX	FREQ	MEDIAN	MODE	SK	KU
XA%	0.92	0.04	0.75	1.00	120	0.91	0.95	-1.44	5.47
WDA%	0.93	0.04	0.78	1.00	120	0.95	0.95	-1.24	3.22
X+%	0.77	0.05	0.62	0.85	120	0.79	0.79	-0.85	1.39
X-%	0.07	0.05	0.00	0.25	104	0.07	0.05	1.46	5.42
Xu%	0.15	0.05	0.05	0.21	120	0.16	0.16	-0.43	-0.53
Isolate/R	0.19	0.03	0.14	0.26	120	0.19	0.16	0.67	-0.53
H	2.47	1.12	1.00	5.00	120	3.00	3.00	0.01	-0.83
(H)	1.48	0.74	0.00	2.00	102	2.00	2.00	-1.06	-0.37
HD	0.25	0.47	0.00	2.00	28	0.00	0.00	1.64	1.80
(Hd)	0.85	0.36	0.00	1.00	102	1.00	1.00	-1.98	1.97
Hx	0.00	[0.00]	0.00	0.00	0	0.00	0.00	----	----
All H Cont	5.05	1.64	2.00	8.00	120	6.00	6.00	-0.58	-0.59
A	8.92	1.18	7.00	11.00	120	9.00	9.00	0.54	-0.43
(A)	1.20	[0.77]	0.00	3.00	96	1.00	1.00	-0.14	-0.88
Ad	1.35	[1.08]	0.00	3.00	76	2.00	2.00	-0.25	-1.49
(Ad)	0.07	[0.25]	0.00	1.00	8	0.00	0.00	3.51	10.56
An	0.67	[0.57]	0.00	2.00	74	1.00	1.00	0.14	-0.66
Art	0.53	0.56	0.00	2.00	60	0.50	0.00	0.43	-0.81
Ay	0.00	[0.00]	0.00	0.00	0	0.00	0.00	----	----
Bl	0.60	[0.59]	0.00	2.00	66	1.00	1.00	0.36	-0.70
Bt	2.17	0.74	1.00	4.00	120	2.00	2.00	0.49	0.33
Cg	1.48	1.03	0.00	3.00	102	1.00	1.00	0.32	-1.10
Cl	0.08	[0.28]	0.00	1.00	10	0.00	0.00	3.05	7.45
Ex	0.08	[0.28]	0.00	1.00	10	0.00	0.00	3.05	7.45
Fi	0.75	[0.44]	0.00	1.00	90	1.00	1.00	-1.16	-0.64
Food	0.53	[0.50]	0.00	1.00	64	1.00	1.00	-0.13	-2.02
Ge	0.00	[0.00]	0.00	0.00	0	0.00	0.00	----	----
Hh	0.60	0.49	0.00	1.00	72	1.00	1.00	-0.41	-1.86
Ls	1.00	0.45	0.00	2.00	108	1.00	1.00	0.00	2.14
Na	0.30	[0.46]	0.00	1.00	36	0.00	0.00	0.88	-1.24
Sc	2.85	[0.40]	2.00	4.00	120	3.00	3.00	-1.16	1.62
Sx	0.00	[0.00]	0.00	0.00	0	0.00	0.00	----	----
Xy	0.00	[0.00]	0.00	0.00	0	0.00	0.00	----	----
Idiographic	0.08	0.28	0.00	1.00	10	0.00	0.00	3.05	7.45
DV	1.00	[0.00]	1.00	1.00	120	1.00	1.00	----	----
INCOM	1.35	[0.51]	1.00	3.00	120	1.00	1.00	1.01	-0.16
DR	0.08	[0.28]	0.00	1.00	10	0.00	0.00	3.05	7.45
FABCOM	0.35	[0.48]	0.00	1.00	42	0.00	0.00	0.63	-1.62
DV2	0.00	[0.00]	0.00	0.00	0	0.00	0.00	----	----
INC2	0.23	[0.43]	0.00	1.00	28	0.00	0.00	1.27	-0.38
DR2	0.02	[0.13]	0.00	1.00	2	0.00	0.00	7.64	57.43
FAB2	0.00	[0.00]	0.00	0.00	0	0.00	0.00	----	----
ALOG	0.37	[0.48]	0.00	1.00	44	0.00	0.00	0.56	-1.72
CONTAM	0.00	0.00	0.00	0.00	0	0.00	0.00	----	----
Sum 6 Sp Sc	3.40	1.10	2.00	6.00	120	3.00	3.00	1.29	0.85
Lvl 2 Sp Sc	0.25	[0.44]	0.00	1.00	30	0.00	0.00	1.16	-0.64
WSum6	8.22	3.79	3.00	17.00	120	7.00	7.00	1.07	0.65
AB	0.00	[0.00]	0.00	0.00	0	0.00	0.00	----	----
AG	1.57	0.62	1.00	3.00	120	1.50	1.00	0.61	-0.55
COP	1.73	0.84	1.00	4.00	120	2.00	2.00	1.41	1.94
CP	0.00	[0.00]	0.00	0.00	0	0.00	0.00	----	----
GOODHR	5.32	1.53	2.00	8.00	120	5.00	5.00	0.02	-0.72
POORHR	1.10	0.65	0.00	3.00	104	1.00	1.00	0.63	1.22
MOR	0.55	[0.62]	0.00	2.00	58	0.00	0.00	0.66	-0.50
PER	0.75	0.44	0.00	1.00	90	1.00	1.00	-1.16	-0.64
PSV	0.05	[0.22]	0.00	1.00	6	0.00	0.00	4.18	15.75

NOTE: Standard Deviations shown in brackets indicate that the value is probably unreliable and/or misleading and should not be used to estimate expected ranges. Ordinarily these variables should not be included in most parametric analyses.

TABLE 23. 11 YEAR OLDS (N = 135)

VARIABLE	MEAN	SD	MIN	MAX	FREQ	MEDIAN	MODE	SK	KU
R	21.29	2.43	15.00	27.00	135	22.00	19.00	0.93	0.29
W	9.61	0.95	9.00	12.00	135	9.00	9.00	1.49	1.06
D	10.01	1.31	9.00	13.00	135	11.00	11.00	0.05	−1.09
Dd	1.67	[1.13]	0.00	4.00	128	0.00	0.00	2.12	3.75
S	1.75	[0.68]	1.00	3.00	135	2.00	2.00	0.36	−0.81
DQ+	8.07	1.22	6.00	10.00	135	8.00	7.00	0.10	−1.08
DQo	12.08	2.14	9.00	17.00	135	12.00	11.00	0.73	0.25
DQv	0.64	[0.88]	0.00	3.00	63	0.00	0.00	1.57	1.99
DQv/+	0.50	[0.69]	0.00	2.00	41	0.00	0.00	1.98	2.39
FQX+	0.21	0.38	0.00	1.00	9	0.00	0.00	3.08	11.42
FQXo	15.83	1.40	13.00	18.00	135	16.00	17.00	−0.29	−1.09
FQXu	3.18	1.26	1.00	6.00	135	3.00	3.00	0.52	0.49
FQX−	2.20	1.87	0.00	7.00	125	2.00	2.00	1.73	2.02
FQXNone	0.18	[0.27]	0.00	1.00	18	0.00	0.00	3.09	7.69
MQ+	0.11	0.45	0.00	1.00	3	0.00	0.00	4.24	13.85
MQo	3.59	1.38	1.00	6.00	135	4.00	3.00	−0.15	−0.69
MQu	0.33	0.47	0.00	1.00	44	0.00	0.00	0.75	−1.46
MQ−	0.20	[0.40]	0.00	1.00	27	0.00	0.00	1.52	0.30
MQNone	0.00	[0.00]	0.00	0.00	0	0.00	0.00	----	----
S−	0.31	[0.46]	0.00	1.00	52	0.00	0.00	0.82	−1.34
M	4.12	1.67	1.00	7.00	135	4.00	3.00	0.08	−0.56
FM	4.48	1.21	2.00	7.00	135	6.00	4.00	−0.51	−0.65
m	1.00	0.89	0.00	2.00	122	1.00	1.00	0.84	1.69
FM+m	5.48	1.21	4.00	8.00	135	7.00	7.00	−0.51	−0.65
FC	2.93	0.95	1.00	4.00	135	3.00	4.00	−0.19	−1.29
CF	3.43	1.13	2.00	6.00	135	4.00	4.00	0.10	−1.14
C	0.28	[0.27]	0.00	1.00	17	0.00	0.00	3.09	7.69
Cn	0.00	[0.00]	0.00	0.00	0	0.00	0.00	----	----
FC+CF+C+Cn	6.44	1.39	4.00	8.00	135	7.00	7.00	−0.57	−0.93
WSum C	4.02	1.15	2.50	8.00	135	5.00	4.00	−0.36	−1.06
Sum C'	1.06	[0.71]	0.00	2.00	105	1.00	1.00	−0.09	−0.99
Sum T	0.94	[0.47]	0.00	2.00	116	1.00	1.00	−0.20	1.55
Sum V	0.00	[0.00]	0.00	0.00	0	0.00	0.00	----	----
Sum Y	0.85	[0.70]	0.00	2.00	91	1.00	1.00	0.21	−0.92
SumShd	2.85	1.10	1.00	4.00	135	3.00	4.00	−0.32	−1.31
Fr+rF	0.21	[0.41]	0.00	1.00	29	0.00	0.00	1.40	−0.03
FD	0.91	[0.84]	0.00	2.00	92	0.00	0.00	0.59	−1.34
F	6.70	2.37	4.00	12.00	135	6.00	5.00	1.12	0.09
PAIR	9.90	1.08	7.00	12.00	135	10.00	10.00	−0.31	0.86
3r(2)/R	0.53	0.04	0.35	0.75	135	0.58	0.50	0.44	0.38
LAMBDA	0.68	0.22	0.27	1.50	135	0.69	0.60	0.89	−0.62
EA	8.14	1.37	7.00	12.00	135	8.00	7.00	0.57	−0.53
es	8.33	1.72	4.00	12.00	135	9.00	7.00	−0.22	−1.08
D	−0.09	0.29	−1.00	0.00	135	0.00	0.00	−2.92	6.63
AdjD	−0.06	0.34	−1.00	1.00	135	0.00	0.00	−1.00	5.32
a (active)	7.89	1.42	6.00	11.00	135	8.00	7.00	0.67	−0.27
p (passive)	2.79	1.60	2.00	8.00	135	2.00	2.00	2.08	3.12
Ma	2.81	1.01	1.00	5.00	135	3.00	3.00	0.29	−0.01
Mp	1.38	1.33	0.00	5.00	104	1.00	1.00	1.26	0.76
Intellect	0.77	0.65	0.00	2.00	135	1.00	1.00	0.26	−0.67
Zf	13.70	1.22	11.00	16.00	135	14.00	15.00	−0.30	−0.72
Zd	0.60	2.74	−4.50	4.50	135	1.00	4.50	−0.07	−1.15
Blends	6.04	1.41	3.00	8.00	135	6.00	7.00	−0.28	−1.05
Col Shd Bl	0.00	[0.00]	0.00	0.00	0	0.00	0.00	----	----
Afr	0.62	0.09	0.47	0.80	135	0.58	0.58	0.33	−0.90
Popular	6.06	0.86	4.00	9.00	135	7.00	5.00	−0.76	−0.78

TABLE 23. 11 YEAR OLDS (N = 135)

VARIABLE	MEAN	SD	MIN	MAX	FREQ	MEDIAN	MODE	SK	KU
XA%	0.90	0.07	0.74	1.00	135	0.91	0.91	-1.51	1.55
WDA%	0.92	0.04	0.78	1.00	135	0.95	0.95	-1.47	2.85
X+%	0.75	0.08	0.52	0.85	135	0.77	0.79	-1.65	2.46
X-%	0.10	0.07	0.00	0.26	125	0.09	0.09	1.41	1.41
Xu%	0.15	0.05	0.05	0.24	135	0.16	0.14	-0.34	-0.35
Isolate/R	0.20	0.05	0.14	0.37	135	0.18	0.17	2.06	4.31
H	2.80	1.27	1.00	5.00	135	3.00	3.00	0.22	-0.71
(H)	1.51	0.66	0.00	2.00	123	2.00	2.00	-1.00	-0.12
HD	0.52	0.66	0.00	2.00	58	0.00	0.00	0.89	-0.30
(Hd)	0.87	0.33	0.00	1.00	118	1.00	1.00	-2.28	3.25
Hx	0.00	[0.00]	0.00	0.00	0	0.00	0.00	----	----
All H Cont	5.70	1.80	2.00	9.00	135	6.00	6.00	-0.22	0.04
A	8.59	1.25	7.00	11.00	135	8.00	8.00	0.83	-0.19
(A)	1.00	[0.83]	0.00	2.00	89	1.00	0.00	0.00	-1.55
Ad	1.54	[0.95]	0.00	3.00	101	2.00	2.00	-0.75	-0.78
(Ad)	0.16	[0.36]	0.00	1.00	21	0.00	0.00	1.92	1.72
An	0.73	[0.64]	0.00	2.00	85	1.00	1.00	0.29	-0.66
Art	0.56	0.50	0.00	1.00	76	1.00	1.00	-0.25	-1.96
Ay	0.21	[0.59]	0.00	2.00	16	0.00	0.00	2.62	5.19
Bl	0.44	[0.57]	0.00	2.00	54	0.00	0.00	0.87	-0.24
Bt	2.10	0.67	1.00	4.00	135	2.00	2.00	0.65	1.16
Cg	1.60	0.99	0.00	3.00	122	1.00	1.00	0.26	-1.15
Cl	0.06	[0.24]	0.00	1.00	8	0.00	0.00	3.77	12.44
Ex	0.03	[0.17]	0.00	1.00	4	0.00	0.00	5.61	29.92
Fi	0.85	[0.36]	0.00	1.00	115	1.00	1.00	-2.00	2.04
Food	0.64	[0.48]	0.00	1.00	87	1.00	1.00	-0.61	-1.65
Ge	0.00	[0.00]	0.00	0.00	0	0.00	0.00	----	----
Hh	0.82	0.46	0.00	2.00	106	1.00	1.00	-0.65	0.55
Ls	1.28	0.61	0.00	2.00	124	1.00	1.00	-0.22	-0.58
Na	0.35	[0.48]	0.00	1.00	47	0.00	0.00	0.64	-1.61
Sc	2.96	[0.36]	2.00	4.00	135	3.00	3.00	-0.57	4.57
Sx	0.00	[0.00]	0.00	0.00	0	0.00	0.00	----	----
Xy	0.09	[0.29]	0.00	1.00	12	0.00	0.00	2.92	6.63
Idio	0.06	0.34	0.00	2.00	4	0.00	0.00	5.61	29.92
DV	1.21	[0.41]	1.00	2.00	135	1.00	1.00	1.46	0.13
INCOM	1.44	[0.63]	0.00	3.00	131	1.00	1.00	0.42	-0.07
DR	0.12	[0.32]	0.00	1.00	16	0.00	0.00	2.38	3.75
FABCOM	0.36	[0.48]	0.00	1.00	48	0.00	0.00	0.61	-1.65
DV2	0.00	[0.00]	0.00	0.00	0	0.00	0.00	----	----
INC2	0.12	[0.32]	0.00	1.00	16	0.00	0.00	2.38	3.75
DR2	0.03	[0.17]	0.00	1.00	4	0.00	0.00	5.61	29.92
FAB2	0.00	[0.00]	0.00	0.00	0	0.00	0.00	----	----
ALOG	0.24	[0.43]	0.00	1.00	33	0.00	0.00	1.20	-0.56
CONTAM	0.00	0.00	0.00	0.00	0	0.00	0.00	----	----
Sum 6 Sp Sc	3.51	1.09	2.00	6.00	135	3.00	3.00	0.58	-0.53
Lvl 2 Sp Sc	0.15	[0.36]	0.00	1.00	20	0.00	0.00	2.00	2.04
WSum6	7.73	3.04	3.00	16.00	135	8.00	7.00	0.77	1.10
AB	0.00	[0.00]	0.00	0.00	0	0.00	0.00	----	----
AG	1.42	0.57	1.00	3.00	135	1.00	1.00	0.93	-0.11
COP	1.56	0.50	1.00	2.00	135	2.00	2.00	-0.22	-1.98
CP	0.00	[0.00]	0.00	0.00	0	0.00	0.00	----	----
GOODHR	5.65	1.49	3.00	8.00	135	5.00	5.00	0.09	-0.83
POORHR	1.12	0.53	0.00	2.00	123	1.00	1.00	0.11	0.38
MOR	0.42	[0.57]	0.00	2.00	52	0.00	0.00	0.93	-0.11
PER	0.88	0.53	0.00	2.00	107	1.00	1.00	-0.11	0.38
PSV	0.04	[0.21]	0.00	1.00	6	0.00	0.00	4.47	18.26

NOTE: Standard Deviations shown in brackets indicate that the value is probably unreliable and/or misleading and should not be used to estimate expected ranges. Ordinarily these variables should not be included in most parametric analyses.

TABLE 23. 12 YEAR OLDS (N = 120)

VARIABLE	MEAN	SD	MIN	MAX	FREQ	MEDIAN	MODE	SK	KU
R	21.40	2.05	14.00	23.00	120	20.00	22.00	-1.03	0.96
W	8.79	1.85	1.00	14.00	120	9.00	9.00	-1.94	7.05
D	10.85	1.96	1.00	13.00	120	11.00	12.00	-3.26	12.20
Dd	1.76	[1.11]	0.00	5.00	117	1.00	1.00	3.51	16.47
S	1.92	[0.76]	0.00	5.00	118	2.00	2.00	1.30	4.92
DQ+	8.16	1.90	2.00	10.00	120	8.00	10.00	-1.42	2.39
DQo	12.12	1.07	9.00	15.00	120	12.00	12.00	-0.13	1.90
DQv	1.03	[0.26]	0.00	2.00	72	1.00	1.00	0.65	2.43
DQv/+	0.38	[0.38]	0.00	2.00	16	0.00	0.00	3.62	13.45
FQX+	0.30	0.54	0.00	2.00	10	0.00	0.00	4.16	16.95
FQXo	15.34	2.32	5.00	17.00	120	16.00	17.00	-2.40	6.80
FQXu	3.77	0.89	1.00	5.00	120	4.00	3.00	-0.95	1.08
FQX-	1.95	1.04	1.00	7.00	120	2.00	2.00	3.71	16.47
FQXNone	0.43	[0.26]	0.00	2.00	42	0.00	0.00	2.65	7.43
MQ+	0.10	0.30	0.00	1.00	5	0.00	0.00	7.45	45.23
MQo	3.21	1.52	1.00	5.00	120	3.00	5.00	-0.33	-1.26
MQu	0.67	0.51	0.00	2.00	78	1.00	1.00	-0.32	-1.01
MQ-	0.22	[0.41]	0.00	1.00	26	0.00	0.00	1.39	-0.06
MQNone	0.02	[0.13]	0.00	1.00	2	0.00	0.00	7.65	57.43
S-	0.57	[0.62]	0.00	3.00	63	1.00	1.00	1.02	2.14
M	4.21	2.06	1.00	7.00	120	4.00	4.00	-0.22	-1.07
FM	5.02	1.66	0.00	9.00	118	6.00	4.00	-1.34	1.64
m	1.00	0.45	0.00	3.00	112	1.00	1.00	2.26	12.57
FM+m	6.02	1.70	1.00	9.00	120	7.00	7.00	-1.44	1.83
FC	2.87	1.17	0.00	4.00	106	3.00	3.00	-1.61	1.77
CF	3.14	1.40	0.00	5.00	112	3.00	3.00	-0.55	-0.30
C	0.39	[0.13]	0.00	1.00	38	0.00	0.00	1.65	7.43
Cn	0.00	[0.00]	0.00	0.00	0	0.00	0.00	----	----
FC+CF+C+Cn	6.03	2.29	0.00	8.00	119	7.00	7.00	-1.49	1.26
WSum C	4.05	1.78	0.00	6.50	120	5.00	6.50	-1.17	0.69
Sum C'	1.08	[0.88]	0.00	3.00	99	1.00	1.00	0.38	-0.47
Sum T	0.88	[0.32]	0.00	1.00	106	1.00	1.00	-2.42	3.91
Sum V	0.07	[0.36]	0.00	2.00	4	0.00	0.00	5.27	26.16
Sum Y	1.01	[0.67]	0.00	2.00	108	2.00	2.00	-1.04	-0.13
SumShd	3.74	1.37	0.00	6.00	114	4.00	4.00	-0.98	1.25
Fr+rF	0.20	[0.13]	0.00	1.00	15	0.00	0.00	3.65	17.43
FD	1.48	[0.83]	0.00	2.00	94	2.00	2.00	-1.11	-0.61
F	5.84	1.65	5.00	13.00	120	5.00	5.00	2.75	7.47
PAIR	9.09	1.89	1.00	10.00	120	10.00	10.00	-2.89	9.00
3r(2)/R	0.54	0.08	0.10	0.50	120	0.55	0.50	-3.53	16.28
LAMBDA	0.66	0.58	0.29	4.25	120	0.70	0.50	5.18	30.28
EA	8.26	2.38	1.00	12.00	120	8.50	7.00	-1.38	1.99
es	8.97	2.59	1.00	13.00	120	8.00	6.00	-2.08	3.95
D	-0.21	0.53	-2.00	1.00	120	0.00	0.00	-1.17	2.25
AdjD	-0.11	0.67	-2.00	2.00	120	0.00	0.00	-0.04	1.74
a (active)	6.53	1.45	2.00	8.00	120	7.00	6.00	-1.34	2.04
p (passive)	4.00	2.01	0.00	8.00	118	3.00	2.00	0.50	-0.57
Ma	2.47	0.80	0.00	4.00	118	2.00	2.00	0.32	0.24
Mp	1.73	1.60	0.00	5.00	92	2.00	2.00	-0.06	-1.04
Intellect	1.05	0.59	0.00	4.00	120	1.00	1.00	2.96	12.69
Zf	13.14	1.96	5.00	16.00	120	14.00	14.00	-2.25	6.48
Zd	1.67	2.11	-4.50	5.00	120	1.50	1.50	-0.24	-0.26
Blends	6.67	2.29	0.00	9.00	118	7.00	8.00	-1.79	2.12
Col Shd Bl	0.05	[0.22]	0.00	1.00	6	0.00	0.00	4.18	15.75
Afr	0.65	0.11	0.21	0.67	120	0.69	0.67	-0.80	0.75
Popular	6.22	1.10	2.00	7.00	120	7.00	6.00	-1.53	2.56

TABLE 23. 12 YEAR OLDS (N = 120)

VARIABLE	MEAN	SD	MIN	MAX	FREQ	MEDIAN	MODE	SK	KU
XA%	0.90	0.06	0.59	0.95	120	0.91	0.91	-4.09	18.15
WDA%	0.93	0.05	0.67	1.00	120	0.95	0.95	-3.57	14.97
X+%	0.75	0.09	0.29	0.88	120	0.77	0.77	-3.32	14.09
X-%	0.10	0.06	0.05	0.41	120	0.09	0.09	4.04	19.33
Xu%	0.15	0.05	0.05	0.29	120	0.15	0.14	-0.27	2.29
Isolate/R	0.15	0.04	0.00	0.33	118	0.16	0.18	0.18	5.42
H	3.38	1.64	1.00	5.00	120	3.00	5.00	-0.36	-1.42
(H)	1.24	0.84	0.00	4.00	97	1.00	1.00	0.38	0.53
HD	0.59	0.69	0.00	3.00	61	1.00	0.00	1.36	2.75
(Hd)	0.78	0.41	0.00	1.00	94	1.00	1.00	-1.39	-0.06
Hx	0.00	[0.00]	0.00	0.00	0	0.00	0.00	----	----
All H Cont	6.00	2.56	2.00	11.00	120	5.00	5.00	-0.23	-1.18
A	7.70	1.29	4.00	13.00	120	8.00	7.00	0.65	4.48
(A)	0.48	[0.50]	0.00	1.00	57	0.00	0.00	0.10	-2.02
Ad	1.97	[0.45]	0.00	3.00	116	2.00	2.00	-2.43	11.96
(Ad)	0.00	[0.00]	0.00	0.00	0	0.00	0.00	----	----
An	1.14	[0.60]	0.00	2.00	106	1.00	1.00	-0.05	-0.27
Art	0.92	0.28	0.00	1.00	110	1.00	1.00	-3.05	7.45
Ay	0.03	[0.18]	0.00	1.00	4	0.00	0.00	5.26	26.16
Bl	0.26	[0.44]	0.00	1.00	31	0.00	0.00	1.11	-0.76
Bt	1.52	0.65	0.00	2.00	110	2.00	2.00	-1.03	-0.03
Cg	1.90	1.06	0.00	4.00	116	1.00	1.00	0.11	-1.63
Cl	0.02	[0.13]	0.00	1.00	2	0.00	0.00	7.64	57.43
Ex	0.00	[0.00]	0.00	0.00	0	0.00	0.00	----	----
Fi	0.97	[0.26]	0.00	2.00	114	1.00	1.00	-1.61	12.13
Food	0.87	[0.34]	0.00	1.00	104	1.00	1.00	-2.18	2.82
Ge	0.02	[0.13]	0.00	1.00	2	0.00	0.00	7.64	57.43
Hh	0.88	0.32	0.00	1.00	106	1.00	1.00	-2.41	3.91
Ls	1.36	0.61	0.00	2.00	112	1.00	1.00	-0.36	-0.65
Na	0.10	[0.35]	0.00	2.00	10	0.00	0.00	3.78	14.82
Sc	2.48	[0.87]	0.00	3.00	112	3.00	3.00	-1.71	2.12
Sx	0.02	[0.13]	0.00	1.00	2	0.00	0.00	7.64	57.43
Xy	0.00	[0.00]	0.00	0.00	0	0.00	0.00	----	----
Idio	0.15	0.51	0.00	3.00	12	0.00	0.00	4.02	17.31
DV	1.21	[0.55]	0.00	2.00	112	1.00	1.00	0.08	-0.13
INCOM	1.35	[0.58]	0.00	3.00	116	1.00	1.00	0.34	-0.10
DR	0.24	[0.43]	0.00	1.00	29	0.00	0.00	1.22	-0.52
FABCOM	0.26	[0.53]	0.00	2.00	26	0.00	0.00	1.95	2.99
DV2	0.03	[0.16]	0.00	1.00	3	0.00	0.00	6.16	36.58
INC2	0.18	[0.56]	0.00	3.00	13	0.00	0.00	3.54	12.65
DR2	0.03	[0.16]	0.00	1.00	3	0.00	0.00	6.16	36.58
FAB2	0.04	[0.20]	0.00	1.00	5	0.00	0.00	4.64	19.91
ALOG	0.00	[0.00]	0.00	0.00	0	0.00	0.00	----	----
CONTAM	0.00	0.00	0.00	0.00	0	0.00	0.00	----	----
Sum 6 Sp Sc	3.33	1.11	1.00	8.00	120	4.00	4.00	0.82	3.59
Lvl 2 Sp Sc	0.27	[0.68]	0.00	4.00	22	0.00	0.00	3.47	14.41
WSum6	6.86	3.85	2.00	26.00	120	7.00	3.00	2.32	9.04
AB	0.05	[0.22]	0.00	1.00	6	0.00	0.00	4.18	15.75
AG	1.08	0.66	0.00	2.00	99	1.00	1.00	-0.08	-0.65
COP	1.23	0.53	0.00	2.00	114	1.00	1.00	0.17	-0.19
CP	0.00	[0.00]	0.00	0.00	0	0.00	0.00	----	----
GOODHR	5.77	1.84	2.00	8.00	120	6.00	6.00	-0.65	-0.89
POORHR	1.01	0.98	0.00	7.00	97	1.00	1.00	3.97	22.18
MOR	0.17	[0.37]	0.00	1.00	20	0.00	0.00	1.81	1.30
PER	0.93	0.36	0.00	2.00	108	1.00	1.00	-0.88	4.40
PSV	0.03	[0.18]	0.00	1.00	4	0.00	0.00	5.26	26.16

NOTE: Standard Deviations shown in brackets indicate that the value is probably unreliable and/or misleading and should not be used to estimate expected ranges. Ordinarily these variables should not be included in most parametric analyses.

TABLE 23. 13 YEAR OLDS (N = 110)

VARIABLE	MEAN	SD	MIN	MAX	FREQ	MEDIAN	MODE	SK	KU
R	21.20	3.30	14.00	33.00	110	20.00	20.00	1.07	3.51
W	8.57	2.15	1.00	14.00	110	9.00	9.00	-1.07	3.04
D	11.15	3.09	1.00	21.00	110	11.00	12.00	-0.25	3.08
Dd	1.46	[1.66]	0.00	6.00	93	1.00	1.00	2.74	7.81
S	1.33	[1.16]	0.00	7.00	106	2.00	1.00	1.93	5.93
DQ+	7.70	2.54	2.00	15.00	110	8.00	8.00	0.24	1.27
DQo	12.40	2.02	8.00	20.00	110	12.00	12.00	0.73	2.74
DQv	0.45	[0.99]	0.00	4.00	24	0.00	0.00	2.31	4.70
DQv/+	0.24	[0.57]	0.00	2.00	18	0.00	0.00	2.33	4.18
FQX+	0.20	0.59	0.00	3.00	14	0.00	0.00	3.25	10.63
FQXo	15.24	3.04	5.00	23.00	110	15.00	17.00	-0.70	2.09
FQXu	3.27	1.53	0.00	8.00	106	3.00	3.00	0.42	1.24
FQX-	2.00	1.42	0.00	7.00	108	2.00	2.00	2.15	4.81
FQXNone	0.07	[0.32]	0.00	2.00	6	0.00	0.00	4.81	23.90
MQ+	0.13	0.43	0.00	2.00	10	0.00	0.00	3.52	11.76
MQo	3.23	1.66	1.00	8.00	110	3.00	5.00	0.34	-0.38
MQu	0.54	0.66	0.00	3.00	51	0.00	0.00	1.23	2.00
MQ-	0.14	[0.51]	0.00	2.00	12	0.00	0.00	2.08	3.61
MQNone	0.02	[0.13]	0.00	1.00	2	0.00	0.00	7.31	52.42
S-	0.52	[0.81]	0.00	4.00	43	0.00	0.00	2.16	5.84
M	4.14	2.24	1.00	11.00	110	4.00	4.00	0.50	-0.01
FM	4.42	1.94	0.00	8.00	108	4.00	6.00	-0.25	-0.89
m	1.25	0.94	0.00	5.00	98	1.00	1.00	1.88	4.46
FM+m	5.67	2.10	1.00	11.00	110	6.00	7.00	-0.28	-0.34
FC	2.95	1.72	0.00	9.00	96	3.00	3.00	0.42	1.72
CF	2.70	1.50	0.00	5.00	102	3.00	3.00	-0.07	-0.98
C	0.07	[0.26]	0.00	1.00	8	0.00	0.00	3.34	9.30
Cn	0.00	[0.00]	0.00	0.00	0	0.00	0.00	----	----
FC+CF+C+Cn	5.73	2.61	0.00	10.00	110	6.50	8.00	-0.71	-0.33
WSum C	4.29	1.94	0.00	7.50	110	4.75	6.50	-0.61	-0.49
Sum C'	1.20	[0.89]	0.00	3.00	87	1.00	1.00	0.48	-0.37
Sum T	0.97	[0.51]	0.00	3.00	90	1.00	1.00	0.64	4.99
Sum V	0.14	[0.48]	0.00	2.00	10	0.00	0.00	3.31	9.70
Sum Y	1.02	[0.81]	0.00	2.00	80	1.00	2.00	-0.22	-1.44
SumShd	3.34	1.44	0.00	6.00	104	4.00	4.00	-0.55	-0.07
Fr+rF	0.45	[0.23]	0.00	1.00	32	0.00	0.00	2.98	4.08
FD	1.27	[0.87]	0.00	3.00	82	2.00	2.00	-0.39	-1.25
F	6.90	2.52	3.00	13.00	110	6.00	5.00	0.93	-0.20
PAIR	8.64	2.30	1.00	14.00	110	9.50	10.00	-1.18	2.59
3r(2)/R	0.49	0.10	0.20	0.66	110	0.48	0.50	-1.84	4.97
LAMBDA	0.67	0.61	0.20	4.33	110	0.38	0.33	4.44	24.00
EA	8.43	2.69	1.00	15.00	110	9.00	7.50	-0.60	0.64
es	9.01	3.01	1.00	14.00	110	10.00	8.00	-0.83	-0.02
D	-0.09	0.82	-2.00	3.00	110	0.00	0.00	0.78	3.45
AdjD	0.10	0.84	-2.00	3.00	110	0.00	0.00	0.74	2.06
a (active)	6.23	1.89	2.00	11.00	110	6.00	6.00	-0.34	0.13
p (passive)	3.61	2.11	0.00	8.00	104	3.00	3.00	0.45	-0.49
Ma	2.49	1.30	0.00	8.00	106	2.00	2.00	1.80	6.06
Mp	1.67	1.44	0.00	5.00	84	2.00	2.00	0.12	-0.80
Intellect	1.22	0.95	0.00	4.00	110	1.00	1.00	1.24	1.45
Zf	12.64	3.02	5.00	23.00	110	13.00	11.00	0.05	2.17
Zd	1.37	2.27	-4.50	5.00	110	1.50	-0.50	-0.35	-0.40
Blends	5.81	2.43	0.00	9.00	108	7.00	7.00	-0.90	-0.34
Col Shd Blend	0.16	[0.37]	0.00	1.00	18	0.00	0.00	1.84	1.42s
Afr	0.69	0.15	0.28	1.00	110	0.58	0.67	0.10	0.52
Popular	6.19	1.34	2.00	9.00	110	7.00	6.00	-0.59	0.79

TABLE 23. 13 YEAR OLDS (N = 110)

VARIABLE	MEAN	SD	MIN	MAX	FREQ	MEDIAN	MODE	SK	KU
XA%	0.90	0.07	0.59	1.00	110	0.91	0.91	-2.84	9.41
WDA%	0.92	0.06	0.67	1.00	110	0.95	0.95	-2.55	8.57
X+%	0.74	0.11	0.29	1.00	110	0.77	0.77	-1.86	5.39
X-%	0.10	0.07	0.00	0.41	108	0.09	0.09	2.66	8.99
Xu%	0.16	0.07	0.00	0.33	106	0.15	0.14	-0.02	0.76
Isolate/R	0.16	0.06	0.00	0.33	108	0.16	0.18	0.58	1.30
H	3.09	1.72	1.00	8.00	110	3.00	5.00	0.41	-0.57
(H)	1.25	1.02	0.00	5.00	84	1.00	1.00	1.06	2.35
HD	0.68	0.83	0.00	3.00	55	0.50	0.00	1.23	1.11
(Hd)	0.56	0.53	0.00	2.00	60	1.00	1.00	0.11	-1.21
Hx	0.00	[0.00]	0.00	0.00	0	0.00	0.00	----	----
All H Cont	5.59	2.46	2.00	11.00	110	5.00	5.00	0.12	-1.03
A	7.96	1.81	4.00	13.00	110	8.00	7.00	0.62	0.65
(A)	0.37	[0.49]	0.00	1.00	41	0.00	0.00	0.53	-1.75
Ad	2.00	[0.81]	0.00	4.00	106	2.00	2.00	0.41	1.71
(Ad)	0.00	[0.00]	0.00	0.00	0	0.00	0.00	----	----
An	0.84	[0.69]	0.00	2.00	74	1.00	1.00	0.21	-0.89
Art	0.86	0.48	0.00	2.00	88	1.00	1.00	-0.36	0.78
Ay	0.11	[0.31]	0.00	1.00	12	0.00	0.00	2.54	4.55
Bl	0.19	[0.40]	0.00	1.00	21	0.00	0.00	1.59	0.55
Bt	1.74	0.98	0.00	5.00	98	2.00	2.00	0.43	1.35
Cg	1.62	1.10	0.00	4.00	98	1.00	1.00	0.47	-0.93
Cl	0.06	[0.23]	0.00	1.00	6	0.00	0.00	3.97	14.08
Ex	0.09	[0.29]	0.00	1.00	10	0.00	0.00	2.88	6.44
Fi	0.76	[0.54]	0.00	2.00	78	1.00	1.00	-0.11	-0.23
Food	0.62	[0.52]	0.00	2.00	66	1.00	1.00	-0.10	-1.15
Ge	0.04	[0.19]	0.00	1.00	4	0.00	0.00	5.02	23.65
Hh	1.07	0.81	0.00	4.00	90	1.00	1.00	1.34	2.87
Ls	1.10	0.97	0.00	6.00	84	1.00	1.00	2.27	10.32
Na	0.22	[0.50]	0.00	2.00	20	0.00	0.00	2.25	4.39
Sc	1.97	[1.14]	0.00	5.00	96	2.00	3.00	-0.17	-0.48
Sx	0.07	[0.42]	0.00	3.00	4	0.00	0.00	6.42	42.22
Xy	0.00	[0.00]	0.00	0.00	0	0.00	0.00	----	----
Idio	0.78	1.14	0.00	4.00	44	0.00	0.00	1.26	0.28
DV	1.01	[0.70]	0.00	3.00	86	1.00	1.00	0.31	0.06
INCOM	1.07	[0.79]	0.00	3.00	84	1.00	1.00	0.33	-0.33
DR	0.30	[0.66]	0.00	4.00	27	0.00	0.00	3.54	16.72
FABCOM	0.42	[0.71]	0.00	3.00	34	0.00	0.00	1.71	2.45
DV2	0.02	[0.13]	0.00	1.00	2	0.00	0.00	7.31	52.43
INC2	0.22	[0.60]	0.00	3.00	16	0.00	0.00	3.06	9.49
DR2	0.04	[0.19]	0.00	1.00	4	0.00	0.00	5.02	23.65
FAB2	0.07	[0.32]	0.00	2.00	6	0.00	0.00	4.81	23.91
ALOG	0.04	[0.19]	0.00	1.00	4	0.00	0.00	5.02	23.65
CONTAM	0.00	0.00	0.00	0.00	0	0.00	0.00	----	----
Sum 6 Sp Sc	3.18	1.86	0.00	11.00	108	3.00	2.00	2.01	6.04
Lvl 2 Sp Sc	0.35	[0.77]	0.00	4.00	24	0.00	0.00	2.73	8.42
WSum6	7.54	6.99	0.00	40.00	108	6.00	3.00	2.88	9.56
AB	0.13	[0.34]	0.00	1.00	14	0.00	0.00	2.26	3.20
AG	1.18	0.91	0.00	4.00	85	1.00	1.00	0.66	0.48
COP	1.65	1.22	0.00	6.00	100	1.00	1.00	1.58	3.11
CP	0.02	[0.13]	0.00	1.00	2	0.00	0.00	7.31	52.43
GOODHR	5.24	1.89	1.00	8.00	110	6.00	6.00	-0.25	-1.04
POORHR	1.31	1.21	0.00	7.00	88	1.00	1.00	2.16	7.57
MOR	0.49	[0.74]	0.00	3.00	40	0.00	0.00	1.42	1.38
PER	1.05	0.89	0.00	5.00	90	1.00	1.00	2.30	7.82
PSV	0.06	[0.23]	0.00	1.00	6	0.00	0.00	3.97	14.08

NOTE: Standard Deviations shown in brackets indicate that the value is probably unreliable and/or misleading and should not be used to estimate expected ranges. Ordinarily these variables should not be included in most parametric analyses.

TABLE 23. 14 YEAR OLDS (N = 105)

VARIABLE	MEAN	SD	MIN	MAX	FREQ	MEDIAN	MODE	SK	KU
R	21.72	3.36	14.00	33.00	105	20.00	20.00	1.11	3.43
W	8.92	2.19	4.00	14.00	105	9.00	9.00	-1.01	2.83
D	11.13	3.16	1.00	21.00	105	11.00	10.00	-0.23	2.82
Dd	1.67	[1.70]	0.00	6.00	98	2.00	1.00	2.67	7.31
S	1.32	[1.09]	0.00	7.00	101	2.00	2.00	1.89	5.56
DQ+	7.81	2.55	2.00	15.00	105	8.00	8.00	0.33	1.36
DQo	12.69	2.06	8.00	20.00	105	12.00	12.00	0.73	2.58
DQv	0.58	[1.01]	0.00	4.00	27	0.00	0.00	2.23	4.30
DQv/+	0.65	[0.58]	0.00	2.00	48	0.00	0.00	2.25	3.79
FQX+	0.14	0.50	0.00	2.00	11	0.00	0.00	3.16	9.97
FQXo	15.17	3.09	5.00	23.00	105	15.00	15.00	-0.64	1.93
FQXu	3.27	1.56	0.00	8.00	101	3.00	3.00	0.42	1.10
FQX-	1.84	1.25	0.00	5.00	103	2.00	2.00	2.10	4.46
FQXNone	0.02	[0.53]	0.00	1.00	4	0.00	0.00	4.69	22.65
MQ+	0.11	0.44	0.00	2.00	6	0.00	0.00	3.42	11.04
MQo	3.21	1.66	1.00	8.00	105	3.00	1.00	0.43	-0.26
MQu	0.51	0.67	0.00	3.00	46	0.00	0.00	1.34	2.18
MQ-	0.13	[0.50]	0.00	2.00	11	0.00	0.00	2.18	4.01
MQNone	0.00	[0.00]	0.00	0.00	0	0.00	0.00	----	----
S-	0.39	[0.82]	0.00	3.00	31	0.00	0.00	2.24	6.00
M	4.06	2.24	1.00	11.00	105	4.00	4.00	0.59	0.16
FM	4.35	1.96	0.00	8.00	103	4.00	6.00	-0.17	-0.92
m	1.27	0.96	0.00	5.00	93	1.00	1.00	1.81	4.08
FM+m	5.62	2.14	1.00	11.00	105	6.00	7.00	-0.21	-0.42
FC	2.93	1.76	0.00	9.00	91	3.00	3.00	0.45	1.59
CF	2.70	1.53	0.00	5.00	97	3.00	3.00	-0.08	-1.05
C	0.10	[0.27]	0.00	1.00	9	0.00	0.00	3.14	7.67
Cn	0.00	[0.00]	0.00	0.00	0	0.00	0.00	----	----
FC+CF+C+Cn	5.71	2.67	1.00	10.00	105	7.00	8.00	-0.69	-0.44
WSum C	4.29	1.98	0.50	7.50	105	5.00	6.50	-0.60	-0.58
Sum C'	1.11	[0.91]	0.00	3.00	82	1.00	1.00	0.44	-0.50
Sum T	0.99	[0.52]	0.00	3.00	85	1.00	1.00	0.66	4.71
Sum V	0.13	[0.50]	0.00	2.00	8	0.00	0.00	3.21	9.06
Sum Y	0.88	[0.84]	0.00	2.00	75	1.00	2.00	-0.14	-1.44
SumShd	3.10	1.47	0.00	6.00	99	4.00	4.00	-0.49	-0.19
Fr+rF	0.38	[0.43]	0.00	1.00	15	0.00	0.00	3.97	10.25
FD	1.24	[0.87]	0.00	3.00	71	1.00	2.00	-0.31	-1.30
F	6.96	2.56	3.00	13.00	105	6.00	5.00	0.87	-0.35
PAIR	8.59	2.34	1.00	14.00	105	9.00	10.00	-1.12	2.38
3r(2)/R	0.47	0.10	0.05	0.56	105	0.45	0.50	-1.79	4.60
LAMBDA	0.67	0.62	0.20	4.33	105	0.38	0.33	4.34	22.96
EA	8.34	2.70	1.00	15.00	105	9.00	7.50	-0.55	0.60
es	8.92	3.06	1.00	13.00	105	9.00	9.00	-0.76	-0.15
D	-0.09	0.84	-2.00	3.00	105	0.00	0.00	0.78	3.19
AdjD	0.09	0.86	-2.00	3.00	105	0.00	0.00	0.74	1.95
a (active)	6.20	1.92	2.00	11.00	105	6.00	7.00	-0.32	0.06
p (passive)	3.49	2.07	0.00	8.00	99	3.00	3.00	0.52	-0.35
Ma	2.59	1.32	0.00	8.00	101	2.00	2.00	1.81	5.93
Mp	1.49	1.36	0.00	5.00	89	2.00	2.00	0.17	-0.74
Intellect	1.23	0.97	0.00	4.00	105	1.00	1.00	1.18	1.22
Zf	12.56	3.06	5.00	23.00	105	13.00	14.00	0.12	2.11
Zd	1.27	2.26	-4.50	5.00	105	1.50	-0.50	-0.30	-0.38
Blends	5.74	2.46	0.00	9.00	103	7.00	7.00	-0.84	-0.47
Col Shd Blend	0.17	[0.38]	0.00	1.00	18	0.00	0.00	1.77	1.15
Afr	0.69	0.16	0.31	0.89	105	0.68	0.67	0.03	0.47
Popular	6.02	1.17	3.00	9.00	105	7.00	6.00	-0.53	0.67

TABLE 23. 14 YEAR OLDS (N = 105)

VARIABLE	MEAN	SD	MIN	MAX	FREQ	MEDIAN	MODE	SK	KU
XA%	0.90	0.07	0.59	1.00	105	0.91	0.91	-2.76	8.82
WDA%	0.92	0.06	0.67	1.00	105	0.94	0.95	-2.48	8.09
X+%	0.74	0.12	0.29	1.00	105	0.77	0.75	-1.80	5.01
X-%	0.10	0.07	0.00	0.41	103	0.09	0.05	2.59	8.43
Xu%	0.16	0.07	0.00	0.33	101	0.15	0.14	-0.03	0.61
Isolate/R	0.16	0.06	0.00	0.33	103	0.16	0.16	0.59	1.15
H	3.00	1.71	1.00	8.00	105	3.00	1.00	0.54	-0.35
(H)	1.23	1.03	0.00	5.00	79	1.00	1.00	1.13	2.44
HD	0.67	0.85	0.00	3.00	50	0.00	0.00	1.27	1.07
(Hd)	0.56	0.54	0.00	2.00	57	1.00	1.00	0.13	-1.19
Hx	0.00	[0.00]	0.00	0.00	0	0.00	0.00	----	----
All H Cont	5.46	2.44	2.00	11.00	105	5.00	5.00	0.22	-0.91
A	7.97	1.85	4.00	13.00	105	8.00	7.00	0.60	0.49
(A)	0.39	[0.49]	0.00	1.00	41	0.00	0.00	0.45	-1.83
Ad	2.00	[0.83]	0.00	4.00	101	2.00	2.00	0.40	1.50
(Ad)	0.00	[0.00]	0.00	0.00	0	0.00	0.00	----	----
An	0.84	[0.71]	0.00	2.00	69	1.00	1.00	0.24	-0.97
Art	0.85	0.50	0.00	2.00	83	1.00	1.00	-0.31	0.62
Ay	0.11	[0.32]	0.00	1.00	12	0.00	0.00	2.46	4.13
Bl	0.20	[0.40]	0.00	1.00	21	0.00	0.00	1.52	0.32
Bt	1.73	1.00	0.00	5.00	93	2.00	2.00	0.44	1.22
Cg	1.55	1.08	0.00	4.00	93	1.00	1.00	0.60	-0.69
Cl	0.06	[0.23]	0.00	1.00	6	0.00	0.00	3.87	13.24
Ex	0.10	[0.30]	0.00	1.00	10	0.00	0.00	2.79	5.94
Fi	0.75	[0.55]	0.00	2.00	73	1.00	1.00	-0.05	-0.32
Food	0.60	[0.53]	0.00	2.00	61	1.00	1.00	-0.01	-1.16
Ge	0.04	[0.19]	0.00	1.00	4	0.00	0.00	4.89	22.40
Hh	1.08	0.83	0.00	4.00	85	1.00	1.00	1.30	2.59
Ls	1.06	0.97	0.00	6.00	79	1.00	1.00	2.46	11.28
Na	0.23	[0.51]	0.00	2.00	20	0.00	0.00	2.17	4.01
Sc	1.93	[1.15]	0.00	5.00	91	2.00	3.00	-0.10	-0.48
Sx	0.08	[0.43]	0.00	3.00	4	0.00	0.00	6.27	40.17
Xy	0.00	[0.00]	0.00	0.00	0	0.00	0.00	----	----
Idio	0.82	1.16	0.00	4.00	44	0.00	0.00	1.19	0.11
DV	0.98	[0.69]	0.00	3.00	81	1.00	1.00	0.37	0.22
INCOM	1.05	[0.79]	0.00	3.00	79	1.00	1.00	0.39	-0.24
DR	0.30	[0.66]	0.00	4.00	25	0.00	0.00	3.60	16.99
FABCOM	0.44	[0.72]	0.00	3.00	34	0.00	0.00	1.64	2.19
DV2	0.02	[0.14]	0.00	1.00	2	0.00	0.00	7.13	49.92
INC2	0.22	[0.60]	0.00	3.00	15	0.00	0.00	3.06	9.40
DR2	0.03	[0.17]	0.00	1.00	3	0.00	0.00	5.74	31.57
FAB2	0.08	[0.33]	0.00	2.00	6	0.00	0.00	4.69	22.65
ALOG	0.04	[0.19]	0.00	1.00	4	0.00	0.00	4.89	22.40
CONTAM	0.00	0.00	0.00	0.00	0	0.00	0.00	----	----
Sum 6 Sp Sc	3.14	1.90	0.00	11.00	103	3.00	2.00	2.06	5.97
Lvl 2 Sp Sc	0.34	[0.78]	0.00	4.00	22	0.00	0.00	2.74	8.37
WSum6	7.52	7.14	0.00	40.00	103	6.00	3.00	2.84	9.12
AB	0.13	[0.34]	0.00	1.00	14	0.00	0.00	2.18	2.84
AG	1.20	0.92	0.00	4.00	81	1.00	1.00	0.63	0.36
COP	1.65	1.24	0.00	6.00	95	1.00	1.00	1.56	2.91
CP	0.02	[0.14]	0.00	1.00	2	0.00	0.00	7.13	49.92
GOODHR	5.14	1.87	1.00	8.00	105	6.00	6.00	-0.19	-1.03
POORHR	1.32	1.24	0.00	7.00	83	1.00	1.00	2.09	7.06
MOR	0.51	[0.75]	0.00	3.00	40	0.00	0.00	1.35	1.17
PER	1.06	0.91	0.00	5.00	85	1.00	1.00	2.24	7.32
PSV	0.06	[0.23]	0.00	1.00	6	0.00	0.00	3.87	13.24

NOTE: Standard Deviations shown in brackets indicate that the value is probably unreliable and/or misleading and should not be used to estimate expected ranges. Ordinarily these variables should not be included in most parametric analyses.

TABLE 23. 15 YEAR OLDS (N = 110)

VARIABLE	MEAN	SD	MIN	MAX	FREQ	MEDIAN	MODE	SK	KU
R	21.94	4.21	14.00	32.00	110	21.00	20.00	0.94	1.14
W	8.87	2.20	3.00	20.00	110	9.00	9.00	1.57	9.58
D	11.42	3.66	0.00	20.00	109	12.00	12.00	-0.31	1.91
Dd	1.65	[1.31]	0.00	7.00	91	1.00	1.00	1.31	3.76
S	1.44	[1.31]	0.00	5.00	104	2.00	1.00	2.66	12.86
DQ+	7.88	2.02	2.00	13.00	110	8.00	8.00	-0.33	0.15
DQo	12.67	3.62	5.00	29.00	110	12.00	12.00	1.49	5.43
DQv	0.75	[1.29]	0.00	4.00	40	0.00	0.00	1.84	2.46
DQv/+	0.14	[0.42]	0.00	2.00	12	0.00	0.00	3.22	10.13
FQX+	0.36	0.70	0.00	3.00	27	0.00	0.00	1.81	2.20
FQXo	16.35	3.34	7.00	29.00	110	16.00	15.00	0.60	2.79
FQXu	3.08	1.57	0.00	11.00	108	3.00	3.00	1.37	5.75
FQX-	1.60	0.91	0.00	6.00	99	2.00	2.00	0.81	3.89
FQXNone	0.04	[0.25]	0.00	2.00	4	0.00	0.00	6.07	39.81
MQ+	0.25	0.57	0.00	3.00	22	0.00	0.00	2.46	6.34
MQo	3.54	2.01	0.00	8.00	108	3.00	1.00	0.20	-0.91
MQu	0.44	0.52	0.00	2.00	48	0.00	0.00	0.43	-1.36
MQ-	0.12	[0.32]	0.00	1.00	13	0.00	0.00	2.40	3.82
MQNone	0.00	[0.00]	0.00	0.00	0	0.00	0.00	----	----
S-	0.38	[0.57]	0.00	2.00	37	0.00	0.00	1.22	0.52
M	4.35	2.17	1.00	9.00	110	4.00	4.00	0.06	-0.97
FM	4.82	1.73	1.00	9.00	110	5.00	6.00	-0.20	-0.80
m	1.17	0.78	0.00	4.00	97	1.00	1.00	1.49	3.79
FM+m	5.99	1.78	2.00	10.00	110	6.00	7.00	-0.14	-0.67
FC	3.14	1.14	0.00	6.00	107	3.00	3.00	-0.56	0.76
CF	2.85	1.53	0.00	6.00	101	3.00	2.00	-0.11	-0.73
C	0.03	[0.16]	0.00	1.00	3	0.00	0.00	5.88	33.24
Cn	0.02	[0.13]	0.00	1.00	2	0.00	0.00	7.31	52.42
FC+CF+C+Cn	6.04	2.01	1.00	10.00	110	7.00	8.00	-0.62	-0.37
WSum C	4.47	1.68	0.50	8.00	110	4.50	3.50	-0.33	-0.64
Sum C'	1.63	[1.35]	0.00	10.00	94	1.00	1.00	2.49	12.61
Sum T	1.06	[0.51]	0.00	3.00	101	1.00	1.00	2.62	13.12
Sum V	0.18	[0.49]	0.00	2.00	12	0.00	0.00	2.75	6.73
Sum Y	1.30	[1.27]	0.00	10.00	83	1.00	2.00	3.35	20.69
SumShd	4.17	2.55	0.00	23.00	109	4.00	4.00	4.04	27.31
Fr+rF	0.50	[0.45]	0.00	2.00	26	0.00	0.00	6.67	53.57
FD	1.33	[0.97]	0.00	5.00	83	1.50	2.00	0.35	0.78
F	6.48	2.71	2.00	17.00	110	5.00	5.00	1.31	2.02
PAIR	9.10	2.00	1.00	14.00	110	10.00	10.00	-1.37	4.47
3r(2)/R	0.44	0.10	0.05	0.79	110	0.45	0.50	-0.58	4.63
LAMBDA	0.65	0.22	0.14	1.71	110	0.36	0.33	2.27	8.94
EA	8.82	2.34	2.00	13.50	110	9.50	9.50	-0.69	0.39
es	9.16	3.40	4.00	17.00	110	10.00	9.00	2.13	12.31
D	-0.45	1.39	-10.00	2.00	110	0.00	0.00	-3.73	20.85
AdjD	-0.25	1.07	-5.00	2.00	110	0.00	0.00	-1.71	5.14
a (active)	6.99	1.73	3.00	12.00	110	7.00	8.00	0.18	0.32
p (passive)	3.36	1.93	0.00	9.00	106	3.00	3.00	0.75	0.31
Ma	2.58	1.44	1.00	7.00	110	2.00	2.00	0.96	0.38
Mp	1.77	1.46	0.00	5.00	81	2.00	2.00	0.48	-0.51
Intellect	1.04	0.83	0.00	4.00	110	1.00	1.00	1.59	3.76
Zf	12.68	2.59	5.00	23.00	110	13.00	13.00	0.01	2.61
Zd	1.03	2.96	-6.50	9.00	110	0.50	-0.50	0.17	0.11
Blends	6.34	2.16	1.00	12.00	110	7.00	7.00	-0.63	0.03
Col Shd Blend	0.22	[0.51]	0.00	2.00	19	0.00	0.00	2.35	4.69
Afr	0.65	0.18	0.27	1.29	110	0.67	0.67	0.97	1.69
Popular	6.33	1.23	3.00	9.00	110	7.00	7.00	-0.59	0.22

TABLE 23. 15 YEAR OLDS (N = 110)

VARIABLE	MEAN	SD	MIN	MAX	FREQ	MEDIAN	MODE	SK	KU
XA%	0.92	0.05	0.57	1.00	110	0.91	0.95	-3.35	23.67
WDA%	0.94	0.05	0.54	1.00	110	0.95	0.95	-4.34	32.40
X+%	0.78	0.07	0.50	1.00	110	0.77	0.75	-0.45	2.72
X-%	0.08	0.05	0.00	0.43	99	0.09	0.05	3.29	23.27
Xu%	0.14	0.06	0.00	0.37	108	0.15	0.14	0.45	1.97
Isolate/R	0.15	0.07	0.00	0.47	108	0.15	0.16	1.76	8.19
H	3.42	1.96	0.00	8.00	109	3.00	5.00	0.49	-0.51
(H)	1.05	0.90	0.00	4.00	75	1.00	1.00	0.52	-0.16
HD	0.57	0.82	0.00	4.00	48	0.00	0.00	1.96	5.02
(Hd)	0.54	0.50	0.00	1.00	59	1.00	1.00	-0.14	-2.01
Hx	0.00	[0.00]	0.00	0.00	0	0.00	0.00	----	----
All H Cont	5.57	2.28	1.00	9.00	110	5.00	5.00	-0.14	-0.95
A	7.98	1.96	3.00	15.00	110	8.00	7.00	0.54	1.91
(A)	0.36	[0.55]	0.00	3.00	37	0.00	0.00	1.55	3.35
Ad	2.08	[1.20]	0.00	9.00	102	2.00	2.00	2.25	11.70
(Ad)	0.06	[0.30]	0.00	2.00	4	0.00	0.00	5.79	34.15
An	0.93	[0.79]	0.00	3.00	73	1.00	1.00	0.24	-1.02
Art	0.86	0.63	0.00	4.00	82	1.00	1.00	1.00	4.67
Ay	0.14	[0.35]	0.00	1.00	15	0.00	0.00	2.14	2.67
Bl	0.22	[0.42]	0.00	1.00	24	0.00	0.00	1.38	-0.09
Bt	1.68	0.82	0.00	4.00	102	2.00	2.00	-0.04	-0.06
Cg	1.47	1.11	0.00	4.00	93	1.00	1.00	0.58	-0.80
Cl	0.09	[0.35]	0.00	2.00	8	0.00	0.00	4.11	17.53
Ex	0.12	[0.32]	0.00	1.00	13	0.00	0.00	2.39	3.82
Fi	0.69	[0.52]	0.00	2.00	73	1.00	1.00	-0.22	-0.72
Food	0.60	[0.51]	0.00	2.00	65	1.00	1.00	-0.20	-1.47
Ge	0.01	[0.10]	0.00	1.00	1	0.00	0.00	10.48	110.00
Hh	0.89	0.60	0.00	4.00	88	1.00	1.00	1.36	7.28
Ls	1.12	0.71	0.00	2.00	88	1.00	1.00	-0.17	-1.00
Na	0.12	[0.35]	0.00	2.00	12	0.00	0.00	3.02	9.12
Sc	1.70	[1.34]	0.00	6.00	77	2.00	3.00	0.02	-0.83
Sx	0.11	[0.44]	0.00	3.00	8	0.00	0.00	4.64	23.43
Xy	0.04	[0.19]	0.00	1.00	4	0.00	0.00	5.02	23.65
Idio	1.09	1.47	0.00	7.00	52	0.00	0.00	1.48	2.28
DV	0.98	[0.70]	0.00	3.00	84	1.00	1.00	0.34	0.03
INCOM	0.88	[0.74]	0.00	4.00	76	1.00	1.00	0.74	1.58
DR	0.13	[0.34]	0.00	1.00	14	0.00	0.00	2.26	3.20
FABCOM	0.23	[0.46]	0.00	2.00	23	0.00	0.00	1.87	2.73
DV2	0.03	[0.16]	0.00	1.00	3	0.00	0.00	5.88	33.24
INC2	0.01	[0.10]	0.00	1.00	1	0.00	0.00	10.48	110.00
DR2	0.01	[0.10]	0.00	1.00	1	0.00	0.00	10.48	110.00
FAB2	0.04	[0.19]	0.00	1.00	4	0.00	0.00	5.02	23.65
ALOG	0.06	[0.27]	0.00	2.00	5	0.00	0.00	5.36	31.19
CONTAM	0.00	0.00	0.00	0.00	0	0.00	0.00	----	----
Sum 6 Sp Sc	2.35	1.38	0.00	5.00	96	2.00	2.00	-0.19	-0.97
Lvl 2 Sp Sc	0.08	[0.28]	0.00	1.00	9	0.00	0.00	3.09	7.71
WSum6	4.71	3.33	0.00	15.00	96	4.00	3.00	0.60	0.27
AB	0.03	[0.16]	0.00	1.00	3	0.00	0.00	5.88	33.24
AG	1.15	0.91	0.00	4.00	82	1.00	1.00	0.53	-0.05
COP	1.54	0.97	0.00	5.00	98	1.00	1.00	0.74	0.98
CP	0.00	[0.00]	0.00	0.00	0	0.00	0.00	----	----
GOODHR	5.01	1.91	0.00	9.00	109	6.00	6.00	-0.38	-0.55
POORHR	1.57	1.22	0.00	6.00	75	1.00	1.00	2.00	4.33
MOR	0.54	[0.83]	0.00	4.00	41	0.00	0.00	1.73	3.06
PER	0.92	0.65	0.00	5.00	89	1.00	1.00	2.31	14.11
PSV	0.04	[0.19]	0.00	1.00	4	0.00	0.00	5.02	23.65

NOTE: Standard Deviations shown in brackets indicate that the value is probably unreliable and/or misleading and should not be used to estimate expected ranges. Ordinarily these variables should not be included in most parametric analyses.

TABLE 23. 16 YEAR OLDS (N = 140)

VARIABLE	MEAN	SD	MIN	MAX	FREQ	MEDIAN	MODE	SK	KU
R	22.89	5.16	14.00	31.00	140	21.00	20.00	0.94	1.70
W	8.96	2.37	3.00	20.00	140	9.00	9.00	1.70	8.32
D	11.91	3.74	0.00	21.00	139	12.00	12.00	-0.23	1.41
Dd	2.02	[1.82]	0.00	7.00	121	2.00	1.00	3.49	15.11
S	1.24	[1.23]	0.00	5.00	132	2.00	2.00	2.70	14.04
DQ+	7.94	2.04	2.00	13.00	140	8.00	8.00	-0.28	-0.13
DQo	13.12	3.47	5.00	27.00	140	12.00	12.00	1.23	4.58
DQv	0.89	[1.35]	0.00	5.00	59	0.00	0.00	1.59	1.62
DQv/+	0.84	[0.53]	0.00	2.00	46	0.00	0.00	2.21	3.98
FQX+	0.54	0.83	0.00	3.00	48	0.00	0.00	1.26	0.31
FQXo	16.43	3.36	7.00	29.00	140	16.00	15.00	0.59	2.16
FQXu	3.19	1.56	0.00	11.00	138	3.00	3.00	1.18	4.32
FQX-	1.58	0.91	0.00	5.00	126	2.00	2.00	0.70	2.97
FQXNone	0.06	[0.26]	0.00	2.00	7	0.00	0.00	5.01	27.20
MQ+	0.35	0.64	0.00	3.00	38	0.00	0.00	1.96	3.75
MQo	3.50	2.01	0.00	8.00	138	3.00	1.00	0.29	-0.86
MQu	0.37	0.50	0.00	2.00	51	0.00	0.00	0.71	-1.07
MQ-	0.09	[0.29]	0.00	1.00	13	0.00	0.00	2.84	6.13
MQNone	0.00	[0.00]	0.00	0.00	0	0.00	0.00	----	----
S-	0.34	[0.55]	0.00	2.00	43	0.00	0.00	1.32	0.81
M	4.31	2.13	1.00	9.00	140	4.00	4.00	0.20	-0.88
FM	4.58	1.66	1.00	9.00	140	4.00	4.00	0.04	-0.73
m	1.14	0.80	0.00	4.00	117	1.00	1.00	1.10	2.43
FM+m	5.72	1.78	2.00	10.00	140	6.00	7.00	0.03	-0.73
FC	3.43	1.34	0.00	8.00	137	3.00	3.00	0.14	1.16
CF	2.78	1.45	0.00	6.00	130	3.00	3.00	-0.05	-0.59
C	0.04	[0.20]	0.00	1.00	6	0.00	0.00	4.56	19.10
Cn	0.01	[0.12]	0.00	1.00	2	0.00	0.00	8.27	67.44
FC+CF+C+Cn	6.26	2.08	1.00	11.00	140	7.00	8.00	-0.56	-0.16
WSum C	4.56	1.66	0.50	8.00	140	5.00	3.50	-0.42	-0.49
Sum C'	1.15	[1.27]	0.00	6.00	118	1.00	1.00	2.48	13.59
Sum T	1.02	[0.48]	0.00	3.00	128	1.00	1.00	2.44	13.39
Sum V	0.19	[0.51]	0.00	2.00	20	0.00	0.00	2.64	6.03
Sum Y	1.04	[1.21]	0.00	5.00	95	2.00	1.00	3.25	20.79
SumShd	3.44	2.35	0.00	23.00	139	4.00	4.00	4.25	31.18
Fr+rF	0.48	[0.41]	0.00	3.00	32	0.00	0.00	6.27	48.14
FD	1.31	[0.93]	0.00	5.00	108	1.00	2.00	0.33	0.77
F	6.85	2.69	2.00	17.00	140	6.00	5.00	0.96	0.93
PAIR	9.04	2.00	1.00	14.00	140	9.00	10.00	-0.90	3.36
3r(2)/R	0.43	0.09	0.05	0.79	140	0.45	0.50	-0.32	3.89
LAMBDA	0.65	0.21	0.24	1.71	140	0.68	0.63	1.85	7.03
EA	8.87	2.23	2.00	13.50	140	9.00	8.50	-0.59	0.63
es	9.21	3.29	4.00	17.00	140	10.00	8.00	2.09	12.09
D	-0.31	1.31	-10.00	2.00	140	0.00	0.00	-3.70	22.64
AdjD	-0.11	1.04	-5.00	2.00	140	0.00	0.00	-1.56	5.47
a (active)	6.82	1.71	3.00	12.00	140	7.00	6.00	0.25	0.13
p (passive)	3.22	1.89	0.00	9.00	133	3.00	2.00	0.70	0.33
Ma	2.62	1.42	1.00	7.00	140	2.00	2.00	0.88	0.20
Mp	1.69	1.38	0.00	5.00	106	2.00	2.00	0.55	-0.32
Intellect	1.14	0.93	0.00	5.00	140	1.00	1.00	1.38	2.72
Zf	12.61	2.64	5.00	23.00	140	13.00	13.00	0.37	3.18
Zd	1.12	2.96	-6.50	9.00	140	0.75	-0.50	0.09	0.15
Blends	6.11	2.13	1.00	12.00	140	7.00	7.00	-0.44	-0.26
Col Shd Blends	0.24	[0.50]	0.00	2.00	28	0.00	0.00	2.08	3.56
Afr	0.65	0.17	0.27	1.29	140	0.67	0.67	0.80	1.61
Popular	6.46	1.27	3.00	10.00	140	7.00	7.00	-0.35	0.39

TABLE 23. 16 YEAR OLDS (N = 140)

VARIABLE	MEAN	SD	MIN	MAX	FREQ	MEDIAN	MODE	SK	KU
XA%	0.93	0.05	0.57	1.00	140	0.92	0.95	-3.12	22.84
WDA%	0.94	0.05	0.54	1.00	140	0.95	0.95	-3.80	29.25
X+%	0.78	0.07	0.50	1.00	140	0.78	0.75	-0.41	2.27
X-%	0.07	0.05	0.00	0.43	126	0.07	0.05	3.07	22.85
Xu%	0.15	0.06	0.00	0.37	138	0.15	0.15	0.45	1.42
Isolate/R	0.16	0.07	0.00	0.47	138	0.16	0.16	1.30	4.09
H	3.39	1.94	0.00	8.00	139	3.00	3.00	0.62	-0.28
(H)	1.07	0.89	0.00	4.00	97	1.00	1.00	0.36	-0.43
HD	0.59	0.81	0.00	4.00	62	0.00	0.00	1.79	4.08
(Hd)	0.46	0.50	0.00	1.00	64	0.00	0.00	0.17	-2.00
Hx	0.00	[0.00]	0.00	0.00	0	0.00	0.00	----	----
All H Cont	5.51	2.12	1.00	9.00	140	5.00	5.00	-0.06	-0.76
A	8.04	1.97	3.00	15.00	140	8.00	7.00	0.46	1.18
(A)	0.32	[0.54]	0.00	3.00	41	0.00	0.00	1.72	3.69
Ad	2.11	[1.15]	0.00	9.00	131	2.00	2.00	1.97	10.34
(Ad)	0.07	[0.33]	0.00	2.00	7	0.00	0.00	4.93	24.56
An	0.81	[0.79]	0.00	3.00	82	1.00	0.00	0.44	-0.97
Art	0.83	0.68	0.00	4.00	97	1.00	1.00	0.78	2.33
Ay	0.19	[0.41]	0.00	2.00	25	0.00	0.00	1.95	2.75
Bl	0.21	[0.43]	0.00	2.00	29	0.00	0.00	1.68	1.61
Bt	1.87	1.03	0.00	6.00	130	2.00	2.00	0.62	1.27
Cg	1.39	1.06	0.00	4.00	116	1.00	1.00	0.64	-0.57
Cl	0.11	[0.36]	0.00	2.00	14	0.00	0.00	3.32	11.31
Ex	0.11	[0.32]	0.00	1.00	16	0.00	0.00	2.45	4.06
Fi	0.63	[0.57]	0.00	2.00	82	1.00	1.00	0.19	-0.76
Food	0.51	[0.52]	0.00	2.00	70	0.50	0.00	0.13	-1.62
Ge	0.01	[0.12]	0.00	1.00	2	0.00	0.00	8.27	67.44
Hh	0.91	0.67	0.00	4.00	108	1.00	1.00	1.14	3.97
Ls	1.07	0.74	0.00	3.00	108	1.00	1.00	0.00	-0.87
Na	0.17	[0.42]	0.00	2.00	22	0.00	0.00	2.35	5.05
Sc	1.51	[1.31]	0.00	6.00	93	2.00	0.00	0.23	-0.82
Sx	0.11	[0.41]	0.00	3.00	11	0.00	0.00	4.57	23.67
Xy	0.04	[0.19]	0.00	1.00	5	0.00	0.00	5.05	23.93
Idiographic	1.31	1.45	0.00	7.00	81	1.00	0.00	1.07	1.04
DV	0.99	[0.71]	0.00	3.00	107	1.00	1.00	0.38	0.11
INCOM	0.83	[0.75]	0.00	4.00	91	1.00	1.00	0.81	1.34
DR	0.14	[0.37]	0.00	2.00	19	0.00	0.00	2.48	5.51
FABCOM	0.21	[0.45]	0.00	2.00	28	0.00	0.00	1.89	2.75
DV2	0.02	[0.15]	0.00	1.00	3	0.00	0.00	6.68	43.26
INC2	0.01	[0.12]	0.00	1.00	2	0.00	0.00	8.27	67.44
DR2	0.01	[0.09]	0.00	1.00	1	0.00	0.00	11.83	140.00
FAB2	0.04	[0.19]	0.00	1.00	5	0.00	0.00	5.05	23.93
ALOG	0.05	[0.25]	0.00	2.00	6	0.00	0.00	5.49	32.88
CONTAM	0.00	0.00	0.00	0.00	0	0.00	0.00	----	----
Sum 6 Sp Sc	2.30	1.34	0.00	5.00	125	2.00	2.00	-0.03	-0.92
Lvl 2 Sp Sc	0.08	[0.27]	0.00	1.00	11	0.00	0.00	3.16	8.14
WSum6	4.57	3.23	0.00	15.00	125	4.00	3.00	0.67	0.32
AB	0.06	[0.25]	0.00	1.00	9	0.00	0.00	3.59	11.06
AG	1.20	0.99	0.00	5.00	106	1.00	1.00	1.02	1.98
COP	1.60	1.10	0.00	5.00	120	1.00	1.00	0.68	0.45
CP	0.00	[0.00]	0.00	0.00	0	0.00	0.00	----	----
GOODHR	5.29	1.80	0.00	9.00	139	6.00	6.00	-0.21	-0.49
POORHR	1.16	1.29	0.00	6.00	96	1.00	1.00	1.67	2.67
MOR	0.58	[0.81]	0.00	4.00	59	0.00	0.00	1.56	2.57
PER	0.96	0.72	0.00	5.00	110	1.00	1.00	1.59	7.12
PSV	0.04	[0.20]	0.00	1.00	6	0.00	0.00	4.56	19.10

NOTE: Standard Deviations shown in brackets indicate that the value is probably unreliable and/or misleading and should not be used to estimate expected ranges. Ordinarily these variables should not be included in most parametric analyses.

TABLE 24. FREQUENCIES FOR 36 VARIABLES FOR 1390 NONPATIENT CHILDREN AND ADOLESCENTS BY AGE

	AGE 5 (N = 90)		AGE 6 (N = 80)		AGE 7 (N = 120)		AGE 8 (N = 120)		AGE 9 (N = 140)		AGE 10 (N = 120)	
	Freq	%	Freq	%	Freq	%	Freq	%	Freq	%	Freq	%
STYLES												
Introversive	0	0%	0	0%	6	5%	16	13%	23	16%	24	20%
Pervasive Introversive	0	0%	0	0%	0	0%	0	0%	1	0%	0	0%
Ambitent	24	27%	20	25%	42	35%	36	30%	48	40%	38	32%
Extratensive	54	60%	51	64%	58	48%	48	40%	49	35%	45	38%
Pervasive Extratensive	48	53%	46	58%	40	33%	24	20%	15	11%	26	22%
Avoidant	12	13%	9	11%	14	12%	20	17%	20	14%	13	11%
EA - es DIFFERENCES: D-SCORES												
D Score > 0	0	0%	0	0%	0	0%	6	5%	7	5%	2	2%
D Score = 0	68	76%	51	64%	69	58%	90	75%	117	84%	100	83%
D Score < 0	22	24%	29	36%	51	43%	24	20%	16	11%	18	15%
D Score < -1	4	4%	4	5%	12	10%	8	7%	9	6%	2	2%
Adj D Score > 0	0	0%	0	0%	0	0%	6	5%	9	6%	6	5%
Adj D Score = 0	72	80%	63	79%	69	58%	98	82%	121	86%	96	80%
Adj D Score < 0	18	20%	17	21%	51	43%	16	13%	10	7%	18	15%
Adj D Score < -1	3	3%	4	5%	5	4%	8	7%	7	5%	2	2%
Zd > +3.0 (Overincorp)	3	3%	0	0%	0	0%	8	7%	28	20%	30	25%
Zd < -3.0 (Underincorp)	23	26%	27	34%	32	27%	19	16%	22	16%	19	16%
FORM QUALITY DEVIATIONS												
XA% > .89	25	28%	41	51%	62	52%	56	47%	61	44%	66	47%
XA% < .70	14	16%	15	19%	12	10%	16	13%	18	13%	9	7%
WDA% < .85	14	16%	8	10%	18	15%	22	18%	24	17%	16	13%
WDA% < .75	4	4%	3	4%	0	0%	0	0%	3	2%	1	0%
X+% < .55	4	4%	0	0%	0	0%	3	3%	4	3%	3	3%
Xu% > .20	49	54%	55	69%	23	19%	32	27%	36	26%	22	18%
X-% > .20	3	3%	2	3%	6	5%	4	4%	4	3%	9	8%
X-% > .30	0	0%	0	0%	0	0%	0	0%	0	0%	0	0%
FC:CF+C RATIO												
FC > (CF+C) + 2	0	0%	0	0%	9	8%	1	1%	0	0%	1	1%
FC > (CF+C) + 1	0	0%	0	0%	12	10%	9	8%	10	7%	14	12%
(CF+C) > FC+1	87	97%	71	89%	17	14%	48	40%	30	21%	60	50%
(CF+C) > FC+2	43	48%	49	61%	11	9%	32	27%	19	14%	21	18%

TABLE 24. (CONTINUED)

	AGE 5 (N = 90) Freq	%	AGE 6 (N = 80) Freq	%	AGE 7 (N = 120) Freq	%	AGE 8 (N = 120) Freq	%	AGE 9 (N = 140) Freq	%	AGE 10 (N = 120) Freq	%
CONSTELLATIONS & INDICES												
HVI Positive	0	0%	0	0%	0	0%	0	0%	0	0%	0	0%
OBS Positive	0	0%	0	0%	0	0%	0	0%	0	0%	0	0%
PTI = 5	0	0%	0	0%	0	0%	0	0%	0	0%	0	0%
PTI = 4	0	0%	0	0%	0	0%	0	0%	0	0%	0	0%
PTI = 3	0	0%	0	0%	0	0%	0	0%	0	0%	0	0%
DEPI = 7	0	0%	0	0%	0	0%	0	0%	0	0%	0	0%
DEPI = 6	0	0%	0	0%	0	0%	0	0%	0	0%	0	0%
DEPI = 5	0	0%	0	0%	0	0%	0	0%	0	0%	0	0%
CDI = 5	1	1%	2	2%	3	3%	3	3%	0	0%	0	0%
CDI = 4	11	12%	10	13%	13	11%	8	7%	9	6%	18	15%
MISCELLANEOUS VARIABLES												
R < 17	17	19%	15	19%	14	12%	40	33%	21	15%	13	11%
R > 27	0	0%	0	0%	0	0%	0	0%	0	0%	0	0%
S > 2	21	23%	4	5%	37	31%	9	8%	12	9%	14	12%
Sum T = 0	33	37%	11	14%	10	8%	8	7%	17	12%	14	12%
Sum T > 1	0	0%	0	0%	2	2%	8	7%	12	9%	8	7%
3r+(2)/R < .33	0	0%	6	8%	0	0%	8	7%	7	5%	4	3%
3r+(2)/R > .44	86	96%	62	78%	82	68%	82	68%	99	71%	110	92%
PureC > 1	53	59%	56	70%	12	10%	40	33%	28	20%	16	13%
Afr < .40	0	0%	12	15%	0	0%	1	1%	8	6%	2	2%
Afr < .50	13	14%	19	24%	9	8%	24	20%	16	11%	16	13%
(FM+m) < Sum Shading	0	0%	0	0%	2	2%	10	8%	14	10%	8	7%
Populars < 4	6	7%	8	10%	3	3%	4	3%	0	0%	4	3%
COP = 0	13	14%	13	16%	12	10%	6	5%	4	3%	6	5%
COP > 2	6	6%	5	6%	16	13%	30	25%	37	26%	21	18%
AG = 0	8	9%	40	50%	0	0%	24	20%	12	9%	3	3%
AG > 2	4	4%	4	5%	3	3%	13	11%	19	14%	18	15%
MOR > 2	3	3%	5	6%	6	5%	3	3%	11	8%	13	11%
Level 2 Sp.Sc. > 0	32	36%	16	20%	19	16%	13	11%	14	10%	10	8%
GHR > PHR	79	88%	69	77%	93	78%	101	84%	98	70%	94	78%
Pure H < 2	4	4%	24	30%	63	52%	32	27%	31	22%	36	30%
Pure H = 0	1	1%	0	0%	0	0%	4	3%	2	1%	4	3%
p > a+1	7	8%	5	6%	16	13%	10	8%	19	14%	12	10%
Mp > Ma	9	10%	9	11%	11	9%	14	12%	17	12%	14	12%

TABLE 24. (CONTINUED)

	AGE 11 (N = 135) Freq	%	AGE 12 (N = 120) Freq	%	AGE 13 (N = 110) Freq	%	AGE 14 (N = 105) Freq	%	AGE 15 (N = 110) Freq	%	AGE 16 (N = 140) Freq	%
STYLES												
Introversive	27	20%	24	20%	30	27%	28	27%	37	34%	46	33%
Pervasive Introversive	0	0%	8	6%	6	5%	6	6%	7	6%	11	8%
Ambitent	37	27%	47	39%	35	32%	32	30%	27	25%	28	20%
Extratensive	51	38%	33	28%	35	32%	35	33%	34	31%	52	37%
Pervasive Extratensive	14	10%	22	18%	18	16%	18	17%	18	16%	23	16%
Avoidant	21	16%	16	13%	10	9%	10	10%	12	10%	14	12%
EA - es DIFFERENCES: D-SCORES												
D Score > 0	0	0%	4	3%	14	13%	10	10%	9	8%	14	10%
D Score = 0	123	91$	90	75%	70	64%	69	66%	71	65%	110	79%
D Score < 0	12	9%	26	22%	26	24%	26	25%	30	27%	16	11%
D Score < -1	5	4%	3	3%	4	4%	3	3%	10	9%	9	6%
Adj D Score > 0	4	3%	14	12%	25	23%	21	20%	16	15%	17	12%
Adj D Score = 0	119	88%	80	67%	65	59%	70	67%	67	61%	86	61%
Adj D Score < 0	11	8%	26	22%	20	18%	14	13%	27	25%	12	9%
Adj D Score < -1	4	3%	2	2%	2	2%	2	2%	6	5%	7	5%
Zd > +3.0 (Overincorp)	36	27%	34	28%	30	27%	21	20%	25	23%	30	21%
Zd < -3.0 (Underincorp)	14	10%	20	17%	15	14%	16	15%	16	15%	14	10%
FORM QUALITY DEVIATIONS												
XA% > .89	111	82%	110	92%	86	78%	81	77%	87	79%	114	81%
XA% < .70	0	0%	4	3%	4	4%	4	4%	2	2%	3	2%
WDA% < .85	6	4%	4	3%	8	7%	8	8%	2	2%	2	1%
WDA% < .75	0	0%	4	3%	4	4%	4	4%	1	1%	1	1%
X+% < .55	12	9%	6	5%	8	7%	8	8%	2	2%	3	2%
Xu% > .20	26	19%	16	13%	16	15%	17	15%	9	8%	16	11%
X-% > .20	18	13%	4	3%	6	5%	7	6%	2	2%	2	1%
X-% > .30	0	0%	2	2%	2	2%	2	2%	1	1%	1	1%
FC:CF+C RATIO												
FC > (CF+C) + 2	3	2%	8	7%	6	5%	4	4%	10	9%	18	13%
FC > (CF+C) + 1	17	13%	12	10%	12	11%	8	8%	20	18%	38	27%
(CF+C) > FC+1	45	33%	24	20%	19	17%	16	15%	23	21%	23	16%
(CF+C) > FC+2	14	10%	0	0%	3	3%	3	3%	2	2%	2	1%

TABLE 24. (CONTINUED)

	AGE 11 (N = 135) Freq	%	AGE 12 (N = 120) Freq	%	AGE 13 (N = 110) Freq	%	AGE 14 (N = 105) Freq	%	AGE 15 (N = 110) Freq	%	AGE 16 (N = 140) Freq	%
CONSTELLATIONS & INDICES												
HVI Positive	5	4%	4	3%	3	3%	6	6%	0	0%	1	1%
OBS Positive	0	0%	0	0%	0	0%	0	0%	1	1%	1	1%
PTI = 5	0	0%	0	0%	0	0%	0	0%	0	0%	0	0%
PTI = 4	0	0%	0	0%	0	0%	0	0%	0	0%	0	0%
PTI = 3	0	0%	2	2%	2	2%	2	2%	1	1%	1	1%
DEPI = 7	0	0%	0	0%	0	0%	0	0%	0	0%	0	0%
DEPI = 6	0	0%	0	0%	0	0%	0	0%	0	0%	0	0%
DEPI = 5	0	0%	1	1%	1	1%	0	0%	0	0%	0	0%
CDI = 5	0	0%	0	0%	0	0%	0	0%	1	1%	1	1%
CDI = 4	12	9%	29	24%	22	20%	13	12%	16	15%	15	11%
MISCELLANEOUS VARIABLES												
R < 17	4	3%	8	7%	10	9%	10	10%	12	11%	13	9%
R > 27	0	0%	0	0%	4	4%	5	5%	8	7%	11	8%
S > 2	18	13%	10	8%	16	15%	13	12%	17	15%	18	13%
Sum T = 0	19	14%	14	12%	20	18%	17	16%	6	5%	12	9%
Sum T > 1	11	8%	0	0%	4	4%	2	2%	9	8%	11	8%
3r+(2)/R < .33	0	0%	6	5%	18	16%	18	17%	7	6%	10	7%
3r+(2)/R > .44	123	91%	85	71%	62	56%	59	56%	49	45%	74	53%
PureC > 1	0	0%	0	0%	0	0%	0	0%	0	0%	0	0%
Afr < .40	0	0%	0	0%	8	7%	6	6%	5	5%	6	4%
Afr < .50	13	10%	6	5%	33	30%	24	23%	19	17%	21	15%
(FM+m) < Sum Shading	10	7%	45	38%	11	10%	9	9%	17	15%	20	14%
Populars < 4	0	0%	12	10%	4	4%	1	1%	3	3%	4	3%
COP = 0	6	4%	4	3%	10	9%	13	12%	12	11%	20	14%
COP > 2	13	10%	6	5%	16	15%	18	17%	15	14%	24	17%
AG = 0	5	4%	19	16%	25	23%	19	18%	28	25%	34	24%
AG > 2	10	7%	21	18%	8	7%	10	10%	8	7%	11	8%
MOR > 2	6	4%	15	13%	2	2%	5	5%	4	4%	5	4%
Level 2 Sp.Sc. > 0	20	15%	22	18%	13	12%	9	9%	9	8%	7	5%
GHR > PHR	105	78%	109	91%	94	85%	89	85%	84	76%	111	79%
Pure H < 2	27	20%	30	25%	28	25%	18	17%	23	21%	14	10%
Pure H = 0	4	3%	0	0%	0	0%	0	0%	1	1%	1	1%
p > a+1	12	9%	10	8%	7	6%	13	12%	13	12%	15	11%
Mp > Ma	20	15%	18	15%	9	8%	8	8%	16	15%	17	12%

TABLE 25. DESCRIPTIVE STATISTICS FOR ADULT OUTPATIENTS (N = 535)

VARIABLE	MEAN	SD	MIN	MAX	FREQ	MEDIAN	MODE	SK	KU
AGE	33.81	12.06	18.00	70.00	535	31.00	23.00	1.12	0.79
Years Educ	13.46	4.65	10.00	20.00	535	14.00	13.00	-0.67	1.39
R	20.25	5.49	14.00	41.00	535	19.00	16.00	1.21	1.03
W	7.88	3.36	1.00	24.00	535	7.00	7.00	0.60	0.82
D	9.11	5.21	0.00	30.00	525	8.00	4.00	0.94	0.65
Dd	3.26	[2.79]	0.00	16.00	465	3.00	1.00	1.39	3.04
S	2.11	[1.81]	0.00	10.00	416	2.00	0.00	0.88	0.95
DQ+	6.09	3.23	0.00	20.00	530	6.00	5.00	0.92	1.40
DQo	12.74	5.19	4.00	32.00	535	11.00	9.00	1.14	1.44
DQv	1.23	[1.50]	0.00	9.00	313	1.00	0.00	1.56	2.53
DQv/+	0.19	[0.56]	0.00	5.00	79	0.00	0.00	4.40	26.22
FQx+	0.58	1.35	0.00	7.00	112	0.00	0.00	2.41	4.69
FQxo	12.20	3.82	6.00	34.00	535	12.00	12.00	1.31	3.62
FQxu	3.80	2.48	0.00	12.00	512	3.00	3.00	0.91	0.43
FQx-	3.20	2.28	0.00	13.00	488	3.00	1.00	0.88	1.00
FQxNone	0.48	[0.85]	0.00	5.00	169	0.00	0.00	2.09	4.72
MQ+	0.44	1.05	0.00	4.00	99	0.00	0.00	2.35	4.26
MQo	2.38	1.65	0.00	9.00	486	2.00	1.00	0.79	0.63
MQu	0.58	0.80	0.00	5.00	227	0.00	0.00	1.43	2.19
MQ-	0.44	[0.73]	0.00	4.00	171	0.00	0.00	1.79	3.39
MQNone	0.00	[0.06]	0.00	1.00	2	0.00	0.00	16.30	264.98
SQual-	0.79	[1.00]	0.00	4.00	264	0.00	0.00	1.26	0.97
M	3.85	2.53	0.00	11.00	498	4.00	4.00	0.82	0.62
FM	2.56	1.85	0.00	13.00	477	2.00	2.00	0.96	1.71
m	1.28	1.27	0.00	7.00	346	1.00	0.00	1.00	1.01
FM+m	3.84	2.45	0.00	14.00	495	4.00	4.00	0.66	1.01
FC	1.37	1.35	0.00	7.00	388	1.00	1.00	1.36	1.99
CF	1.22	1.32	0.00	8.00	336	1.00	0.00	1.31	2.25
C	0.53	[0.88]	0.00	4.00	183	0.00	0.00	1.74	2.67
Cn	0.01	[0.11]	0.00	1.00	6	0.00	0.00	9.30	84.98
Sum Color	3.14	2.01	0.00	11.00	501	3.00	2.00	0.80	0.73
WSumC	2.71	1.91	0.00	10.00	501	2.50	1.50	1.04	1.59
Sum C'	1.01	[1.25]	0.00	7.00	303	1.00	0.00	1.60	2.72
Sum T	0.52	[0.84]	0.00	3.00	191	0.00	0.00	1.70	2.23
Sum V	0.44	[0.77]	0.00	3.00	153	0.00	0.00	1.67	1.80
Sum Y	1.02	[1.14]	0.00	7.00	328	1.00	0.00	1.48	3.02
Sum Shading	2.99	2.72	0.00	12.00	463	2.00	1.00	1.10	0.55
Fr+rF	0.19	[0.63]	0.00	6.00	63	0.00	0.00	5.07	33.65
FD	0.91	[1.02]	0.00	5.00	317	1.00	0.00	1.53	3.06
F	9.22	4.90	2.00	30.00	535	8.00	7.00	1.24	2.12
(2)	7.85	3.71	1.00	23.00	535	7.00	5.00	1.21	1.88
3r+(2)/R	0.41	0.14	0.12	1.25	535	0.40	0.33	1.04	3.88
Lambda	1.14	1.26	0.11	7.67	535	0.78	1.00	3.21	12.06
EA	6.56	3.46	0.00	19.00	533	6.00	7.50	0.99	1.23
es	6.83	4.19	1.00	23.00	535	6.00	5.00	0.65	-0.20
D Score	-0.09	1.34	-4.00	5.00	535	0.00	0.00	-0.20	2.26
AdjD	0.25	1.16	-3.00	5.00	535	0.00	0.00	0.53	2.49
a (active)	4.22	2.69	0.00	17.00	510	4.00	3.00	0.89	1.18
p (passive)	3.48	2.46	0.00	13.00	483	3.00	2.00	0.54	-0.31
Ma	2.06	1.81	0.00	8.00	430	2.00	2.00	1.10	0.91
Mp	1.80	1.49	0.00	8.00	409	2.00	2.00	0.88	1.32
Intellect	1.66	1.74	0.00	10.00	363	1.00	0.00	1.20	1.20
Zf	11.09	3.83	2.00	26.00	535	11.00	10.00	0.53	1.48
Zd	0.27	4.54	-14.00	13.00	521	-0.50	5.00	0.06	-0.33
Blends	3.12	2.42	0.00	13.00	458	3.00	1.00	0.61	-0.21
Blends/R	0.16	0.12	0.00	0.57	458	0.14	0.00	0.63	-0.13
Col-Shd Blends	0.63	[0.80]	0.00	4.00	247	0.00	0.00	1.24	1.28
Afr	0.58	0.19	0.13	1.25	535	0.55	0.50	1.31	1.84

TABLE 25. ADULT OUTPATIENTS (N = 535) (Continued)

VARIABLE	MEAN	SD	MIN	MAX	FREQ	MEDIAN	MODE	SK	KU
Populars	5.73	2.17	0.00	10.00	529	6.00	4.00	-0.09	-0.61
XA%	0.82	0.11	0.50	1.00	535	0.82	0.94	-0.28	-0.36
WDA%	0.85	0.10	0.60	1.00	535	0.85	0.83	-0.46	-0.14
X+%	0.64	0.14	0.27	0.95	535	0.63	0.52	-0.16	-0.63
X-%	0.16	0.10	0.00	0.46	488	0.15	0.00	0.45	-0.30
Xu%	0.18	0.09	0.00	0.42	512	0.18	0.21	0.18	-0.49
Isolate/R	0.13	0.14	0.00	0.81	415	0.11	0.00	2.43	8.87
H	2.28	1.44	0.00	9.00	505	2.00	1.00	0.88	1.12
(H)	1.17	1.21	0.00	6.00	332	1.00	0.00	0.90	0.25
HD	1.45	1.53	0.00	8.00	393	1.00	1.00	1.97	4.82
(Hd)	0.55	0.86	0.00	5.00	189	0.00	0.00	1.62	2.83
Hx	0.03	[0.21]	0.00	2.00	11	0.00	0.00	8.01	67.67
All H Cont	5.44	2.79	0.00	16.00	519	5.00	4.00	0.62	0.36
A	7.62	2.70	2.00	20.00	535	7.00	5.00	0.68	0.24
(A)	0.32	[0.64]	0.00	3.00	134	0.00	0.00	2.40	6.30
Ad	1.94	[1.89]	0.00	11.00	431	2.00	1.00	1.75	3.68
(Ad)	0.11	[0.33]	0.00	2.00	52	0.00	0.00	3.19	10.17
An	0.78	[1.21]	0.00	11.00	238	0.00	0.00	2.66	11.95
Art	1.06	1.13	0.00	5.00	318	1.00	0.00	0.86	-0.01
Ay	0.18	[0.41]	0.00	2.00	93	0.00	0.00	1.99	2.94
Bl	0.22	[0.55]	0.00	3.00	89	0.00	0.00	2.91	9.13
Bt	1.09	1.21	0.00	5.00	321	1.00	0.00	1.11	0.50
Cg	1.68	1.70	0.00	8.00	359	1.00	0.00	1.00	0.57
Cl	0.16	[0.44]	0.00	2.00	67	0.00	0.00	2.90	7.88
Ex	0.15	[0.40]	0.00	2.00	73	0.00	0.00	2.63	6.56
Fi	0.29	[0.51]	0.00	2.00	142	0.00	0.00	1.48	1.26
Food	0.25	[0.50]	0.00	2.00	116	0.00	0.00	1.88	2.77
Ge	0.07	[0.37]	0.00	4.00	24	0.00	0.00	7.95	74.77
Hh	0.64	0.93	0.00	4.00	204	0.00	0.00	1.33	1.15
Ls	0.68	1.09	0.00	6.00	205	0.00	0.00	2.12	5.55
Na	0.22	[0.67]	0.00	4.00	79	0.00	0.00	4.09	18.61
Sc	0.51	[0.78]	0.00	5.00	201	0.00	0.00	2.17	7.50
Sx	0.58	[0.99]	0.00	5.00	188	0.00	0.00	2.06	4.40
Xy	0.12	[0.33]	0.00	1.00	66	0.00	0.00	2.29	3.29
Idio	1.09	1.24	0.00	6.00	309	1.00	0.00	1.16	1.04
DV	0.80	[1.04]	0.00	5.00	272	1.00	0.00	1.81	4.40
INCOM	0.98	[1.11]	0.00	6.00	310	1.00	0.00	1.23	1.34
DR	0.26	[0.77]	0.00	5.00	74	0.00	0.00	3.55	13.47
FABCOM	0.41	[0.66]	0.00	3.00	173	0.00	0.00	1.49	1.56
DV2	0.09	[0.30]	0.00	2.00	45	0.00	0.00	3.34	10.88
INC2	0.17	[0.47]	0.00	2.00	69	0.00	0.00	2.83	7.26
DR2	0.14	[0.74]	0.00	10.00	45	0.00	0.00	9.94	121.29
FAB2	0.26	[0.64]	0.00	3.00	94	0.00	0.00	2.70	7.03
ALOG	0.13	[0.42]	0.00	3.00	52	0.00	0.00	3.77	15.59
CONTAM	0.00	0.00	0.00	0.00	0	0.00	0.00	----	----
Sum 6 Sp Sc	3.24	2.91	0.00	21.00	484	3.00	1.00	1.83	5.74
Lvl 2 Sp Sc	0.66	[1.29]	0.00	11.00	200	0.00	0.00	4.07	24.14
WSum6	9.36	10.84	0.00	97.00	484	7.00	1.00	3.23	17.78
AB	0.21	[0.47]	0.00	3.00	98	0.00	0.00	2.43	6.75
AG	0.89	1.22	0.00	8.00	257	0.00	0.00	2.25	8.70
COP	0.97	1.10	0.00	6.00	304	1.00	0.00	1.38	2.76
CP	0.01	[0.09]	0.00	1.00	4	0.00	0.00	11.46	129.98
GOODHR	3.46	1.75	0.00	10.00	509	4.00	4.00	0.31	0.59
POORHR	2.58	2.15	0.00	12.00	466	2.00	2.00	1.44	2.83
MOR	1.06	[1.33]	0.00	7.00	314	1.00	0.00	1.69	2.70
PER	1.04	1.65	0.00	11.00	235	0.00	0.00	2.51	9.21
PSV	0.20	[0.58]	0.00	3.00	74	0.00	0.00	3.39	12.00

NOTE: Standard Deviations shown in brackets indicate that the value is probably unreliable and/or misleading and should not be used to estimate expected ranges. Ordinarily these variables should not be included in most parametric analyses.

TABLE 26. FREQUENCIES FOR 36 VARIABLES FOR ADULT OUTPATIENTS
(N = 535)

DEMOGRAPHY VARIABLES

MARITAL STATUS			AGE			RACE		
Single	170	32%	18-25	154	29%	White	453	85%
Lives w/S.O.	32	6%	26-35	194	36%	Black	43	8%
Married	264	49%	36-45	102	19%	Hispanic	27	5%
Separated	28	5%	46-55	35	7%	Asian	12	2%
Divorced	37	7%	56-65	36	7%			
Widowed	4	1%	OVER 65	14	3%			

						EDUCATION		
SEX						UNDER 12	58	11%
Male	208	39%				12 Years	148	28%
Female	327	61%				13-15 Yrs	224	42%
						16+ Yrs	105	20%

RATIOS, PERCENTAGES AND SPECIAL INDICES

STYLES			FORM QUALITY DEVIATIONS		
Introversive	151	28%	XA% > .89	127	24%
Pervasive	113	21%	XA% < .70	62	12%
Ambitent	110	21%	WDA% < .85	249	47%
Extratensive	73	14%	WDA% < .75	79	15%
Pervasive	45	8%	X+% < .55	146	27%
Avoidant	201	38%	Xu% > .20	211	39%
			X-% > .20	164	31%
D-SCORES			X-% > .30	42	8%
D Score > 0	125	23%			
D Score = 0	262	49%	FC:CF+C RATIO		
D Score < 0	148	28%	FC > (CF+C) + 2	37	7%
D Score < -1	55	10%	FC > (CF+C) + 1	87	16%
			(CF+C) > FC+1	140	26%
Adj D Score > 0	168	31%	(CF+C) > FC+2	71	13%
Adj D Score = 0	277	52%			
Adj D Score < 0	90	17%			
Adj D Score < -1	27	5%	S-Constellation Positive	1	0%
			HVI Positive	61	11%
Zd > +3.0 (Overincorp)	159	30%	OBS Positive	44	8%
Zd < -3.0 (Underincorp)	134	25%			

PTI = 5	3	1%	DEPI = 7	2	0%	CDI = 5	42	8%
PTI = 4	3	1%	DEPI = 6	24	4%	CDI = 4	123	23%
PTI = 3	7	1%	DEPI = 5	82	15%			

MISCELLANEOUS VARIABLES

R < 17	165	31%	(2AB+Art+Ay) > 5	22	4%
R > 27	65	12%	Populars < 4	76	14%
DQv > 2	89	17%	Populars > 7	131	24%
S > 2	206	39%	COP = 0	231	43%
Sum T = 0	344	64%	COP > 2	40	7%
Sum T > 1	56	10%	AG = 0	278	52%
3r+(2)/R < .33	141	26%	AG > 2	19	4%
3r+(2)/R > .44	166	31%	MOR > 2	70	13%
Fr + rF > 0	63	12%	Level 2 Sp.Sc. > 0	200	37%
PureC > 0	183	34%	GHR > PHR	328	61%
PureC > 1	74	14%	Pure H < 2	188	35%
Afr < .40	109	20%	Pure H = 0	30	6%
Afr < .50	258	48%	p > a+1	158	30%
(FM+m) < Sum Shading	164	31%	Mp > Ma	170	32%

TABLE 27. DESCRIPTIVE STATISTICS FOR OUTPATIENT INTROVERSIVES
(N = 151)

VARIABLE	MEAN	SD	MIN	MAX	FREQ	MEDIAN	MODE	SK	KU
AGE	30.81	8.62	18.00	57.00	151	29.00	29.00	0.65	-0.02
Years Educ	14.19	3.70	11.00	20.00	151	14.00	14.00	0.92	1.31
R	20.64	5.81	14.00	38.00	151	18.00	16.00	1.15	0.32
W	7.95	2.71	4.00	15.00	151	7.00	7.00	0.96	0.27
D	9.46	5.58	2.00	30.00	151	7.00	7.00	1.47	1.35
Dd	3.23	[2.23]	0.00	12.00	127	4.00	4.00	0.39	0.51
S	2.31	[1.59]	0.00	7.00	138	2.00	1.00	0.87	0.69
DQ+	8.62	3.44	3.00	20.00	151	8.00	8.00	0.94	0.15
DQo	11.31	3.94	5.00	30.00	151	11.00	11.00	1.63	5.61
DQv	0.52	[1.10]	0.00	7.00	40	0.00	0.00	2.83	9.91
DQv/+	0.19	[0.67]	0.00	5.00	18	0.00	0.00	5.49	35.51
FQx+	1.56	2.03	0.00	7.00	65	0.00	0.00	0.79	-1.02
FQxo	12.31	3.79	7.00	34.00	151	11.00	10.00	2.60	9.84
FQxu	3.87	3.01	0.00	11.00	139	3.00	2.00	0.81	-0.49
FQx-	2.72	2.00	0.00	13.00	141	3.00	1.00	1.54	4.65
FQxNone	0.18	[0.60]	0.00	5.00	17	0.00	0.00	4.76	29.44
MQ+	1.25	1.59	0.00	4.00	64	0.00	0.00	0.68	-1.26
MQo	3.37	1.63	1.00	9.00	151	3.00	2.00	0.71	0.22
MQu	0.93	0.99	0.00	3.00	87	1.00	0.00	0.75	-0.52
MQ-	0.79	[1.01]	0.00	4.00	68	0.00	0.00	1.06	0.40
MQNone	0.01	[0.11]	0.00	1.00	2	0.00	0.00	8.60	72.95
S-	0.99	[0.92]	0.00	4.00	107	1.00	1.00	1.31	2.01
M	6.36	2.30	4.00	11.00	151	6.00	6.00	0.78	-0.76
FM	2.95	1.95	0.00	13.00	147	3.00	2.00	1.60	4.20
m	1.60	1.30	0.00	5.00	106	2.00	2.00	0.36	-0.33
FM+m	4.55	2.35	1.00	13.00	151	4.00	4.00	1.21	2.41
FC	1.66	1.39	0.00	6.00	128	1.00	1.00	1.33	1.64
CF	1.02	0.76	0.00	3.00	117	1.00	1.00	0.70	0.64
C	0.22	[0.54]	0.00	3.00	25	0.00	0.00	2.68	7.30
Cn	0.01	[0.11]	0.00	1.00	2	0.00	0.00	8.60	72.95
Sum Color	2.91	1.81	0.00	8.00	139	2.00	2.00	0.71	0.38
WSumC	2.17	1.43	0.00	6.50	139	1.50	1.50	0.72	0.13
Sum C'	0.89	[1.09]	0.00	4.00	81	1.00	0.00	1.24	0.80
Sum T	0.72	[0.95]	0.00	3.00	72	0.00	0.00	1.36	0.96
Sum V	0.62	[0.89]	0.00	3.00	61	0.00	0.00	1.28	0.68
Sum Y	1.20	[1.00]	0.00	7.00	125	1.00	1.00	2.07	7.90
Sum Shading	3.44	2.59	0.00	12.00	146	2.00	2.00	0.86	-0.15
Fr+rF	0.18	[0.75]	0.00	6.00	16	0.00	0.00	6.54	47.92
FD	1.09	[0.90]	0.00	4.00	114	1.00	1.00	0.93	0.83
F	7.30	2.97	2.00	15.00	151	7.00	7.00	0.50	-0.36
(2)	9.07	4.44	3.00	23.00	151	8.00	6.00	1.33	1.21
3r+(2)/R	0.46	0.16	0.12	1.25	151	0.44	0.28	1.47	6.26
Lambda	0.57	0.21	0.11	0.92	151	0.63	0.33	-0.35	-0.89
EA	8.53	3.47	4.00	16.50	151	7.50	5.50	0.74	-0.54
es	7.99	3.56	2.00	18.00	151	7.00	5.00	0.61	-0.54
D Score	0.03	1.40	-4.00	5.00	151	0.00	0.00	1.08	3.50
AdjD	0.40	1.20	-3.00	5.00	151	0.00	0.00	1.67	4.63
a (active)	5.37	2.70	3.00	17.00	151	5.00	3.00	1.14	1.25
p (passive)	5.54	2.24	1.00	13.00	151	6.00	7.00	0.13	0.42
Ma	3.22	1.94	0.00	8.00	149	2.00	2.00	0.85	-0.23
Mp	3.15	1.43	1.00	8.00	151	3.00	4.00	1.05	2.18
Intellect	1.56	1.35	0.00	7.00	117	2.00	2.00	1.34	2.92
Zf	13.11	3.70	7.00	26.00	151	12.00	12.00	0.95	0.72
Zd	2.62	4.73	-12.00	10.00	151	3.50	5.00	-0.53	-0.12
Blends	4.15	2.29	0.00	8.00	139	4.00	3.00	0.02	-0.90
Blends/R	0.20	0.11	0.00	0.50	139	0.21	0.23	0.40	0.56
Col-Shd Blends	1.01	[0.92]	0.00	3.00	102	1.00	1.00	0.71	-0.23
Afr	0.53	0.19	0.13	1.25	151	0.48	0.50	1.59	4.20

TABLE 27. OUTPATIENT INTROVERSIVES (N = 151) (Continued)

VARIABLE	MEAN	SD	MIN	MAX	FREQ	MEDIAN	MODE	SK	KU
Populars	7.09	1.90	2.00	10.00	151	8.00	8.00	-0.72	-0.38
XA%	0.87	0.08	0.54	1.00	151	0.85	0.84	-0.97	1.79
WDA%	0.88	0.07	0.63	1.00	151	0.88	0.85	-0.81	1.59
X+%	0.69	0.13	0.27	0.89	151	0.73	0.52	-0.84	0.20
X-%	0.13	0.08	0.00	0.46	141	0.12	0.16	0.93	2.18
Xu%	0.18	0.11	0.00	0.35	139	0.14	0.11	0.13	-1.15
Isolate/R	0.14	0.10	0.00	0.50	138	0.12	0.11	1.21	1.79
H	3.02	1.46	1.00	8.00	151	3.00	2.00	0.97	0.86
(H)	1.64	1.12	0.00	6.00	131	2.00	2.00	1.06	2.32
HD	1.74	1.90	0.00	8.00	106	2.00	2.00	1.66	2.55
(Hd)	0.44	0.68	0.00	2.00	51	0.00	0.00	1.24	0.23
Hx	0.00	[0.00]	0.00	0.00	0	0.00	0.00	----	----
All H Cont	6.84	2.65	3.00	14.00	151	7.00	7.00	0.58	-0.32
A	7.52	2.46	3.00	20.00	151	7.00	6.00	1.02	3.57
(A)	0.51	[0.95]	0.00	3.00	42	0.00	0.00	1.78	1.86
Ad	1.63	[1.17]	0.00	7.00	126	2.00	2.00	1.16	3.46
(Ad)	0.06	[0.29]	0.00	2.00	7	0.00	0.00	5.28	29.37
An	0.43	[0.79]	0.00	4.00	44	0.00	0.00	2.14	5.13
Art	0.99	0.91	0.00	3.00	93	1.00	0.00	0.23	-1.29
Ay	0.24	[0.44]	0.00	2.00	35	0.00	0.00	1.47	0.81
Bl	0.13	[0.44]	0.00	2.00	13	0.00	0.00	3.56	11.85
Bt	1.41	1.18	0.00	4.00	109	1.00	2.00	0.54	-0.35
Cg	2.29	1.80	0.00	8.00	117	2.00	2.00	0.52	-0.13
Cl	0.11	[0.39]	0.00	2.00	13	0.00	0.00	3.69	13.45
Ex	0.17	[0.38]	0.00	1.00	26	0.00	0.00	1.75	1.09
Fi	0.36	[0.53]	0.00	2.00	51	0.00	0.00	1.09	0.16
Food	0.11	[0.32]	0.00	1.00	17	0.00	0.00	2.47	4.19
Ge	0.05	[0.23]	0.00	1.00	8	0.00	0.00	4.03	14.44
Hh	0.99	1.02	0.00	3.00	80	1.00	0.00	0.31	-1.45
Ls	0.93	1.44	0.00	6.00	64	0.00	0.00	1.80	2.96
Na	0.13	[0.44]	0.00	3.00	16	0.00	0.00	4.37	22.89
Sc	0.85	[1.02]	0.00	5.00	83	1.00	0.00	1.81	4.97
Sx	0.58	[1.01]	0.00	4.00	48	0.00	0.00	1.86	3.09
Xy	0.28	[0.45]	0.00	1.00	42	0.00	0.00	1.00	-1.01
Idio	1.38	1.46	0.00	6.00	87	1.00	0.00	0.82	-0.06
DV	0.66	[0.77]	0.00	4.00	79	1.00	0.00	1.45	3.42
INCOM	1.25	[1.26]	0.00	4.00	94	1.00	0.00	0.70	-0.60
DR	0.19	[0.65]	0.00	3.00	15	0.00	0.00	3.62	12.37
FABCOM	0.51	[0.77]	0.00	3.00	56	0.00	0.00	1.46	1.53
DV2	0.03	[0.18]	0.00	1.00	5	0.00	0.00	5.27	26.13
INC2	0.25	[0.56]	0.00	2.00	29	0.00	0.00	2.13	3.52
DR2	0.33	[1.29]	0.00	10.00	23	0.00	0.00	6.16	42.17
FAB2	0.32	[0.57]	0.00	2.00	40	0.00	0.00	1.62	1.68
ALOG	0.10	[0.41]	0.00	3.00	11	0.00	0.00	5.32	32.33
CONTAM	0.00	0.00	0.00	0.00	0	0.00	0.00	----	----
Sum 6 Sp Sc	3.64	3.60	0.00	21.00	147	3.00	1.00	2.21	6.79
Lvl 2 Sp Sc	0.93	[1.90]	0.00	11.00	68	0.00	0.00	3.68	14.92
WSum6	11.55	15.06	0.00	97.00	147	8.00	1.00	3.09	13.40
AB	0.17	[0.51]	0.00	3.00	18	0.00	0.00	3.63	14.46
AG	1.48	1.50	0.00	8.00	112	1.00	2.00	2.31	7.91
COP	1.23	1.33	0.00	6.00	90	1.00	0.00	1.25	2.28
CP	0.00	[0.00]	0.00	0.00	0	0.00	0.00	----	----
GOODHR	4.37	1.57	0.00	10.00	149	4.00	3.00	0.48	1.08
POORHR	3.36	2.42	0.00	12.00	150	2.00	2.00	1.59	2.65
MOR	1.00	[1.05]	0.00	5.00	106	1.00	1.00	2.02	5.22
PER	0.82	1.17	0.00	4.00	62	0.00	0.00	1.33	0.84
PSV	0.05	[0.23]	0.00	1.00	8	0.00	0.00	4.03	14.44

NOTE: Standard Deviations shown in brackets indicate that the value is probably unreliable and/or misleading and should not be used to estimate expected ranges. Ordinarily these variables should not be included in most parametric analyses.

TABLE 28. FREQUENCIES FOR 36 VARIABLES FOR OUTPATIENT INTROVERSIVES (N = 151)

DEMOGRAPHY VARIABLES

MARITAL STATUS			AGE			RACE		
Single	56	37%	18-25	44	29%	White	129	85%
Lives w/S.O.	8	5%	26-35	67	44%	Black	9	6%
Married	72	48%	36-45	31	21%	Hispanic	4	3%
Separated	6	4%	46-55	7	5%	Asian	9	6%
Divorced	9	6%	56-65	2	1%			
Widowed	0	0%	OVER 65	0	0%			

SEX						EDUCATION		
Male	75	50%				UNDER 12	8	5%
Female	76	50%				12 Years	23	15%
						13-15 Yrs	83	55%
						16+ Yrs	37	25%

RATIOS, PERCENTAGES AND SPECIAL INDICES

STYLES			FORM QUALITY DEVIATIONS		
Introversive	151	100%	XA% > .89	64	42%
Pervasive	113	75%	XA% < .70	5	3%
Ambitent	0	0%	WDA% < .85	33	22%
Extratensive	0	0%	WDA% < .75	5	3%
Pervasive	0	0%	X+% < .55	29	19%
Avoidant	0	0%	Xu% > .20	55	36%
			X-% > .20	14	9%
D-SCORES			X-% > .30	5	3%
D Score > 0	30	20%			
D Score = 0	82	54%			
D Score < 0	39	26%	FC:CF+C RATIO		
D Score < -1	15	10%	FC > (CF+C) + 2	21	14%
			FC > (CF+C) + 1	27	18%
Adj D Score > 0	46	30%	(CF+C) > FC+1	7	5%
Adj D Score = 0	85	56%	(CF+C) > FC+2	4	3%
Adj D Score < 0	20	13%			
Adj D Score < -1	1	1%	S-Constellation Positive	0	0%
			HVI Positive	20	13%
Zd > +3.0 (Overincorp)	89	59%	OBS Positive	35	23%
Zd < -3.0 (Underincorp)	24	16%			

PTI = 5	0	0%	DEPI = 7	2	1%	CDI = 5	0	0%
PTI = 4	3	2%	DEPI = 6	10	7%	CDI = 4	24	16%
PTI = 3	3	2%	DEPI = 5	10	7%			

MISCELLANEOUS VARIABLES

R < 17	44	29%	(2AB+Art+Ay) > 5	2	1%
R > 27	24	16%	Populars < 4	8	5%
DQv > 2	10	7%	Populars > 7	85	56%
S > 2	60	40%	COP = 0	61	40%
Sum T = 0	79	52%	COP > 2	22	15%
Sum T > 1	20	13%	AG = 0	39	26%
3r+(2)/R < .33	40	26%	AG > 2	12	8%
3r+(2)/R > .44	75	50%	MOR > 2	13	9%
Fr + rF > 0	16	11%	Level 2 Sp.Sc. > 0	68	45%
PureC > 0	25	17%	GHR > PHR	108	72%
PureC > 1	7	5%	Pure H < 2	15	10%
Afr < .40	22	15%	Pure H = 0	0	0%
Afr < .50	79	52%	p > a+1	75	50%
(FM+m) < Sum Shading	48	32%	Mp > Ma	62	41%

TABLE 29. DESCRIPTIVE STATISTICS FOR OUTPATIENTS EXTRATENSIVES

(N = 73)

VARIABLE	MEAN	SD	MIN	MAX	FREQ	MEDIAN	MODE	SK	KU
AGE	33.60	10.47	22.00	56.00	73	29.00	28.00	1.25	0.27
Years Educ	12.89	3.22	10.00	19.00	73	13.00	13.00	0.81	-0.64
R	20.49	5.92	14.00	40.00	73	19.00	16.00	0.84	0.05
W	9.97	3.64	4.00	19.00	73	10.00	13.00	-0.20	-0.70
D	7.22	5.27	0.00	22.00	63	6.00	14.00	0.41	-0.78
Dd	3.30	[3.74]	0.00	11.00	61	2.00	1.00	1.34	0.35
S	2.51	[2.02]	0.00	7.00	56	4.00	4.00	0.16	-1.09
DQ+	5.19	2.29	1.00	12.00	73	5.00	3.00	0.44	-0.72
DQo	12.36	5.36	5.00	31.00	73	11.00	9.00	0.95	0.52
DQv	2.59	[1.82]	0.00	6.00	67	2.00	1.00	0.32	-1.31
DQv/+	0.36	[0.63]	0.00	3.00	22	0.00	0.00	2.26	6.53
FQx+	0.01	0.12	0.00	1.00	1	0.00	0.00	8.54	73.00
FQxo	12.69	3.61	7.00	24.00	73	12.00	11.00	0.65	0.92
FQxu	3.36	2.29	0.00	11.00	72	3.00	1.00	0.80	0.32
FQx-	3.27	2.07	0.00	6.00	71	2.00	2.00	0.34	-1.51
FQxNone	1.16	[1.17]	0.00	5.00	47	1.00	0.00	0.85	0.17
MQ+	0.01	0.12	0.00	1.00	1	0.00	0.00	8.54	73.00
MQo	1.80	1.80	0.00	7.00	61	1.00	1.00	1.91	3.50
MQu	0.30	0.46	0.00	1.00	22	0.00	0.00	0.88	-1.25
MQ-	0.00	[0.00]	0.00	0.00	0	0.00	0.00	----	----
MQNone	0.00	[0.00]	0.00	0.00	0	0.00	0.00	----	----
S-	0.55	[0.60]	0.00	2.00	36	0.00	0.00	0.59	-0.55
M	2.11	1.78	0.00	7.00	61	2.00	2.00	1.49	2.50
FM	2.77	1.30	1.00	7.00	73	2.00	2.00	0.48	-0.19
m	1.70	1.15	0.00	7.00	67	1.00	1.00	1.63	5.50
FM+m	4.47	2.06	1.00	14.00	73	5.00	5.00	1.19	5.01
FC	0.99	0.92	0.00	4.00	52	1.00	1.00	1.34	2.28
CF	2.60	1.68	0.00	6.00	62	3.00	2.00	0.33	-0.17
C	1.30	[1.23]	0.00	4.00	49	1.00	0.00	0.68	-0.48
Cn	0.00	[0.00]	0.00	0.00	0	0.00	0.00	----	----
Sum Color	4.89	1.74	3.00	9.00	73	4.00	4.00	1.22	0.56
WSumC	5.05	1.93	3.00	9.50	73	4.50	3.00	1.05	0.23
Sum C'	1.88	[1.62]	0.00	7.00	58	1.00	1.00	0.96	0.94
Sum T	0.47	[0.58]	0.00	2.00	31	0.00	0.00	0.79	-0.33
Sum V	0.64	[0.77]	0.00	2.00	34	0.00	0.00	0.71	-0.94
Sum Y	1.18	[1.21]	0.00	5.00	47	1.00	0.00	0.91	0.18
Sum Shading	4.16	2.52	1.00	12.00	73	4.00	5.00	1.05	1.12
Fr+rF	0.27	[0.73]	0.00	4.00	11	0.00	0.00	3.02	9.92
FD	1.20	[1.17]	0.00	5.00	50	1.00	1.00	0.88	0.16
F	7.86	3.47	3.00	19.00	73	7.00	6.00	1.21	0.56
(2)	6.84	3.39	1.00	13.00	73	8.00	8.00	0.05	-1.12
3r+(2)/R	0.36	0.14	0.13	0.75	73	0.38	0.38	-0.09	0.21
Lambda	0.64	0.22	0.23	0.93	73	0.60	0.93	-0.30	-0.93
EA	7.16	3.60	3.00	16.50	73	6.50	6.00	1.31	1.47
es	8.63	3.41	3.00	23.00	73	9.00	11.00	0.88	3.35
D Score	-0.30	1.44	-4.00	2.00	73	0.00	-1.00	-0.48	0.66
AdjD	0.04	1.34	-2.00	3.00	73	0.00	-1.00	0.78	-0.03
a (active)	4.03	1.62	2.00	8.00	73	3.00	5.00	0.58	-0.39
p (passive)	2.55	2.14	0.00	9.00	62	2.00	1.00	0.77	-0.21
Ma	1.07	1.42	0.00	5.00	40	1.00	0.00	1.71	2.48
Mp	1.04	0.89	0.00	3.00	47	1.00	2.00	0.04	-1.48
Intellect	2.29	2.26	0.00	7.00	50	1.00	0.00	0.50	-1.32
Zf	11.08	2.19	9.00	21.00	73	10.00	10.00	1.97	5.04
Zd	-0.74	3.73	-14.00	8.50	71	-0.50	-0.50	-0.22	2.50
Blends	3.77	1.96	0.00	11.00	72	4.00	4.00	0.77	1.48
Blends/R	0.19	0.10	0.00	0.44	72	0.14	0.14	0.56	-0.34
Col-Shd Blends	0.75	[0.81]	0.00	2.00	38	1.00	0.00	0.48	-1.32
Afr	0.66	0.13	0.32	0.92	73	0.64	0.64	1.41	2.55

TABLE 29. OUTPATIENTS EXTRATENSIVES (N = 73) (Continued)

VARIABLE	MEAN	SD	MIN	MAX	FREQ	MEDIAN	MODE	SK	KU
Populars	5.19	1.88	2.00	10.00	73	5.00	5.00	-0.06	-0.63
XA%	0.78	0.10	0.60	1.00	73	0.76	0.76	-0.10	-0.65
WDA%	0.79	0.11	0.60	1.00	73	0.83	0.83	-0.44	-0.92
X+%	0.63	0.09	0.41	0.80	73	0.63	0.63	0.10	-0.36
X-%	0.16	0.10	0.00	0.40	71	0.13	0.21	1.12	1.17
Xu%	0.16	0.08	0.00	0.35	72	0.19	0.21	0.04	-0.76
Isolate/R	0.23	0.25	0.04	0.81	73	0.14	0.07	1.73	1.58
H	1.29	0.91	0.00	5.00	60	1.00	1.00	1.00	3.33
(H)	1.14	1.25	0.00	3.00	40	1.00	0.00	0.56	-1.36
HD	0.81	0.74	0.00	2.00	45	1.00	1.00	0.32	-1.09
(Hd)	0.36	0.56	0.00	2.00	23	0.00	0.00	1.32	0.83
Hx	0.06	[0.23]	0.00	1.00	4	0.00	0.00	3.99	14.35
All H Cont	3.59	2.01	0.00	7.00	63	4.00	4.00	-0.18	-0.39
A	7.04	2.14	4.00	14.00	73	6.00	6.00	0.70	0.20
(A)	0.37	[0.49]	0.00	1.00	27	0.00	0.00	0.55	-1.75
Ad	2.16	[2.72]	0.00	8.00	55	1.00	1.00	1.53	0.82
(Ad)	0.37	[0.54]	0.00	2.00	25	0.00	0.00	1.08	0.18
An	0.64	[1.12]	0.00	4.00	24	0.00	0.00	1.84	2.59
Art	1.52	1.41	0.00	5.00	50	1.00	0.00	0.51	-0.88
Ay	0.11	[0.36]	0.00	2.00	7	0.00	0.00	3.45	12.43
Bl	0.49	[0.90]	0.00	3.00	22	0.00	0.00	1.90	2.67
Bt	1.36	1.17	0.00	4.00	59	1.00	1.00	1.13	0.58
Cg	1.99	2.37	0.00	6.00	38	1.00	0.00	0.71	-1.14
Cl	0.21	[0.41]	0.00	1.00	15	0.00	0.00	1.48	0.22
Ex	0.30	[0.49]	0.00	2.00	21	0.00	0.00	1.24	0.38
Fi	0.23	[0.43]	0.00	1.00	17	0.00	0.00	1.29	-0.34
Food	0.26	[0.60]	0.00	2.00	13	0.00	0.00	2.18	3.48
Ge	0.04	[0.20]	0.00	1.00	3	0.00	0.00	4.72	20.86
Hh	0.88	1.26	0.00	4.00	30	0.00	0.00	1.31	0.73
Ls	0.81	1.01	0.00	6.00	40	1.00	0.00	2.23	8.62
Na	0.80	[1.37]	0.00	4.00	26	0.00	0.00	1.70	1.44
Sc	0.58	[0.80]	0.00	3.00	29	0.00	0.00	1.09	0.05
Sx	0.62	[0.86]	0.00	4.00	30	0.00	0.00	1.37	1.88
Xy	0.10	[0.30]	0.00	1.00	7	0.00	0.00	2.80	6.02
Idio	0.59	1.09	0.00	6.00	25	0.00	0.00	2.67	8.77
DV	1.78	[1.50]	0.00	5.00	60	2.00	2.00	1.06	0.48
INCOM	0.89	[0.57]	0.00	2.00	57	1.00	1.00	-0.02	0.12
DR	0.38	[0.83]	0.00	3.00	14	0.00	0.00	1.89	2.15
FABCOM	0.59	[0.70]	0.00	2.00	34	0.00	0.00	0.78	-0.60
DV2	0.14	[0.35]	0.00	1.00	10	0.00	0.00	2.15	2.72
INC2	0.06	[0.23]	0.00	1.00	4	0.00	0.00	3.99	14.35
DR2	0.10	[0.38]	0.00	2.00	5	0.00	0.00	4.19	17.63
FAB2	0.00	[0.00]	0.00	0.00	0	0.00	0.00	----	----
ALOG	0.32	[0.66]	0.00	2.00	15	0.00	0.00	1.88	2.04
CONTAM	0.00	0.00	0.00	0.00	0	0.00	0.00	----	----
Sum 6 Sp Sc	4.25	2.37	0.00	9.00	71	4.00	4.00	0.65	0.18
Lvl 2 Sp Sc	0.29	[0.61]	0.00	3.00	17	0.00	0.00	2.74	8.98
WSum6	9.71	4.68	0.00	20.00	71	11.00	12.00	-0.31	-0.36
AB	0.33	[0.47]	0.00	1.00	24	0.00	0.00	0.74	-1.49
AG	0.49	0.71	0.00	2.00	27	0.00	0.00	1.10	-0.13
COP	0.51	0.71	0.00	2.00	28	0.00	0.00	1.05	-0.22
CP	0.06	[0.23]	0.00	1.00	4	0.00	0.00	3.99	14.35
GOODHR	2.69	1.49	0.00	8.00	63	3.00	3.00	0.20	1.68
POORHR	1.27	1.23	0.00	4.00	47	1.00	0.00	0.75	-0.06
MOR	1.25	[1.48]	0.00	5.00	49	1.00	1.00	1.54	1.44
PER	1.63	1.51	0.00	4.00	50	1.00	0.00	0.38	-1.41
PSV	0.37	[0.57]	0.00	2.00	24	0.00	0.00	1.24	0.63

NOTE: Standard Deviations shown in brackets indicate that the value is probably unreliable and/or misleading and should not be used to estimate expected ranges. Ordinarily these variables should not be included in most parametric analyses.

TABLE 30. FREQUENCIES FOR 36 VARIABLES FOR OUTPATIENT EXTRATENSIVES   (N = 73)

DEMOGRAPHY VARIABLES

MARITAL STATUS			AGE			RACE		
Single	36	49%	18-25	16	22%	White	58	79%
Lives w/S.O.	2	3%	26-35	39	53%	Black	8	11%
Married	21	29%	36-45	4	6%	Hispanic	6	8%
Separated	4	5%	46-55	6	8%	Asian	1	1%
Divorced	10	14%	56-65	8	11%			
Widowed	0	0%	OVER 65	0	0%			

SEX						EDUCATION		
						UNDER 12	13	18%
Male	21	29%				12 Years	15	21%
Female	52	71%				13-15 Yrs	29	40%
						16+ Yrs	16	22%

RATIOS, PERCENTAGES AND SPECIAL INDICES

STYLES			FORM QUALITY DEVIATIONS		
Introversive	0	0%	XA% > .89	8	11%
Pervasive	0	0%	XA% < .70	12	16%
Ambitent	0	0%	WDA% < .85	48	66%
Extratensive	73	100%	WDA% < .75	27	37%
Pervasive	45	62%	X+% < .55	12	16%
Avoidant	0	0%	Xu% > .20	29	40%
			X-% > .20	24	33%
D-SCORES			X-% > .30	6	8%
D Score > 0	17	23%			
D Score = 0	24	33%	FC:CF+C RATIO		
D Score < 0	32	44%	FC > (CF+C) + 2	0	0%
D Score < -1	7	10%	FC > (CF+C) + 1	0	0%
			(CF+C) > FC+1	65	89%
Adj D Score > 0	21	29%	(CF+C) > FC+2	36	49%
Adj D Score = 0	22	30%			
Adj D Score < 0	30	41%			
Adj D Score < -1	5	7%	S-Constellation Positive	1	1%
			HVI Positive	11	15%
Zd > +3.0 (Overincorp) 11 15%			OBS Positive	2	3%
Zd < -3.0 (Underincorp) 16 22%					

PTI = 5	0	0%	DEPI = 7	0	0%	CDI = 5	12	16%
PTI = 4	0	0%	DEPI = 6	3	4%	CDI = 4	14	19%
PTI = 3	0	0%	DEPI = 5	33	45%			

MISCELLANEOUS VARIABLES

R < 17	28	38%	(2AB+Art+Ay) > 5	4	5%
R > 27	14	19%	Populars < 4	19	26%
DQv > 2	35	48%	Populars > 7	4	5%
S > 2	39	53%	COP = 0	45	62%
Sum T = 0	42	58%	COP > 2	0	0%
Sum T > 1	3	4%	AG = 0	46	63%
3r+(2)/R < .33	20	27%	AG > 2	0	0%
3r+(2)/R > .44	13	18%	MOR > 2	12	16%
Fr + rF > 0	11	15%	Level 2 Sp.Sc. > 0	17	23%
PureC > 0	49	67%	GHR > PHR	54	74%
PureC > 1	28	38%	Pure H < 2	44	60%
Afr < .40	13	18%	Pure H = 0	13	18%
Afr < .50	33	45%	p > a+1	12	16%
(FM+m) < Sum Shading	19	26%	Mp > Ma	21	29%

TABLE 31. DESCRIPTIVE STATISTICS FOR OUTPATIENT AMBITENTS (N = 110)

VARIABLE	MEAN	SD	MIN	MAX	FREQ	MEDIAN	MODE	SK	KU
AGE	37.08	15.22	18.00	70.00	110	34.00	23.00	1.01	-0.02
Years Education	13.41	2.72	10.00	17.00	110	13.00	13.00	-1.85	10.69
R	18.91	4.44	14.00	35.00	110	18.00	16.00	1.19	1.01
W	8.80	3.19	4.00	24.00	110	9.00	7.00	1.60	5.53
D	7.03	3.89	2.00	19.00	110	7.00	4.00	0.98	0.32
Dd	3.08	[2.00]	0.00	11.00	100	3.00	4.00	0.66	1.26
S	2.08	[1.82]	0.00	9.00	79	2.00	0.00	0.77	0.77
DQ+	6.91	2.34	2.00	15.00	110	7.00	7.00	0.35	1.70
DQo	10.63	3.78	4.00	21.00	110	10.00	11.00	1.19	1.15
DQv	1.19	[1.25]	0.00	9.00	81	1.00	1.00	2.88	14.35
DQv/+	0.18	[0.39]	0.00	1.00	20	0.00	0.00	1.67	0.81
FQx+	0.48	0.80	0.00	4.00	39	0.00	0.00	2.20	6.09
FQxo	11.39	3.83	6.00	22.00	110	11.00	13.00	0.60	0.07
FQxu	3.51	2.02	0.00	12.00	107	3.00	2.00	1.17	2.82
FQx-	3.03	1.94	0.00	9.00	100	4.00	4.00	0.39	0.58
FQxNone	0.50	[0.65]	0.00	4.00	50	0.00	0.00	1.97	7.81
MQ+	0.28	0.54	0.00	3.00	27	0.00	0.00	2.16	5.65
MQo	2.79	1.22	0.00	7.00	108	3.00	3.00	0.07	0.29
MQu	0.56	0.89	0.00	5.00	37	0.00	0.00	1.79	4.27
MQ-	0.30	[0.53]	0.00	2.00	29	0.00	0.00	1.59	1.69
MQNone	0.00	[0.00]	0.00	0.00	0	0.00	0.00	----	----
S-	0.93	[1.20]	0.00	4.00	48	0.00	0.00	0.95	-0.29
M	3.93	1.51	0.00	10.00	108	4.00	4.00	1.00	4.36
FM	3.93	1.74	0.00	8.00	108	4.00	5.00	0.14	-0.34
m	1.58	1.32	0.00	6.00	82	2.00	2.00	0.78	0.74
FM+m	5.51	1.92	2.00	13.00	110	6.00	6.00	0.72	1.64
FC	1.98	1.66	0.00	7.00	87	2.00	2.00	0.84	0.35
CF	1.63	1.37	0.00	8.00	85	1.00	1.00	1.09	2.95
C	0.54	[0.77]	0.00	4.00	44	0.00	0.00	1.62	3.21
Cn	0.00	[0.00]	0.00	0.00	0	0.00	0.00	----	----
Sum Color	4.14	2.09	1.00	11.00	110	4.00	4.00	0.69	0.71
WSumC	3.42	1.66	1.50	10.00	110	3.50	3.50	1.44	3.39
Sum C'	1.47	[1.46]	0.00	5.00	82	1.00	1.00	1.19	0.60
Sum T	0.84	[1.06]	0.00	3.00	51	0.00	0.00	0.94	-0.49
Sum V	0.60	[0.94]	0.00	3.00	36	0.00	0.00	1.22	0.05
Sum Y	1.28	[1.20]	0.00	5.00	71	1.00	0.00	0.55	-0.51
Sum Shading	4.19	3.30	0.00	11.00	96	3.00	3.00	0.58	-0.77
Fr+rF	0.16	[0.43]	0.00	3.00	15	0.00	0.00	3.60	17.11
FD	1.18	[1.32]	0.00	5.00	75	1.00	1.00	1.69	2.70
F	5.53	2.42	2.00	12.00	110	5.00	4.00	1.22	0.50
(2)	6.81	2.70	4.00	16.00	110	5.00	5.00	0.98	0.41
3r+(2)/R	0.38	0.11	0.24	0.93	110	0.34	0.33	1.64	5.66
Lambda	0.43	0.20	0.15	0.92	110	0.36	0.36	0.97	0.08
EA	7.35	3.03	1.50	19.00	110	7.50	7.50	1.42	4.44
es	9.70	4.13	2.00	17.00	110	9.00	12.00	0.29	-1.10
D Score	-0.66	1.38	-4.00	2.00	110	0.00	0.00	-0.75	-0.01
AdjD	-0.11	1.31	-3.00	4.00	110	0.00	0.00	-0.27	1.01
a (active)	5.99	2.43	2.00	14.00	110	6.00	5.00	0.61	1.58
p (passive)	3.45	2.18	0.00	7.00	105	3.00	2.00	0.34	-1.10
Ma	2.56	1.71	0.00	7.00	95	2.00	2.00	0.48	-0.08
Mp	1.36	1.12	0.00	4.00	75	1.50	2.00	0.11	-1.23
Intellect	1.74	1.97	0.00	10.00	72	1.00	0.00	1.37	2.00
Zf	12.26	3.31	5.00	26.00	110	12.50	10.00	1.32	4.54
Zd	0.53	4.52	-6.50	13.00	106	-0.25	-3.50	0.37	-0.72
Blends	4.30	2.47	1.00	13.00	110	4.00	1.00	0.54	0.10
Blends/R	0.23	0.13	0.05	0.57	110	0.24	0.07	0.32	-0.77
Col-Shd Blends	0.69	[0.85]	0.00	4.00	54	0.00	0.00	1.36	2.38
Afr	0.56	0.21	0.18	1.10	110	0.58	0.48	1.24	0.71

TABLE 31. OUTPATIENTS AMBITENTS (N = 110) (Continued)

VARIABLE	MEAN	SD	MIN	MAX	FREQ	MEDIAN	MODE	SK	KU
Populars	5.14	2.50	0.00	10.00	104	5.00	5.00	-0.05	-0.57
XA%	0.81	0.12	0.60	1.00	110	0.83	0.89	-0.27	-0.87
WDA%	0.85	0.09	0.67	1.00	110	0.85	0.94	-0.17	-0.92
X+%	0.63	0.15	0.28	0.95	110	0.65	0.68	-0.03	-0.74
X-%	0.16	0.11	0.00	0.36	100	0.15	0.27	0.16	-1.25
Xu%	0.18	0.09	0.00	0.41	107	0.18	0.21	0.24	-0.52
Isolate/R	0.12	0.09	0.00	0.38	90	0.11	0.00	0.69	0.09
H	2.36	1.40	0.00	9.00	108	2.00	1.00	1.14	3.32
(H)	1.44	1.24	0.00	4.00	86	1.00	1.00	0.74	-0.50
HD	1.41	0.88	0.00	5.00	96	1.00	1.00	0.73	1.92
(Hd)	0.56	0.83	0.00	4.00	40	0.00	0.00	1.39	1.54
Hx	0.01	[0.10]	0.00	1.00	1	0.00	0.00	10.48	110.00
All H Cont	5.77	2.71	0.00	16.00	108	5.00	5.00	0.85	0.89
A	6.85	2.46	4.00	13.00	110	6.50	5.00	1.30	1.00
(A)	0.16	[0.37]	0.00	1.00	18	0.00	0.00	1.84	1.42
Ad	1.93	[1.58]	0.00	6.00	91	1.00	1.00	0.70	-0.27
(Ad)	0.06	[0.25]	0.00	1.00	7	0.00	0.00	3.62	11.35
An	0.74	[0.96]	0.00	5.00	57	1.00	0.00	2.05	5.91
Art	1.02	1.09	0.00	5.00	69	1.00	1.00	1.21	1.24
Ay	0.16	[0.36]	0.00	1.00	17	0.00	0.00	1.93	1.79
Bl	0.24	[0.45]	0.00	2.00	25	0.00	0.00	1.56	1.28
Bt	0.89	0.90	0.00	3.00	68	1.00	1.00	0.90	0.18
Cg	1.39	1.40	0.00	7.00	74	1.00	0.00	1.29	2.86
Cl	0.16	[0.36]	0.00	1.00	17	0.00	0.00	1.93	1.79
Ex	0.21	[0.53]	0.00	2.00	17	0.00	0.00	2.50	5.28
Fi	0.34	[0.53]	0.00	2.00	34	0.00	0.00	1.25	0.61
Food	0.23	[0.42]	0.00	1.00	25	0.00	0.00	1.32	-0.26
Ge	0.14	[0.68]	0.00	4.00	5	0.00	0.00	5.25	27.13
Hh	0.46	0.71	0.00	2.00	37	0.00	0.00	1.21	0.05
Ls	0.74	0.91	0.00	5.00	55	0.50	0.00	1.45	3.34
Na	0.15	[0.43]	0.00	3.00	14	0.00	0.00	3.78	18.75
Sc	0.11	[0.46]	0.00	4.00	9	0.00	0.00	6.33	49.31
Sx	0.62	[0.90]	0.00	3.00	47	0.00	0.00	1.61	1.91
Xy	0.05	[0.21]	0.00	1.00	5	0.00	0.00	4.42	17.90
Idio	1.25	1.01	0.00	6.00	93	1.00	1.00	1.59	3.92
DV	0.70	[1.04]	0.00	5.00	48	0.00	0.00	2.04	5.14
INCOM	0.66	[0.85]	0.00	3.00	53	0.00	0.00	1.46	1.78
DR	0.29	[0.88]	0.00	4.00	16	0.00	0.00	3.56	12.30
FABCOM	0.46	[0.70]	0.00	2.00	37	0.00	0.00	1.23	0.14
DV2	0.12	[0.38]	0.00	2.00	11	0.00	0.00	3.38	11.63
INC2	0.13	[0.41]	0.00	2.00	11	0.00	0.00	3.39	11.34
DR2	0.01	[0.10]	0.00	1.00	1	0.00	0.00	10.48	110.00
FAB2	0.13	[0.47]	0.00	2.00	8	0.00	0.00	3.61	11.64
ALOG	0.04	[0.19]	0.00	1.00	4	0.00	0.00	5.02	23.65
CONTAM	0.00	0.00	0.00	0.00	0	0.00	0.00	----	----
Sum 6 Sp Sc	2.52	2.83	0.00	11.00	81	1.00	0.00	1.67	2.78
Lvl 2 Sp Sc	0.38	[0.85]	0.00	4.00	25	0.00	0.00	2.69	7.77
WSum6	6.57	9.72	0.00	40.00	81	3.50	0.00	2.46	5.89
AB	0.28	[0.47]	0.00	2.00	30	0.00	0.00	1.24	0.23
AG	1.14	1.30	0.00	6.00	60	1.00	0.00	1.31	2.32
COP	1.45	1.33	0.00	5.00	70	2.00	2.00	0.51	-0.35
CP	0.00	[0.00]	0.00	0.00	0	0.00	0.00	----	----
GOODHR	3.93	1.62	0.00	10.00	108	4.00	5.00	0.12	1.13
POORHR	2.56	1.95	0.00	10.00	98	2.00	2.00	1.06	1.40
MOR	1.18	[1.38]	0.00	4.00	62	1.00	0.00	0.98	-0.30
PER	0.70	1.46	0.00	11.00	35	0.00	0.00	3.91	22.61
PSV	0.13	[0.43]	0.00	2.00	10	0.00	0.00	3.51	11.76

NOTE: Standard Deviations shown in brackets indicate that the value is probably unreliable and/or misleading and should not be used to estimate expected ranges. Ordinarily these variables should not be included in most parametric analyses.

TABLE 32. FREQUENCIES FOR 36 VARIABLES FOR OUTPATIENT AMBITENTS
(N = 110)

DEMOGRAPHY VARIABLES

MARITAL STATUS			AGE			RACE		
Single	33	30%	18-25	31	28%	White	93	85%
Lives w/S.O.	12	11%	26-35	33	30%	Black	11	10%
Married	49	45%	36-45	22	20%	Hispanic	6	5%
Separated	5	5%	46-55	4	4%	Asian	0	0%
Divorced	11	10%	56-65	8	7%			
Widowed	0	0%	OVER 65	12	11%			
						EDUCATION		
SEX						UNDER 12	9	8%
Male	38	35%				12 Years	38	35%
Female	72	65%				13-15 Yrs	46	42%
						16+ Yrs	17	15%

RATIOS, PERCENTAGES AND SPECIAL INDICES

STYLES			FORM QUALITY DEVIATIONS		
Introversive	0	0%	XA% > .89	22	20%
Pervasive	0	0%	XA% < .70	19	17%
Ambitent	110	100%	WDA% < .85	52	47%
Extratensive	0	0%	WDA% < .75	20	18%
Pervasive	0	0%	X+% < .55	35	32%
Avoidant	0	0%	Xu% > .20	46	42%
			X-% > .20	43	39%
D-SCORES			X-% > .30	15	14%
D Score > 0	21	19%			
D Score = 0	39	35%			
D Score < 0	50	45%	FC:CF+C RATIO		
D Score < -1	25	23%	FC > (CF+C) + 2	12	11%
			FC > (CF+C) + 1	22	20%
Adj D Score > 0	31	28%	(CF+C) > FC+1	28	25%
Adj D Score = 0	50	45%	(CF+C) > FC+2	8	7%
Adj D Score < 0	29	26%			
Adj D Score < -1	16	15%			
			S-Constellation Positive	0	0%
Zd > +3.0 (Overincorp)	31	28%	HVI Positive	22	20%
Zd < -3.0 (Underincorp)	36	33%	OBS Positive	6	5%

PTI = 5	3	3%	DEPI = 7	0	0%	CDI = 5	2	2%
PTI = 4	0	0%	DEPI = 6	3	3%	CDI = 4	21	19%
PTI = 3	0	0%	DEPI = 5	13	12%			

MISCELLANEOUS VARIABLES

R < 17	38	35%	(2AB+Art+Ay) > 5	8	7%
R > 27	6	5%	Populars < 4	26	24%
DQv > 2	12	11%	Populars > 7	21	19%
S > 2	46	42%	COP = 0	40	36%
Sum T = 0	59	54%	COP > 2	16	15%
Sum T > 1	28	25%	AG = 0	50	45%
3r+(2)/R < .33	24	22%	AG > 2	6	5%
3r+(2)/R > .44	25	23%	MOR > 2	20	18%
Fr + rF > 0	15	14%	Level 2 Sp.Sc. > 0	25	23%
PureC > 0	44	40%	GHR > PHR	74	67%
PureC > 1	12	11%	Pure H < 2	40	36%
Afr < .40	34	31%	Pure H = 0	2	2%
Afr < .50	51	46%	p > a+1	16	15%
(FM+m) < Sum Shading	26	24%	Mp > Ma	21	19%

TABLE 33. DESCRIPTIVE STATISTICS FOR HIGH LAMBDA OUTPATIENTS

(N = 201)

VARIABLE	MEAN	SD	MIN	MAX	FREQ	MEDIAN	MODE	SK	KU
AGE	34.35	12.40	18.00	66.00	201	31.00	23.00	0.83	-0.15
Years Educ	12.88	4.13	10.00	20.00	201	12.00	12.00	-1.53	2.15
R	20.61	5.52	14.00	41.00	201	19.00	16.00	1.32	1.74
W	6.58	3.25	1.00	18.00	201	6.00	4.00	0.46	-0.35
D	10.66	4.97	4.00	25.00	201	10.00	14.00	0.68	0.09
Dd	3.38	[3.13]	0.00	16.00	177	2.00	1.00	1.56	3.59
S	1.84	[1.85]	0.00	10.00	143	1.00	0.00	1.36	2.75
DQ+	4.08	2.13	0.00	10.00	196	4.00	5.00	0.40	0.52
DQo	15.11	5.70	7.00	32.00	201	16.00	16.00	0.76	0.42
DQv	1.28	[1.42]	0.00	6.00	125	1.00	0.00	1.33	1.65
DQv/+	0.14	[0.51]	0.00	3.00	19	0.00	0.00	4.22	18.88
FQx+	0.10	0.58	0.00	4.00	7	0.00	0.00	6.25	38.85
FQxo	12.37	3.89	6.00	29.00	201	12.00	12.00	1.07	2.21
FQxu	4.06	2.30	0.00	12.00	194	3.00	3.00	0.87	0.59
FQx-	3.64	2.62	0.00	11.00	176	3.00	4.00	0.68	0.11
FQxNone	0.44	[0.83]	0.00	3.00	55	0.00	0.00	1.88	2.60
MQ+	0.08	0.45	0.00	3.00	7	0.00	0.00	5.94	34.98
MQo	1.63	1.35	0.00	8.00	166	1.00	1.00	0.97	1.21
MQu	0.44	0.57	0.00	2.00	81	0.00	0.00	0.87	-0.23
MQ-	0.41	[0.57]	0.00	2.00	74	0.00	0.00	1.02	0.07
MQNone	0.00	[0.00]	0.00	0.00	0	0.00	0.00	----	----
S-	0.66	[1.02]	0.00	4.00	73	0.00	0.00	1.42	0.91
M	2.56	1.79	0.00	11.00	178	2.00	2.00	0.76	1.23
FM	1.44	1.26	0.00	5.00	149	1.00	1.00	0.67	-0.44
m	0.72	1.07	0.00	5.00	91	0.00	0.00	2.01	4.38
FM+m	2.16	1.86	0.00	8.00	161	2.00	1.00	0.87	0.20
FC	0.96	1.05	0.00	5.00	121	1.00	0.00	1.27	1.70
CF	0.65	1.01	0.00	4.00	72	0.00	0.00	1.42	1.07
C	0.49	[0.81]	0.00	3.00	65	0.00	0.00	1.57	1.56
Cn	0.02	[0.14]	0.00	1.00	4	0.00	0.00	6.92	46.45
Sum Color	2.12	1.44	0.00	6.00	179	2.00	1.00	0.70	0.38
WSumC	1.87	1.46	0.00	7.00	179	1.50	1.00	0.84	0.48
Sum C'	0.53	[0.74]	0.00	3.00	82	0.00	0.00	1.46	1.94
Sum T	0.22	[0.53]	0.00	3.00	37	0.00	0.00	2.94	10.32
Sum V	0.13	[0.41]	0.00	2.00	22	0.00	0.00	3.19	9.94
Sum Y	0.69	[1.10]	0.00	6.00	85	0.00	0.00	2.40	7.17
Sum Shading	1.58	1.72	0.00	8.00	148	1.00	1.00	1.57	2.21
Fr+rF	0.17	[0.58]	0.00	3.00	21	0.00	0.00	3.73	13.95
FD	0.51	[0.70]	0.00	2.00	78	0.00	0.00	1.02	-0.26
F	13.18	4.82	7.00	30.00	201	12.00	11.00	1.24	1.81
(2)	7.88	3.43	3.00	21.00	201	7.00	6.00	0.94	0.70
3r+(2)/R	0.41	0.14	0.14	0.79	201	0.39	0.39	0.57	0.15
Lambda	2.14	1.59	1.00	7.67	201	1.75	1.00	2.23	4.58
EA	4.43	2.29	0.00	14.50	199	4.00	2.50	0.59	0.66
es	3.74	2.77	1.00	14.00	201	3.00	2.00	1.62	3.05
D Score	0.20	1.11	-4.00	2.00	201	0.00	0.00	-0.94	3.68
AdjD	0.42	0.89	-2.00	4.00	201	0.00	0.00	0.47	1.37
a (active)	2.45	1.94	0.00	13.00	176	2.00	2.00	1.37	3.63
p (passive)	2.28	1.79	0.00	7.00	165	2.00	2.00	0.74	-0.14
Ma	1.27	1.22	0.00	8.00	146	1.00	1.00	1.54	4.48
Mp	1.29	1.23	0.00	4.00	136	1.00	0.00	0.81	-0.08
Intellect	1.45	1.59	0.00	6.00	124	1.00	0.00	1.13	0.81
Zf	8.95	3.59	2.00	21.00	201	9.00	11.00	0.30	0.37
Zd	-1.26	3.92	-11.50	9.50	193	-1.00	-1.00	-0.06	-0.40
Blends	1.46	1.57	0.00	7.00	137	1.00	1.00	1.20	0.86
Blends/R	0.07	0.08	0.00	0.29	137	0.05	0.00	1.11	0.40
Col-Shd Blends	0.27	[0.46]	0.00	2.00	53	0.00	0.00	1.21	-0.10
Afr	0.48	0.20	0.23	1.13	201	0.50	0.46	1.07	0.73

TABLE 33. HIGH LAMBDA OUTPATIENTS (N = 201) (Continued)

VARIABLE	MEAN	SD	MIN	MAX	FREQ	MEDIAN	MODE	SK	KU
Populars	5.21	1.78	1.00	10.00	201	5.00	4.00	0.33	-0.06
XA%	0.80	0.11	0.50	1.00	201	0.80	1.00	0.14	-0.11
WDA%	0.85	0.10	0.64	1.00	201	0.83	1.00	----	-0.76
X+%	0.61	0.13	0.33	0.89	201	0.60	0.52	0.11	-0.56
X-%	0.17	0.11	0.00	0.44	176	0.19	0.00	0.07	-0.66
Xu%	0.19	0.09	0.00	0.42	194	0.19	0.14	0.31	0.22
Isolate/R	0.09	0.11	0.00	0.36	114	0.06	0.00	1.10	0.24
H	2.03	1.33	0.00	5.00	186	2.00	1.00	0.55	-0.70
(H)	0.68	1.07	0.00	4.00	75	0.00	0.00	1.51	1.23
HD	1.49	1.66	0.00	8.00	146	1.00	1.00	1.78	3.46
(Hd)	0.69	1.04	0.00	5.00	75	0.00	0.00	1.46	1.90
Hx	0.05	[0.30]	0.00	2.00	6	0.00	0.00	6.11	36.98
All H Cont	4.89	2.64	0.00	15.00	197	4.00	3.00	0.74	0.63
A	8.33	3.00	2.00	16.00	201	8.00	7.00	0.16	-0.90
(A)	0.24	[0.45]	0.00	2.00	47	0.00	0.00	1.52	1.15
Ad	2.09	[2.09]	0.00	11.00	159	2.00	2.00	1.66	3.26
(Ad)	0.07	[0.25]	0.00	1.00	13	0.00	0.00	3.56	10.83
An	1.10	[1.50]	0.00	11.00	113	1.00	0.00	2.46	9.77
Art	0.98	1.14	0.00	4.00	106	1.00	0.00	0.90	-0.36
Ay	0.18	[0.41]	0.00	2.00	34	0.00	0.00	2.11	3.67
Bl	0.18	[0.48]	0.00	3.00	29	0.00	0.00	2.99	9.76
Bt	0.87	1.33	0.00	5.00	85	0.00	0.00	1.59	1.41
Cg	1.28	1.28	0.00	6.00	130	1.00	0.00	1.03	1.19
Cl	0.17	[0.52]	0.00	2.00	22	0.00	0.00	2.92	7.13
Ex	0.05	[0.24]	0.00	2.00	9	0.00	0.00	5.22	29.65
Fi	0.23	[0.49]	0.00	2.00	40	0.00	0.00	2.05	3.49
Food	0.35	[0.57]	0.00	2.00	61	0.00	0.00	1.39	0.97
Ge	0.05	[0.23]	0.00	2.00	8	0.00	0.00	5.61	34.47
Hh	0.39	0.71	0.00	4.00	57	0.00	0.00	2.19	5.93
Ls	0.40	0.82	0.00	3.00	46	0.00	0.00	1.93	2.59
Na	0.12	[0.36]	0.00	2.00	23	0.00	0.00	2.92	8.37
Sc	0.44	[0.57]	0.00	2.00	80	0.00	0.00	0.89	-0.20
Sx	0.55	[1.06]	0.00	5.00	63	0.00	0.00	2.50	6.37
Xy	0.06	[0.24]	0.00	1.00	12	0.00	0.00	3.74	12.14
Idio	0.98	1.17	0.00	4.00	104	1.00	0.00	0.95	-0.15
DV	0.61	[0.78]	0.00	2.00	85	0.00	0.00	0.81	-0.88
INCOM	0.99	[1.23]	0.00	6.00	106	1.00	0.00	1.33	1.75
DR	0.25	[0.76]	0.00	5.00	29	0.00	0.00	4.17	19.91
FABCOM	0.25	[0.48]	0.00	2.00	46	0.00	0.00	1.71	2.08
DV2	0.10	[0.29]	0.00	1.00	19	0.00	0.00	2.79	5.86
INC2	0.17	[0.48]	0.00	2.00	25	0.00	0.00	2.88	7.45
DR2	0.10	[0.34]	0.00	2.00	16	0.00	0.00	3.86	15.44
FAB2	0.39	[0.82]	0.00	3.00	46	0.00	0.00	2.20	3.89
ALOG	0.12	[0.37]	0.00	2.00	22	0.00	0.00	3.12	9.76
CONTAM	0.00	0.00	0.00	0.00	0	0.00	0.00	----	----
Sum 6 Sp Sc	2.97	2.39	0.00	11.00	185	2.00	1.00	1.27	1.76
Lvl 2 Sp Sc	0.75	[1.02]	0.00	4.00	90	0.00	0.00	1.37	1.13
WSum6	9.10	8.74	0.00	48.00	185	7.00	8.00	1.96	4.96
AB	0.15	[0.41]	0.00	2.00	26	0.00	0.00	2.82	7.69
AG	0.47	0.80	0.00	4.00	58	0.00	0.00	1.49	1.31
COP	0.68	0.67	0.00	3.00	116	1.00	1.00	0.67	0.25
CP	0.00	[0.00]	0.00	0.00	0	0.00	0.00	----	----
GOODHR	2.81	1.65	0.00	9.00	189	3.00	4.00	0.58	0.95
POORHR	2.48	2.06	0.00	11.00	171	2.00	2.00	1.22	1.82
MOR	0.96	[1.43]	0.00	7.00	97	0.00	0.00	1.95	3.80
PER	1.18	2.01	0.00	10.00	88	0.00	0.00	2.52	7.54
PSV	0.29	[0.78]	0.00	3.00	32	0.00	0.00	2.81	6.86

NOTE: Standard Deviations shown in brackets indicate that the value is probably unreliable and/or misleading and should not be used to estimate expected ranges. Ordinarily these variables should not be included in most parametric analyses.

TABLE 34. FREQUENCIES FOR 36 VARIABLES FOR HIGH LAMBDA OUTPATIENTS (N = 201)

DEMOGRAPHY VARIABLES

MARITAL STATUS			AGE			RACE		
Single	45	22%	18-25	63	31%	White	173	86%
Lives w/S.O.	10	5%	26-35	51	25%	Black	15	7%
Married	122	61%	36-45	49	24%	Hispanic	11	5%
Separated	13	6%	46-55	18	9%	Asian	2	1%
Divorced	7	3%	56-65	18	9%			
Widowed	4	2%	OVER 65	2	1%			
						EDUCATION		
SEX						UNDER 12	28	14%
Male	74	37%				12 Years	72	36%
Female	127	63%				13-15 Yrs	66	33%
						16+ Yrs	35	17%

RATIOS, PERCENTAGES AND SPECIAL INDICES

STYLES			FORM QUALITY DEVIATIONS		
Introversive	0	0%	XA% > .89	33	16%
Pervasive	0	0%	XA% < .70	26	13%
Ambitent	0	0%	WDA% < .85	116	58%
Extratensive	0	0%	WDA% < .75	27	13%
Pervasive	0	0%	X+% < .55	70	35%
Avoidant	201	100%	Xu% > .20	81	40%
			X-% > .20	83	41%
D-SCORES			X-% > .30	16	8%
D Score > 0	57	28%			
D Score = 0	117	58%			
D Score < 0	27	13%	FC:CF+C RATIO		
D Score < -1	8	4%	FC > (CF+C) + 2	4	2%
			FC > (CF+C) + 1	38	19%
Adj D Score > 0	70	35%	(CF+C) > FC+1	40	20%
Adj D Score = 0	120	60%	(CF+C) > FC+2	23	11%
Adj D Score < 0	11	5%			
Adj D Score < -1	5	2%			
			S-Constellation Positive	0	0%
Zd > +3.0 (Overincorp)	28	14%	HVI Positive	8	4%
Zd < -3.0 (Underincorp)	58	29%	OBS Positive	1	0%

PTI = 5	0	0%	DEPI = 7	0	0%	CDI = 5	28	14%
PTI = 4	0	0%	DEPI = 6	8	4%	CDI = 4	64	32%
PTI = 3	4	2%	DEPI = 5	26	13%			

MISCELLANEOUS VARIABLES

R < 17	55	27%	(2AB+Art+Ay) > 5	8	4%
R > 27	21	10%	Populars < 4	23	11%
DQv > 2	32	16%	Populars > 7	21	10%
S > 2	61	30%	COP = 0	85	42%
Sum T = 0	164	82%	COP > 2	2	1%
Sum T > 1	5	2%	AG = 0	143	71%
3r+(2)/R < .33	5	28%	AG > 2	1	0%
3r+(2)/R > .44	53	26%	MOR > 2	25	12%
Fr + rF > 0	21	10%	Level 2 Sp.Sc. > 0	90	45%
PureC > 0	65	32%	GHR > PHR	92	46%
PureC > 1	27	13%	Pure H < 2	89	44%
Afr < .40	49	24%	Pure H = 0	15	7%
Afr < .50	98	49%	p > a+1	55	27%
(FM+m) < Sum Shading	71	35%	Mp > Ma	66	33%

TABLE 35. DESCRIPTIVE STATISTICS FOR INPATIENTS DEPRESSIVES

LAMBDA < 1.0 (N = 193)

VARIABLE	MEAN	SD	MIN	MAX	FREQ	MEDIAN	MODE	SK	KU
AGE	40.02	13.01	18.00	71.00	193	40.00	46.00	0.19	-0.80
Years Educ	11.83	6.02	10.00	20.00	193	12.50	12.00	-1.09	0.04
R	22.56	7.20	14.00	43.00	193	21.00	17.00	0.99	0.52
W	9.33	4.27	0.00	18.00	184	10.00	11.00	-0.52	-0.52
D	9.75	5.94	1.00	27.00	193	8.00	4.00	0.95	0.76
Dd	3.49	[3.88]	0.00	14.00	157	2.00	0.00	1.67	2.07
S	2.24	[2.07]	0.00	9.00	148	2.00	0.00	0.97	0.74
DQ+	6.83	3.33	1.00	18.00	193	6.00	4.00	0.77	0.71
DQo	12.82	6.15	4.00	33.00	193	11.00	11.00	1.44	2.25
DQv	2.60	[2.10]	0.00	7.00	155	2.00	0.00	0.57	-0.52
DQv/+	0.31	[0.65]	0.00	3.00	42	0.00	0.00	2.10	3.71
FQx+	0.04	0.27	0.00	3.00	6	0.00	0.00	8.39	82.67
FQxo	11.65	3.79	5.00	20.00	193	11.00	11.00	0.21	-0.61
FQxu	5.49	3.20	1.00	13.00	193	6.00	2.00	0.51	-0.32
FQx-	4.35	2.82	0.00	11.00	180	4.00	2.00	0.53	-0.41
FQxNone	1.03	[1.31]	0.00	4.00	103	1.00	0.00	1.26	0.44
MQ+	0.03	0.19	0.00	2.00	4	0.00	0.00	8.13	72.02
MQo	2.65	1.50	0.00	6.00	185	2.00	2.00	0.55	-0.26
MQu	0.73	1.04	0.00	5.00	88	0.00	0.00	2.00	5.35
MQ-	0.52	[0.83]	0.00	4.00	67	0.00	0.00	1.76	3.39
MQNone	0.05	[0.22]	0.00	1.00	10	0.00	0.00	4.07	14.77
S-	0.84	[1.05]	0.00	4.00	96	0.00	0.00	1.19	0.84
M	3.98	2.10	1.00	9.00	193	4.00	4.00	0.59	-0.17
FM	3.97	2.92	0.00	14.00	187	3.00	2.00	1.82	4.11
m	1.89	2.15	0.00	11.00	139	1.00	0.00	2.14	6.29
FM+m	5.86	3.76	0.00	15.00	190	5.00	3.00	0.92	0.35
FC	1.75	1.98	0.00	11.00	124	1.00	0.00	1.59	3.73
CF	1.79	1.42	0.00	8.00	156	2.00	1.00	0.87	1.19
C	0.73	[1.01]	0.00	4.00	85	0.00	0.00	1.50	2.02
Cn	0.03	[0.16]	0.00	1.00	5	0.00	0.00	6.01	34.55
Sum Color	4.29	2.53	0.00	12.00	181	4.00	2.00	0.28	-0.33
WSumC	3.76	2.19	0.00	9.00	181	4.00	2.00	0.22	-0.78
Sum C'	2.44	[1.92]	0.00	8.00	158	2.00	1.00	0.61	-0.12
Sum T	0.90	[1.50]	0.00	7.00	84	0.00	0.00	2.43	6.34
Sum V	1.27	[1.29]	0.00	5.00	121	1.00	0.00	0.82	-0.04
Sum Y	2.03	[1.22]	0.00	4.00	170	2.00	3.00	-0.18	-1.20
Sum Shading	6.64	3.76	1.00	18.00	193	6.00	4.00	0.90	0.08
Fr+rF	0.12	[0.36]	0.00	2.00	21	0.00	0.00	3.04	9.24
FD	1.04	[1.14]	0.00	4.00	114	1.00	0.00	0.99	0.15
F	7.56	3.85	2.00	21.00	193	7.00	4.00	1.56	3.34
(2)	7.49	3.39	3.00	18.00	193	7.00	5.00	0.86	0.11
3r+(2)/R	0.36	0.14	0.16	0.67	193	0.33	0.21	0.56	-0.59
Lambda	0.52	0.21	0.15	0.95	193	0.50	0.50	0.14	-1.05
EA	7.74	3.64	2.00	18.00	193	6.50	5.00	0.80	0.26
es	12.51	5.08	4.00	27.00	193	12.00	9.00	0.52	0.31
D Score	-1.54	1.87	-6.00	3.00	193	-2.00	-2.00	-0.41	0.04
AdjD	-0.81	1.74	-6.00	3.00	193	-1.00	-1.00	-0.90	1.81
a (active)	5.80	3.05	0.00	14.00	186	6.00	6.00	0.22	-0.20
p (passive)	4.11	2.48	0.00	11.00	188	3.00	3.00	0.96	0.77
Ma	2.29	1.66	0.00	7.00	160	2.00	2.00	0.74	0.61
Mp	1.71	1.25	0.00	5.00	159	2.00	1.00	0.53	-0.15
Intellect	2.47	2.01	0.00	10.00	150	2.00	0.00	0.64	0.16
Zf	12.45	4.31	4.00	25.00	193	13.00	14.00	-0.02	-0.28
Zd	-1.16	5.05	-12.00	13.00	180	-0.50	-2.50	-0.08	-0.12
Blends	5.46	3.09	1.00	15.00	193	6.00	6.00	0.59	0.14
Blends/R	0.25	0.14	0.04	0.61	193	0.27	0.32	0.28	-0.37
Col-Shd Blends	1.19	[1.23]	0.00	5.00	127	1.00	1.00	1.21	1.21
Afr	0.46	0.16	0.16	0.94	193	0.40	0.36	0.65	0.04

TABLE 35. INPATIENT DEPRESSIVES LAMBDA < 1.0 (N = 193) (Continued)

VARIABLE	MEAN	SD	MIN	MAX	FREQ	MEDIAN	MODE	SK	KU
Populars	5.42	2.00	2.00	8.00	193	5.00	8.00	-0.06	-1.26
XA%	0.76	0.10	0.59	1.00	193	0.77	0.71	0.25	-0.39
WDA%	0.80	0.10	0.57	1.00	193	0.79	0.71	0.22	-0.19
X+%	0.53	0.12	0.28	0.80	193	0.53	0.47	0.00	-0.51
X-%	0.19	0.10	0.00	0.41	180	0.17	0.13	0.13	-0.73
Xu%	0.24	0.11	0.04	0.47	193	0.25	0.32	-0.10	-0.75
Isolate/R	0.19	0.11	0.00	0.52	178	0.17	0.32	0.26	-0.41
H	1.96	1.34	0.00	7.00	179	2.00	1.00	1.13	1.75
(H)	1.10	0.91	0.00	3.00	144	1.00	1.00	0.68	-0.17
HD	1.23	1.38	0.00	6.00	115	1.00	0.00	1.17	1.15
(Hd)	0.71	0.90	0.00	4.00	93	0.00	0.00	1.43	2.24
Hx	0.03	[0.17]	0.00	1.00	6	0.00	0.00	5.44	27.95
All H Cont	5.00	2.50	1.00	15.00	193	5.00	7.00	0.96	1.52
A	7.91	3.06	3.00	14.00	193	8.00	8.00	0.37	-0.81
(A)	0.61	[1.16]	0.00	5.00	65	0.00	0.00	2.63	7.16
Ad	1.97	[1.65]	0.00	6.00	156	2.00	1.00	0.72	-0.41
(Ad)	0.25	[0.48]	0.00	2.00	44	0.00	0.00	1.73	2.15
An	0.84	[1.15]	0.00	5.00	92	0.00	0.00	1.65	2.73
Art	1.73	1.64	0.00	5.00	130	1.00	0.00	0.49	-1.13
Ay	0.29	[0.45]	0.00	1.00	55	0.00	0.00	0.96	-1.09
Bl	0.57	[1.19]	0.00	6.00	51	0.00	0.00	2.84	9.28
Bt	1.13	1.25	0.00	4.00	110	1.00	0.00	0.82	-0.53
Cg	1.79	1.48	0.00	8.00	161	1.00	1.00	1.18	2.10
Cl	0.35	[0.60]	0.00	2.00	54	0.00	0.00	1.54	1.29
Ex	0.11	[0.39]	0.00	2.00	16	0.00	0.00	3.76	13.99
Fi	0.64	[0.73]	0.00	3.00	100	1.00	0.00	1.07	1.10
Food	0.37	[0.63]	0.00	3.00	58	0.00	0.00	1.88	3.78
Ge	0.11	[0.33]	0.00	2.00	20	0.00	0.00	2.96	8.40
Hh	0.48	0.64	0.00	2.00	78	0.00	0.00	0.98	-0.12
Ls	1.18	1.21	0.00	5.00	118	1.00	0.00	0.88	0.27
Na	0.50	[0.73]	0.00	3.00	71	0.00	0.00	1.16	0.18
Sc	0.78	[1.23]	0.00	5.00	73	0.00	0.00	1.73	2.65
Sx	0.91	[1.41]	0.00	5.00	74	0.00	0.00	1.41	0.84
Xy	0.16	[0.41]	0.00	2.00	28	0.00	0.00	2.53	6.01
Idio	2.08	1.69	0.00	7.00	162	2.00	1.00	0.99	0.81
DV	0.78	[1.07]	0.00	6.00	91	0.00	0.00	2.11	7.02
INCOM	1.25	[1.18]	0.00	4.00	127	1.00	0.00	0.63	-0.55
DR	1.15	[1.63]	0.00	5.00	78	0.00	0.00	1.01	-0.59
FABCOM	0.61	[1.20]	0.00	5.00	59	0.00	0.00	2.52	6.25
DV2	0.29	[0.69]	0.00	4.00	38	0.00	0.00	3.21	12.36
INC2	0.74	[1.08]	0.00	5.00	88	0.00	0.00	1.81	3.19
DR2	0.84	[1.53]	0.00	6.00	66	0.00	0.00	2.02	3.23
FAB2	0.58	[0.90]	0.00	5.00	78	0.00	0.00	2.12	5.22
ALOG	0.17	[0.39]	0.00	2.00	32	0.00	0.00	2.02	2.92
CONTAM	0.00	0.00	0.00	0.00	0	0.00	0.00	----	----
Sum 6 Sp Sc	6.40	2.73	1.00	13.00	193	7.00	4.00	0.15	-0.60
Lvl 2 Sp Sc	2.44	[2.40]	0.00	12.00	159	2.00	1.00	1.41	2.02
WSum6	22.62	13.65	2.00	65.00	193	22.00	39.00	0.65	-0.14
AB	0.23	[0.62]	0.00	3.00	26	0.00	0.00	2.71	6.37
AG	0.71	1.06	0.00	4.00	75	0.00	0.00	1.44	1.24
COP	0.86	0.92	0.00	3.00	105	1.00	0.00	0.66	-0.71
CP	0.07	[0.25]	0.00	1.00	13	0.00	0.00	3.47	10.21
GOODHR	2.56	1.38	0.00	8.00	190	2.00	3.00	0.98	1.64
POORHR	3.35	2.20	0.00	8.00	176	3.00	5.00	0.37	-0.63
MOR	1.80	[2.00]	0.00	7.00	135	1.00	1.00	1.28	0.74
PER	1.98	2.09	0.00	8.00	133	1.00	0.00	0.90	-0.38
PSV	0.28	[0.66]	0.00	2.00	32	0.00	0.00	2.08	2.61

NOTE: Standard Deviations shown in brackets indicate that the value is probably unreliable and/or misleading and should not be used to estimate expected ranges. Ordinarily these variables should not be included in most parametric analyses.

TABLE 36. FREQUENCIES FOR 36 VARIABLES FOR INPATIENT DEPRESSIVES
LAMBDA < 1.0   (N = 193)

DEMOGRAPHY VARIABLES

MARITAL STATUS			AGE			RACE		
Single	67	35%	18-25	37	19%	White	154	80%
Lives w/S.O.	0	0%	26-35	34	18%	Black	16	8%
Married	95	49%	36-45	42	22%	Hispanic	13	7%
Separated	12	6%	46-55	56	29%	Asian	10	5%
Divorced	16	8%	56-65	18	9%			
Widowed	3	2%	OVER 65	6	3%			
						EDUCATION		
SEX						UNDER 12	4	2%
Male	94	49%				12 Years	57	30%
Female	99	51%				13-15 Yrs	66	34%
						16+ Yrs	66	34%

RATIOS, PERCENTAGES AND SPECIAL INDICES

STYLES			FORM QUALITY DEVIATIONS		
Introversive	53	27%	XA% > .89	15	8%
Pervasive	21	11%	XA% < .70	39	20%
Ambitent	104	54%	WDA% < .85	129	67%
Extratensive	36	19%	WDA% < .75	55	28%
Pervasive	17	9%	X+% < .55	102	53%
Avoidant	0	0%	Xu% > .20	129	67%
			X-% > .20	80	41%
D-SCORES			X-% > .30	24	12%
D Score > 0	25	13%			
D Score = 0	41	21%	FC:CF+C RATIO		
D Score < 0	127	66%	FC > (CF+C) + 2	25	13%
D Score < -1	107	55%	FC > (CF+C) + 1	37	19%
			(CF+C) > FC+1	75	39%
Adj D Score > 0	39	20%	(CF+C) > FC+2	36	19%
Adj D Score = 0	48	25%			
Adj D Score < 0	106	55%			
Adj D Score < -1	55	28%			
			S-Constellation Positive	0	0%
Zd > +3.0 (Overincorp)	46	24%	HVI Positive	18	9%
Zd < -3.0 (Underincorp)	57	30%	OBS Positive	0	0%

PTI = 5	1	1%	DEPI = 7	19	9%	CDI = 5	29	15%
PTI = 4	5	3%	DEPI = 6	54	28%	CDI = 4	62	32%
PTI = 3	12	6%	DEPI = 5	66	34%			

MISCELLANEOUS VARIABLES

R < 17	41	21%	(2AB+Art+Ay) > 5	13	7%
R > 27	49	25%	Populars < 4	35	18%
DQv > 2	90	47%	Populars > 7	51	26%
S > 2	72	37%	COP = 0	88	46%
Sum T = 0	109	56%	COP > 2	9	5%
Sum T > 1	39	20%	AG = 0	118	61%
3r+(2)/R < .33	84	44%	AG > 2	16	8%
3r+(2)/R > .44	54	28%	MOR > 2	53	27%
Fr + rF > 0	21	11%	Level 2 Sp.Sc. > 0	159	82%
PureC > 0	85	44%	GHR > PHR	60	31%
PureC > 1	39	20%	Pure H < 2	86	45%
Afr < .40	79	41%	Pure H = 0	14	7%
Afr < .50	114	59%	p > a+1	48	25%
(FM+m) < Sum Shading	110	57%	Mp > Ma	57	30%

TABLE 37. DESCRIPTIVE STATISTICS FOR INPATIENT DEPRESSIVES

LAMBDA > 0.99   (N = 86)

VARIABLE	MEAN	SD	MIN	MAX	FREQ	MEDIAN	MODE	SK	KU
AGE	38.30	11.64	18.00	63.00	86	37.00	33.00	0.11	-0.68
Years Educ	12.95	4.93	11.00	16.00	86	13.00	16.00	-1.79	2.18
R	24.55	11.21	14.00	55.00	86	21.50	16.00	1.49	1.39
W	6.39	2.91	1.00	14.00	86	6.00	7.00	0.74	0.89
D	11.57	6.16	4.00	30.00	86	10.00	7.00	1.15	1.09
Dd	6.58	[7.48]	0.00	30.00	83	4.00	4.00	1.96	3.36
S	2.93	[2.80]	0.00	10.00	78	2.00	1.00	1.61	1.77
DQ+	3.38	1.95	0.00	8.00	79	3.00	2.00	0.23	-0.47
DQo	18.61	9.85	7.00	46.00	86	14.50	13.00	1.36	1.41
DQv	2.34	[1.85]	0.00	8.00	74	2.00	1.00	0.98	1.14
DQv/+	0.22	[0.54]	0.00	2.00	14	0.00	0.00	2.41	4.84
FQx+	0.04	0.19	0.00	1.00	3	0.00	0.00	5.16	25.21
FQxo	12.87	5.27	4.00	28.00	86	11.00	17.00	1.02	0.90
FQxu	4.95	3.44	1.00	14.00	86	4.00	3.00	1.00	0.57
FQx-	5.87	4.31	1.00	18.00	86	5.00	2.00	1.42	1.64
FQxNone	0.81	[1.23]	0.00	6.00	42	0.00	0.00	2.68	9.03
MQ+	0.04	0.19	0.00	1.00	3	0.00	0.00	5.16	25.21
MQo	1.48	1.11	0.00	5.00	71	1.00	1.00	0.79	0.69
MQu	0.28	0.64	0.00	2.00	15	0.00	0.00	2.09	2.82
MQ-	0.58	[0.73]	0.00	2.00	38	0.00	0.00	0.83	-0.63
MQNone	0.00	[0.00]	0.00	0.00	0	0.00	0.00	----	----
S-	1.51	[1.55]	0.00	5.00	58	1.00	0.00	0.88	-0.33
M	2.37	1.70	0.00	6.00	74	2.00	2.00	0.56	-0.23
FM	1.64	2.03	0.00	8.00	55	1.00	0.00	1.78	3.24
m	0.92	1.05	0.00	3.00	45	1.00	0.00	0.78	-0.69
FM+m	2.56	2.73	0.00	11.00	68	1.00	1.00	1.67	3.03
FC	1.28	1.55	0.00	6.00	49	1.00	0.00	1.29	1.16
CF	0.94	1.06	0.00	3.00	46	1.00	0.00	0.73	-0.77
C	0.66	[1.00]	0.00	4.00	38	0.00	0.00	1.95	3.56
Cn	0.05	[0.21]	0.00	1.00	4	0.00	0.00	4.38	17.63
Sum Color	2.93	2.10	0.00	8.00	76	2.00	2.00	0.44	-0.59
WSumC	2.58	1.83	0.00	6.00	76	2.00	4.00	0.18	-1.24
Sum C'	1.31	[1.29]	0.00	4.00	54	1.00	0.00	0.47	-1.19
Sum T	0.81	[1.08]	0.00	4.00	39	0.00	0.00	1.24	0.89
Sum V	0.57	[0.91]	0.00	3.00	32	0.00	0.00	1.72	2.12
Sum Y	1.40	[1.77]	0.00	8.00	50	1.00	0.00	1.97	4.87
Sum Shading	4.09	3.30	0.00	16.00	83	3.00	2.00	1.67	3.86
Fr+rF	0.04	[0.19]	0.00	1.00	3	0.00	0.00	5.16	25.21
FD	0.36	[0.59]	0.00	2.00	26	0.00	0.00	1.43	1.06
F	14.43	6.28	7.00	33.00	86	12.00	9.00	1.51	2.24
(2)	6.71	4.85	1.00	21.00	86	6.00	7.00	1.63	2.54
3r+(2)/R	0.27	0.12	0.06	0.63	86	0.27	0.19	0.28	-0.35
Lambda	2.09	2.91	1.00	15.00	86	1.34	1.18	4.19	16.50
EA	4.95	2.19	0.00	9.00	82	5.50	6.00	-0.44	-0.52
es	6.65	4.72	1.00	17.00	86	4.00	4.00	0.81	-0.55
D Score	-0.67	1.39	-4.00	1.00	86	0.00	0.00	-1.00	----.
AdjD	-0.22	0.91	-3.00	1.00	86	0.00	0.00	-1.15	1.72
a (active)	2.49	2.01	0.00	6.00	70	2.00	2.00	0.49	-1.04
p (passive)	2.50	2.15	0.00	7.00	69	2.00	2.00	0.74	-0.55
Ma	1.24	1.33	0.00	5.00	61	1.00	1.00	1.63	2.47
Mp	1.19	1.07	0.00	4.00	56	1.00	2.00	0.50	-0.26
Intellect	1.95	2.02	0.00	9.00	65	1.00	1.00	1.60	3.23
Zf	8.51	3.09	1.00	16.00	86	9.00	9.00	-0.23	0.93
Zd	0.04	3.91	-12.50	5.00	80	1.75	3.00	-1.34	1.83
Blends	1.90	1.65	0.00	6.00	63	2.00	0.00	0.51	-0.59
Blends/R	0.08	0.07	0.00	0.19	63	0.09	0.00	0.14	-1.30
Col-Shd Blends	0.45	[0.50]	0.00	1.00	39	0.00	0.00	0.19	-2.01
Afr	0.49	0.17	0.27	1.00	86	0.45	0.45	1.54	3.06

TABLE 37. INPATIENT DEPRESSIVES LAMBDA > 0.99 (N = 86) (Continued)

VARIABLE	MEAN	SD	MIN	MAX	FREQ	MEDIAN	MODE	SK	KU
Populars	5.13	1.86	2.00	10.00	86	5.00	4.00	0.47	-0.21
XA%	0.73	0.11	0.47	0.90	86	0.73	0.73	-0.45	-0.30
WDA%	0.81	0.11	0.50	1.00	86	0.81	0.81	-0.81	1.11
X+%	0.54	0.11	0.27	0.81	86	0.50	0.65	-0.20	-0.08
X-%	0.23	0.09	0.06	0.44	86	0.23	0.13	0.28	-0.67
Xu%	0.20	0.09	0.04	0.38	86	0.21	0.24	-0.10	-0.72
Isolate/R	0.10	0.10	0.00	0.29	55	0.09	0.00	0.41	-1.11
H	1.87	1.41	0.00	5.00	81	1.00	1.00	1.15	0.26
(H)	0.98	1.25	0.00	6.00	52	1.00	1.00	2.39	7.39
HD	1.55	1.61	0.00	6.00	61	1.00	0.00	1.37	1.46
(Hd)	1.09	1.51	0.00	5.00	47	1.00	0.00	1.73	2.17
Hx	0.00	[0.00]	0.00	0.00	0	0.00	0.00	----	----
All H Cont	5.49	3.60	1.00	15.00	86	4.00	4.00	0.77	-0.15
A	7.41	3.75	3.00	17.00	86	6.00	5.00	1.49	1.13
(A)	0.29	[0.46]	0.00	1.00	25	0.00	0.00	0.93	-1.15
Ad	3.44	[4.27]	0.00	19.00	70	3.00	3.00	2.79	8.11
(Ad)	0.06	[0.24]	0.00	1.00	5	0.00	0.00	3.84	13.08
An	1.74	[2.26]	0.00	7.00	45	1.00	0.00	1.15	0.06
Art	1.40	1.80	0.00	9.00	62	1.00	1.00	2.79	9.28
Ay	0.30	[0.65]	0.00	2.00	17	0.00	0.00	1.94	2.29
Bl	0.38	[0.90]	0.00	3.00	14	0.00	0.00	2.06	2.70
Bt	0.74	1.27	0.00	5.00	34	0.00	0.00	2.27	5.14
Cg	1.59	1.29	0.00	5.00	71	1.00	1.00	1.11	1.24
Cl	0.09	[0.29]	0.00	1.00	8	0.00	0.00	2.85	6.28
Ex	0.22	[0.50]	0.00	2.00	16	0.00	0.00	2.21	4.27
Fi	0.20	[0.40]	0.00	1.00	17	0.00	0.00	1.54	0.40
Food	0.41	[0.66]	0.00	2.00	27	0.00	0.00	1.36	0.64
Ge	0.30	[0.70]	0.00	4.00	20	0.00	0.00	3.63	16.35
Hh	0.78	1.28	0.00	4.00	32	0.00	0.00	1.67	1.66
Ls	0.42	0.58	0.00	2.00	32	0.00	0.00	1.05	0.15
Na	0.35	[0.55]	0.00	2.00	27	0.00	0.00	1.28	0.74
Sc	0.40	[0.56]	0.00	2.00	31	0.00	0.00	1.04	0.12
Sx	0.48	[0.73]	0.00	2.00	29	0.00	0.00	1.19	-0.07
Xy	0.22	[0.60]	0.00	2.00	11	0.00	0.00	2.52	4.72
Idio	1.07	1.01	0.00	3.00	56	1.00	1.00	0.61	-0.70
DV	0.24	[0.55]	0.00	2.00	16	0.00	0.00	2.20	3.89
INCOM	0.98	[1.31]	0.00	6.00	47	1.00	0.00	2.13	5.64
DR	0.49	[0.66]	0.00	2.00	34	0.00	0.00	1.03	-0.09
FABCOM	0.28	[0.52]	0.00	2.00	21	0.00	0.00	1.73	2.19
DV2	0.09	[0.29]	0.00	1.00	8	0.00	0.00	2.85	6.28
INC2	0.40	[0.67]	0.00	2.00	25	0.00	0.00	1.45	0.78
DR2	0.07	[0.26]	0.00	1.00	6	0.00	0.00	3.43	10.05
FAB2	0.22	[0.54]	0.00	2.00	14	0.00	0.00	2.41	4.84
ALOG	0.06	[0.24]	0.00	1.00	5	0.00	0.00	3.84	13.08
CONTAM	0.00	0.00	0.00	0.00	0	0.00	0.00	----	----
Sum 6 Sp Sc	2.83	2.48	0.00	11.00	75	2.00	2.00	1.65	2.91
Lvl 2 Sp Sc	0.78	[1.08]	0.00	4.00	40	0.00	0.00	1.60	2.33
WSum6	8.80	9.02	0.00	34.00	75	6.00	6.00	1.60	1.96
AB	0.13	[0.43]	0.00	2.00	8	0.00	0.00	3.50	11.81
AG	0.17	0.54	0.00	3.00	11	0.00	0.00	3.90	17.10
COP	0.45	0.50	0.00	1.00	39	0.00	0.00	0.19	-2.01
CP	0.00	[0.00]	0.00	0.00	0	0.00	0.00	----	----
GOODHR	3.16	1.77	1.00	9.00	86	3.00	2.00	1.17	2.08
POORHR	2.69	2.43	0.00	7.00	62	2.00	0.00	0.38	-1.28
MOR	0.99	[0.73]	0.00	2.00	63	1.00	1.00	0.01	-1.08
PER	1.87	3.05	0.00	9.00	35	0.00	0.00	1.56	1.02
PSV	0.55	[0.76]	0.00	2.00	33	0.00	0.00	0.98	-0.56

NOTE: Standard Deviations shown in brackets indicate that the value is probably unreliable and/or misleading and should not be used to estimate expected ranges. Ordinarily these variables should not be included in most parametric analyses.

TABLE 38. FREQUENCIES FOR 36 VARIABLES FOR INPATIENT DEPRESSIVES LAMBDA > 0.99 (N = 86)

DEMOGRAPHY VARIABLES

MARITAL STATUS			AGE			RACE		
Single	14	16%	18-25	18	21%	White	75	87%
Lives w/S.O.	0	0%	26-35	22	26%	Black	6	7%
Married	60	70%	36-45	26	30%	Hispanic	5	6%
Separated	1	1%	46-55	15	17%	Asian	0	0%
Divorced	6	7%	56-65	5	6%			
Widowed	5	6%	OVER 65	0	0%			
						EDUCATION		
SEX						UNDER 12	3	3%
Male	10	12%				12 Years	24	28%
Female	76	88%				13-15 Yrs	26	30%
						16+ Yrs	33	38%

RATIOS, PERCENTAGES AND SPECIAL INDICES

STYLES			FORM QUALITY DEVIATIONS		
Introversive	0	0%	XA% > .89	1	1%
Pervasive	0	0%	XA% < .70	26	30%
Ambitent	0	0%	WDA% < .85	47	55%
Extratensive	0	0%	WDA% < .75	14	16%
Pervasive	0	0%	X+% < .55	44	51%
Avoidant	86	100%	Xu% > .20	43	50%
			X-% > .20	46	53%
D-SCORES			X-% > .30	20	23%
D Score > 0	11	13%			
D Score = 0	47	55%			
D Score < 0	28	33%	FC:CF+C RATIO		
D Score < -1	25	29%	FC > (CF+C) + 2	3	3%
			FC > (CF+C) + 1	14	16%
			(CF+C) > FC+1	24	28%
Adj D Score > 0	14	16%	(CF+C) > FC+2	13	15%
Adj D Score = 0	50	58%			
Adj D Score < 0	22	26%			
Adj D Score < -1	8	9%	S-Constellation Positive	0	0%
			HVI Positive	5	6%
Zd > +3.0 (Overincorp)	9	10%	OBS Positive	0	0%
Zd < -3.0 (Underincorp)	18	21%			

PTI = 5	0	0%	DEPI = 7	0	0%	CDI = 5	16	19%
PTI = 4	0	0%	DEPI = 6	8	9%	CDI = 4	41	48%
PTI = 3	0	0%	DEPI = 5	48	56%			

MISCELLANEOUS VARIABLES

R < 17	24	28%	(2AB+Art+Ay) > 5	3	3%
R > 27	20	23%	Populars < 4	20	23%
DQv > 2	33	38%	Populars > 7	6	7%
S > 2	37	43%	COP = 0	47	55%
Sum T = 0	47	55%	COP > 2	0	0%
Sum T > 1	22	26%	AG = 0	75	87%
3r+(2)/R < .33	60	70%	AG > 2	2	2%
3r+(2)/R > .44	7	8%	MOR > 2	0	0%
Fr + rF > 0	3	3%	Level 2 Sp.Sc. > 0	40	47%
PureC > 0	38	44%	GHR > PHR	42	49%
PureC > 1	8	9%	Pure H < 2	49	57%
Afr < .40	18	21%	Pure H = 0	5	6%
Afr < .50	50	58%	p > a+1	12	14%
(FM+m) < Sum Shading	59	69%	Mp > Ma	33	38%

TABLE 39. DESCRIPTIVE STATISTICS FOR INPATIENT SCHIZOPHRENICS
LAMBDA < 1.0 (N = 200)

VARIABLE	MEAN	SD	MIN	MAX	FREQ	MEDIAN	MODE	SK	KU
AGE	29.15	11.02	18.00	66.00	200	25.00	21.00	1.37	1.22
Years Educ	12.86	4.16	11.00	19.00	200	14.00	12.00	-1.90	3.72
R	24.80	9.46	14.00	55.00	200	22.00	28.00	1.20	1.10
W	10.11	5.38	2.00	22.00	200	10.00	10.00	0.52	-0.33
D	9.62	6.91	0.00	32.00	196	9.00	4.00	1.08	1.22
Dd	5.07	[5.50]	0.00	21.00	192	3.00	2.00	1.97	3.07
S	2.99	[2.35]	0.00	10.00	176	2.00	1.00	0.83	0.12
DQ+	8.76	3.85	1.00	19.00	200	9.00	7.00	0.22	-0.26
DQo	14.35	8.42	3.00	42.00	200	12.00	13.00	1.74	2.45
DQv	1.49	[2.04]	0.00	8.00	128	1.00	0.00	2.05	3.69
DQv/+	0.20	[0.47]	0.00	2.00	34	0.00	0.00	2.34	4.87
FQx+	0.07	0.33	0.00	2.00	10	0.00	0.00	4.95	24.80
FQxo	9.32	3.72	2.00	20.00	200	9.00	8.00	0.31	-0.09
FQxu	5.37	3.37	1.00	14.00	200	4.00	3.00	0.70	-0.44
FQx-	9.35	5.79	1.00	27.00	200	7.00	7.00	1.26	1.15
FQxNone	0.69	[1.06]	0.00	4.00	86	0.00	0.00	1.93	3.40
MQ+	0.06	0.31	0.00	2.00	8	0.00	0.00	5.46	29.94
MQo	3.29	1.98	0.00	7.00	194	3.00	1.00	0.28	-0.98
MQu	1.34	1.26	0.00	5.00	148	1.00	1.00	1.24	1.46
MQ-	2.88	[2.67]	0.00	10.00	180	2.00	1.00	1.21	0.35
MQNone	0.12	[0.41]	0.00	3.00	20	0.00	0.00	4.46	24.71
S-	1.57	[1.69]	0.00	6.00	126	1.00	0.00	1.03	0.34
M	7.69	4.10	0.00	19.00	198	7.00	8.00	0.44	-0.05
FM	3.23	2.85	0.00	13.00	174	2.00	1.00	1.20	1.37
m	1.39	1.17	0.00	5.00	146	1.00	2.00	0.65	0.08
FM+m	4.62	3.26	0.00	15.00	188	4.00	3.00	1.01	0.78
FC	2.07	1.73	0.00	7.00	164	1.50	1.00	0.72	-0.25
CF	1.63	1.52	0.00	5.00	144	1.00	0.00	0.75	-0.47
C	0.44	[0.78]	0.00	3.00	62	0.00	0.00	1.99	3.57
Cn	0.02	[0.14]	0.00	1.00	4	0.00	0.00	6.90	46.20
Sum Color	4.16	2.73	0.00	11.00	186	4.00	4.00	0.59	-0.03
WSumC	3.33	2.45	0.00	10.50	186	3.00	2.00	0.82	0.38
Sum C'	2.03	[1.82]	0.00	7.00	162	1.50	1.00	0.92	-0.14
Sum T	0.66	[1.29]	0.00	7.00	76	0.00	0.00	3.32	12.74
Sum V	0.69	[1.19]	0.00	7.00	78	0.00	0.00	2.81	10.33
Sum Y	2.78	[2.87]	0.00	9.00	130	2.00	0.00	0.69	-0.81
Sum Shading	6.16	4.80	0.00	23.00	180	6.00	6.00	1.27	2.29
Fr+rF	0.27	[0.62]	0.00	2.00	36	0.00	0.00	2.11	2.98
FD	0.79	[1.07]	0.00	6.00	94	0.00	0.00	1.75	4.39
F	8.19	5.78	1.00	27.00	200	6.50	5.00	1.58	2.07
(2)	9.73	5.12	0.00	29.00	196	9.00	9.00	0.90	2.42
3r+(2)/R	0.42	0.17	0.00	0.75	196	0.41	0.33	-0.25	-0.24
Lambda	0.49	0.28	0.05	0.96	200	0.41	0.96	0.33	-1.25
EA	11.02	4.93	0.50	26.00	200	10.50	8.00	0.63	0.86
es	10.78	5.95	2.00	28.00	200	9.00	8.00	0.59	-0.40
D Score	0.12	2.10	-7.00	7.00	200	0.00	0.00	-0.39	2.56
AdjD	0.91	1.77	-4.00	7.00	200	0.00	0.00	0.42	0.94
a (active)	7.27	3.72	1.00	20.00	200	6.50	6.00	0.90	0.88
p (passive)	5.26	3.50	0.00	14.00	196	4.00	4.00	0.76	-0.33
Ma	4.61	2.86	0.00	19.00	194	4.00	6.00	1.40	4.93
Mp	3.26	2.67	0.00	9.00	172	2.00	1.00	0.66	-0.61
Intellect	1.84	3.32	0.00	28.00	112	1.00	0.00	5.22	37.55
Zf	14.70	4.91	6.00	26.00	200	13.00	13.00	0.87	-0.14
Zd	1.38	4.83	-9.00	13.50	196	2.00	0.50	0.06	-0.17
Blends	5.68	3.57	0.00	19.00	196	5.00	3.00	1.18	1.55
Blends/R	0.23	0.13	0.00	0.61	196	0.20	0.14	1.10	1.43
Col-Shd Blends	0.81	[1.25]	0.00	7.00	86	0.00	0.00	2.11	5.63
Afr	0.53	0.20	0.18	1.00	200	0.50	0.33	0.52	-0.54

TABLE 39. INPATIENT SCHIZOPHRENICS LAMBDA < 1.0 (N = 200) (Continued)

VARIABLE	MEAN	SD	MIN	MAX	FREQ	MEDIAN	MODE	SK	KU
Populars	4.96	2.04	1.00	10.00	200	5.00	6.00	0.21	-0.11
XA%	0.61	0.14	0.30	0.95	200	0.61	0.73	-0.17	-0.43
WDA%	0.67	0.13	0.38	1.00	200	0.70	0.71	-0.47	0.15
X+%	0.40	0.15	0.13	0.74	200	0.40	0.25	0.26	-0.68
X-%	0.36	0.13	0.05	0.67	200	0.33	0.25	0.17	-0.54
Xu%	0.21	0.10	0.05	0.43	200	0.21	0.27	0.28	-0.57
Isolate/R	0.18	0.14	0.00	0.54	176	0.14	0.11	0.99	0.46
H	3.81	2.45	0.00	9.00	176	4.00	5.00	0.27	-0.58
(H)	1.90	1.53	0.00	8.00	188	1.00	1.00	1.90	4.13
HD	1.62	2.09	0.00	8.00	124	1.00	0.00	1.81	2.96
(Hd)	0.88	0.98	0.00	4.00	114	1.00	0.00	1.16	1.30
Hx	0.27	[0.71]	0.00	4.00	32	0.00	0.00	3.01	9.64
All H Cont	8.21	3.94	2.00	21.00	200	8.00	8.00	0.66	0.84
A	8.51	4.15	2.00	27.00	200	7.00	7.00	2.02	6.22
(A)	0.62	[0.91]	0.00	3.00	78	0.00	0.00	1.32	0.68
Ad	2.42	[1.96]	0.00	8.00	156	2.00	0.00	0.50	-0.40
(Ad)	0.23	[0.57]	0.00	2.00	32	0.00	0.00	2.36	4.31
An	1.08	[1.39]	0.00	8.00	104	1.00	0.00	1.76	4.79
Art	0.83	1.52	0.00	7.00	72	0.00	0.00	2.42	5.94
Ay	0.21	[0.43]	0.00	2.00	40	0.00	0.00	1.80	2.24
Bl	0.34	[0.73]	0.00	5.00	50	0.00	0.00	3.35	16.13
Bt	0.87	1.11	0.00	4.00	100	0.50	0.00	1.31	1.09
Cg	2.31	1.89	0.00	9.00	174	2.00	1.00	1.22	1.74
Cl	0.41	[0.89]	0.00	4.00	46	0.00	0.00	2.50	6.34
Ex	0.08	[0.27]	0.00	1.00	16	0.00	0.00	3.12	7.81
Fi	0.44	[0.59]	0.00	2.00	78	0.00	0.00	0.97	-0.03
Food	0.25	[0.57]	0.00	3.00	40	0.00	0.00	2.84	9.33
Ge	0.24	[0.59]	0.00	2.00	32	0.00	0.00	2.31	3.93
Hh	0.39	0.83	0.00	3.00	48	0.00	0.00	2.30	4.44
Ls	0.65	0.99	0.00	4.00	78	0.00	0.00	1.57	1.87
Na	0.89	[1.11]	0.00	4.00	100	0.50	0.00	1.14	0.36
Sc	0.56	[0.77]	0.00	3.00	84	0.00	0.00	1.34	1.36
Sx	1.51	[2.24]	0.00	8.00	102	1.00	0.00	1.76	2.27
Xy	0.20	[0.55]	0.00	3.00	28	0.00	0.00	3.01	9.18
Idio	3.02	2.46	0.00	10.00	172	3.00	1.00	1.09	1.30
DV	1.00	[1.44]	0.00	7.00	98	0.00	0.00	2.12	5.40
INCOM	1.56	[1.54]	0.00	6.00	134	1.00	0.00	0.88	0.25
DR	1.11	[1.61]	0.00	7.00	102	1.00	0.00	2.02	4.15
FABCOM	0.69	[1.16]	0.00	5.00	70	0.00	0.00	1.80	2.62
DV2	0.38	[0.88]	0.00	5.00	48	0.00	0.00	3.42	13.83
INC2	1.48	[1.82]	0.00	7.00	118	1.00	0.00	1.43	1.42
DR2	1.92	[2.65]	0.00	10.00	124	1.00	0.00	1.67	1.89
FAB2	2.38	[2.13]	0.00	9.00	152	2.00	2.00	0.91	0.38
ALOG	1.21	[2.00]	0.00	14.00	94	0.00	0.00	3.27	16.04
CONTAM	0.17	0.43	0.00	2.00	30	0.00	0.00	2.52	5.92
Sum 6 Sp Sc	11.90	7.44	2.00	32.00	200	11.00	8.00	0.88	0.31
Lvl 2 Sp Sc	6.16	[5.48]	0.00	25.00	184	4.00	3.00	1.25	1.41
WSum6	52.31	38.94	4.00	173.00	200	35.00	23.00	1.16	0.92
AB	0.40	[1.47]	0.00	14.00	46	0.00	0.00	8.14	73.63
AG	1.62	2.00	0.00	9.00	122	1.00	0.00	1.67	2.97
COP	1.12	1.00	0.00	4.00	142	1.00	1.00	0.89	0.51
CP	0.05	[0.22]	0.00	1.00	10	0.00	0.00	4.16	15.47
GOODHR	3.14	2.00	0.00	9.00	188	3.00	3.00	0.81	0.83
POORHR	6.79	4.38	0.00	18.00	194	6.00	6.00	0.88	0.25
MOR	1.77	[1.82]	0.00	7.00	128	2.00	0.00	1.04	0.80
PER	1.69	2.61	0.00	15.00	120	1.00	0.00	3.10	12.14
PSV	0.08	[0.34]	0.00	2.00	12	0.00	0.00	4.53	20.83

NOTE: Standard Deviations shown in brackets indicate that the value is probably unreliable and/or misleading and should not be used to estimate expected ranges. Ordinarily these variables should not be included in most parametric analyses.

TABLE 40. FREQUENCIES FOR 36 VARIABLES FOR INPATIENT SCHIZOPHRENICS LAMBDA < 1.0 (N = 200)

DEMOGRAPHY VARIABLES

MARITAL STATUS			AGE			RACE		
Single	136	68%	18-25	102	51%	White	190	95%
Lives w/S.O.	0	0%	26-35	54	27%	Black	8	4%
Married	54	27%	36-45	22	11%	Hispanic	2	1%
Separated	4	2%	46-55	12	6%	Asian	0	0%
Divorced	4	2%	56-65	8	4%			
Widowed	2	1%	OVER 65	2	1%			
						EDUCATION		
SEX						UNDER 12	8	4%
Male	96	48%				12 Years	98	49%
Female	104	52%				13-15 Yrs	51	26%
						16+ Yrs	43	22%

RATIOS, PERCENTAGES AND SPECIAL INDICES

STYLES			FORM QUALITY DEVIATIONS		
Introversive	142	71%	XA% > .89	2	1%
Pervasive	90	45%	XA% < .70	134	67%
Ambitent	38	19%	WDA% < .85	184	92%
Extratensive	20	10%	WDA% < .75	142	71%
Pervasive	16	8%	X+% < .55	168	84%
Avoidant	0	0%	Xu% > .20	100	50%
			X-% > .20	180	90%
D-SCORES			X-% > .30	118	59%
D Score > 0	68	34%			
D Score = 0	78	39%	FC:CF+C RATIO		
D Score < 0	54	27%	FC > (CF+C) + 2	34	17%
D Score < -1	24	12%	FC > (CF+C) + 1	52	26%
			(CF+C) > FC+1	52	26%
Adj D Score > 0	94	47%	(CF+C) > FC+2	38	19%
Adj D Score = 0	82	41%			
Adj D Score < 0	24	12%			
Adj D Score < -1	10	5%	S-Constellation Positive	2	1%
			HVI Positive	44	22%
Zd > +3.0 (Overincorp) 76		38%	OBS Positive	0	0%
Zd < -3.0 (Underincorp) 50		25%			

PTI = 5	74	37%	DEPI = 7	6	3%	CDI = 5	6	3%
PTI = 4	49	25%	DEPI = 6	20	10%	CDI = 4	22	11%
PTI = 3	24	12%	DEPI = 5	34	17%			

MISCELLANEOUS VARIABLES

R < 17	42	21%	(2AB+Art+Ay) > 5	14	7%
R > 27	68	34%	Populars < 4	50	25%
DQv > 2	30	15%	Populars > 7	14	7%
S > 2	96	48%	COP = 0	58	29%
Sum T = 0	124	62%	COP > 2	20	10%
Sum T > 1	22	11%	AG = 0	78	39%
3r+(2)/R < .33	48	24%	AG > 2	52	26%
3r+(2)/R > .44	84	42%	MOR > 2	60	30%
Fr + rF > 0	36	18%	Level 2 Sp.Sc. > 0	184	92%
PureC > 0	62	31%	GHR > PHR	32	16%
PureC > 1	16	8%	Pure H < 2	34	17%
Afr < .40	62	31%	Pure H = 0	24	12%
Afr < .50	90	45%	p > a+1	36	18%
(FM+m) < Sum Shading	100	50%	Mp > Ma	70	35%

TABLE 41. DESCRIPTIVE STATISTICS FOR INPATIENT SCHIZOPHRENICS
LAMBDA > 0.99   (N = 128)

VARIABLE	MEAN	SD	MIN	MAX	FREQ	MEDIAN	MODE	SK	KU
AGE	30.19	21.28	18.00	179.00	128	23.50	19.00	5.48	36.55
Years Educ	11.69	5.22	10.00	18.00	128	12.00	12.00	-1.24	0.43
R	21.27	8.10	14.00	45.00	128	19.00	14.00	1.55	1.72
W	7.20	4.48	1.00	28.00	128	6.00	4.00	1.86	5.96
D	9.89	6.64	0.00	28.00	126	9.00	9.00	1.04	0.84
Dd	4.17	[3.51]	0.00	16.00	120	3.00	2.00	1.55	2.34
S	2.38	[2.24]	0.00	9.00	92	2.00	0.00	0.80	-0.04
DQ+	3.42	2.95	0.00	10.00	92	3.00	0.00	0.39	-0.82
DQo	16.34	7.01	6.00	36.00	128	15.50	11.00	1.11	0.89
DQv	1.30	[1.49]	0.00	9.00	82	1.00	0.00	2.33	9.44
DQv/+	0.20	[0.48]	0.00	2.00	22	0.00	0.00	2.33	4.86
FQx+	0.00	0.00	0.00	0.00	0	0.00	0.00	----	----
FQxo	8.92	3.60	4.00	18.00	128	8.00	8.00	0.99	0.15
FQxu	3.81	2.88	0.00	13.00	120	3.00	4.00	1.13	1.39
FQx-	8.03	4.31	1.00	23.00	128	8.00	8.00	1.18	2.24
FQxNone	0.50	[0.87]	0.00	4.00	40	0.00	0.00	1.89	3.52
MQ+	0.00	0.00	0.00	0.00	0	0.00	0.00	----	----
MQo	0.91	0.97	0.00	4.00	76	1.00	0.00	1.14	1.40
MQu	0.45	0.73	0.00	2.00	40	0.00	0.00	1.27	0.09
MQ-	0.95	[1.26]	0.00	7.00	70	1.00	0.00	2.34	7.91
MQNone	0.02	[0.13]	0.00	1.00	2	0.00	0.00	7.90	61.44
S-	1.64	[1.56]	0.00	6.00	86	1.50	0.00	0.76	-0.02
M	2.33	2.04	0.00	10.00	100	2.00	0.00	1.06	1.61
FM	1.34	1.69	0.00	6.00	70	1.00	0.00	1.24	0.71
m	0.72	1.07	0.00	5.00	56	0.00	0.00	1.83	3.35
FM+m	2.06	2.40	0.00	9.00	86	1.00	0.00	1.38	1.33
FC	0.75	0.77	0.00	3.00	72	1.00	0.00	0.67	-0.35
CF	0.83	1.06	0.00	4.00	64	0.50	0.00	1.24	0.61
C	0.28	[0.65]	0.00	3.00	24	0.00	0.00	2.42	5.34
Cn	0.09	[0.39]	0.00	2.00	8	0.00	0.00	4.27	17.68
Sum Color	1.95	1.83	0.00	10.00	100	2.00	1.00	1.57	4.21
WSumC	1.63	1.71	0.00	10.00	100	1.25	0.00	2.13	7.38
Sum C'	0.77	[1.09]	0.00	5.00	60	0.00	0.00	1.81	3.37
Sum T	0.06	[0.24]	0.00	1.00	8	0.00	0.00	3.65	11.56
Sum V	0.16	[0.37]	0.00	1.00	20	0.00	0.00	1.91	1.70
Sum Y	0.89	[1.50]	0.00	7.00	56	0.00	0.00	2.39	5.87
Sum Shading	1.88	2.07	0.00	10.00	86	1.50	0.00	1.59	3.20
Fr+rF	0.03	[0.18]	0.00	1.00	4	0.00	0.00	5.45	28.17
FD	0.17	[0.42]	0.00	2.00	20	0.00	0.00	2.39	5.26
F	14.28	5.43	7.00	32.00	128	13.00	10.00	1.29	1.70
(2)	6.38	4.90	0.00	21.00	114	6.00	0.00	1.14	1.48
3r+(2)/R	0.29	0.18	0.00	0.71	114	0.32	0.00	-0.08	-0.93
Lambda	3.49	4.76	1.00	29.00	128	1.80	1.11	3.57	13.99
EA	3.95	2.73	0.00	12.00	124	3.50	2.00	1.07	0.63
es	3.94	3.39	0.00	13.00	110	3.00	2.00	1.00	0.42
D Score	-0.02	0.95	-3.00	3.00	128	0.00	0.00	-0.08	3.26
AdjD	0.16	0.84	-2.00	3.00	128	0.00	0.00	0.51	2.31
a (active)	2.34	2.14	0.00	8.00	96	2.00	2.00	0.94	0.44
p (passive)	2.09	2.04	0.00	10.00	98	2.00	2.00	1.56	3.03
Ma	1.17	1.30	0.00	5.00	72	1.00	0.00	0.90	0.02
Mp	1.20	1.35	0.00	6.00	84	1.00	1.00	1.59	2.58
Intellect	1.11	1.71	0.00	9.00	64	0.50	0.00	2.38	6.67
Zf	9.47	4.13	2.00	23.00	128	10.50	11.00	0.45	0.29
Zd	0.46	3.77	-6.00	9.00	124	0.75	1.50	0.08	-0.98
Blends	1.20	1.42	0.00	6.00	72	1.00	0.00	1.37	2.05
Blends/R	0.06	0.06	0.00	0.21	72	0.04	0.00	0.76	-0.57
Col-Shd Blends	0.28	[0.63]	0.00	3.00	26	0.00	0.00	2.44	5.87
Afr	0.49	0.18	0.27	1.25	128	0.48	0.27	1.36	3.43

TABLE 41. INPATIENT SCHIZOPHRENICS LAMBDA > 0.99 (Continued) (N = 128)

VARIABLE	MEAN	SD	MIN	MAX	FREQ	MEDIAN	MODE	SK	KU
Populars	3.67	1.81	1.00	8.00	128	4.00	4.00	0.30	-0.62
XA%	0.60	0.13	0.28	0.89	128	0.60	0.53	0.18	0.57
WDA%	0.65	0.14	0.35	0.88	128	0.67	0.50	-0.39	-0.57
X+%	0.43	0.11	0.14	0.77	128	0.41	0.36	0.78	1.54
X-%	0.38	0.14	0.05	0.72	128	0.39	0.47	-0.18	0.55
Xu%	0.17	0.10	0.00	0.42	120	0.18	0.07	0.48	-0.09
Isolate/R	0.11	0.10	0.00	0.43	92	0.06	0.00	0.83	-0.07
H	1.67	1.78	0.00	9.00	90	1.00	0.00	1.64	3.56
(H)	0.91	0.97	0.00	3.00	76	1.00	0.00	0.93	-0.05
HD	1.73	1.99	0.00	9.00	82	1.00	0.00	1.68	3.45
(Hd)	0.56	1.06	0.00	6.00	42	0.00	0.00	2.87	10.49
Hx	0.03	[0.18]	0.00	1.00	4	0.00	0.00	5.45	28.17
All H Cont	4.88	3.55	0.00	19.00	118	4.00	3.00	1.12	2.51
A	8.17	3.44	3.00	19.00	128	8.00	5.00	0.84	0.36
(A)	0.55	[1.14]	0.00	7.00	40	0.00	0.00	3.45	15.41
Ad	1.42	[1.82]	0.00	10.00	76	1.00	0.00	2.10	6.50
(Ad)	0.16	[0.51]	0.00	3.00	14	0.00	0.00	3.89	16.52
An	1.19	[1.52]	0.00	6.00	76	1.00	0.00	1.70	2.46
Art	0.56	0.83	0.00	3.00	46	0.00	0.00	1.14	-0.05
Ay	0.23	[0.70]	0.00	5.00	22	0.00	0.00	5.13	31.81
Bl	0.34	[0.78]	0.00	5.00	32	0.00	0.00	3.79	18.92
Bt	0.81	1.22	0.00	5.00	58	0.00	0.00	2.02	4.34
Cg	1.05	1.41	0.00	7.00	72	1.00	0.00	2.22	5.98
Cl	0.23	[0.46]	0.00	2.00	28	0.00	0.00	1.74	2.18
Ex	0.13	[0.33]	0.00	1.00	16	0.00	0.00	2.29	3.32
Fi	0.17	[0.45]	0.00	2.00	18	0.00	0.00	2.71	6.88
Food	0.36	[0.88]	0.00	4.00	26	0.00	0.00	2.93	8.61
Ge	0.06	[0.24]	0.00	1.00	8	0.00	0.00	3.65	11.56
Hh	0.44	1.36	0.00	6.00	18	0.00	0.00	3.38	10.32
Ls	0.30	0.88	0.00	5.00	20	0.00	0.00	3.86	15.95
Na	0.36	[0.74]	0.00	3.00	30	0.00	0.00	2.15	4.02
Sc	0.48	[0.71]	0.00	2.00	46	0.00	0.00	1.13	-0.11
Sx	1.06	[1.64]	0.00	5.00	50	0.00	0.00	1.30	0.16
Xy	0.13	[0.33]	0.00	1.00	16	0.00	0.00	2.29	3.32
Idio	1.66	2.03	0.00	9.00	82	1.00	0.00	1.83	3.73
DV	0.83	[1.24]	0.00	6.00	62	0.00	0.00	2.16	5.01
INCOM	1.41	[1.47]	0.00	6.00	90	1.00	1.00	1.37	1.65
DR	0.58	[0.79]	0.00	2.00	50	0.00	0.00	0.90	-0.79
FABCOM	0.48	[0.62]	0.00	2.00	54	0.00	0.00	0.88	-0.21
DV2	0.42	[1.19]	0.00	9.00	36	0.00	0.00	6.05	41.90
INC2	0.64	[1.13]	0.00	4.00	42	0.00	0.00	1.88	2.73
DR2	1.48	[3.05]	0.00	14.00	50	0.00	0.00	2.80	7.91
FAB2	0.64	[1.13]	0.00	6.00	44	0.00	0.00	2.35	6.90
ALOG	0.27	[0.65]	0.00	3.00	22	0.00	0.00	2.53	5.86
CONTAM	0.13	0.42	0.00	2.00	12	0.00	0.00	3.49	11.83
Sum 6 Sp Sc	6.88	5.96	0.00	31.00	118	5.00	3.00	1.92	4.34
Lvl 2 Sp Sc	3.19	[4.30]	0.00	18.00	88	2.00	0.00	2.05	4.11
WSum6	26.31	28.35	0.00	129.00	118	18.00	6.00	2.01	4.03
AB	0.16	[0.54]	0.00	3.00	12	0.00	0.00	3.79	14.57
AG	0.50	0.89	0.00	3.00	36	0.00	0.00	1.58	1.22
COP	0.33	0.69	0.00	3.00	28	0.00	0.00	2.11	3.70
CP	0.03	[0.18]	0.00	1.00	4	0.00	0.00	5.45	28.17
GOODHR	1.73	1.41	0.00	5.00	100	1.50	1.00	0.62	-0.27
POORHR	3.84	3.08	0.00	17.00	118	4.00	1.00	1.39	3.60
MOR	0.81	[1.30]	0.00	5.00	54	0.00	0.00	2.00	3.57
PER	1.08	2.30	0.00	11.00	52	0.00	0.00	3.27	10.94
PSV	0.28	[0.52]	0.00	2.00	32	0.00	0.00	1.65	1.91

NOTE: Standard Deviations shown in brackets indicate that the value is probably unreliable and/or misleading and should not be used to estimate expected ranges. Ordinarily these variables should not be included in most parametric analyses.

TABLE 42. FREQUENCIES FOR 36 VARIABLES FOR INPATIENT SCHIZOPHRENICS LAMBDA > 0.99 (N = 128)

DEMOGRAPHY VARIABLES

MARITAL STATUS			AGE			RACE		
Single	82	64%	18-25	70	55%	White	120	94%
Lives w/S.O.	0	0%	26-35	24	19%	Black	4	2%
Married	36	28%	36-45	22	17%	Hispanic	4	3%
Separated	2	2%	46-55	8	6%	Asian	0	0%
Divorced	8	6%	56-65	2	2%			
Widowed	0	0%	OVER 65	2	2%			
						EDUCATION		
SEX						UNDER 12	23	18%
Male	72	56%				12 Years	64	50%
Female	56	44%				13-15 Yrs	19	15%
						16+ Yrs	22	17%

RATIOS, PERCENTAGES AND SPECIAL INDICES

STYLES			FORM QUALITY DEVIATIONS		
Introversive	0	0%	XA% > .89	0	0%
Pervasive	0	0%	XA% < .70	110	86%
Ambitent	0	0%	WDA% < .85	114	89%
Extratensive	0	0%	WDA% < .75	94	73%
Pervasive	0	0%	X+% < .55	110	86%
Avoidant	128	100%	Xu% > .20	36	28%
			X-% > .20	114	89%
D-SCORES			X-% > .30	100	78%
D Score > 0	22	17%			
D Score = 0	80	63%	FC:CF+C RATIO		
D Score < 0	26	20%	FC > (CF+C) + 2	0	0%
D Score < -1	4	3%	FC > (CF+C) + 1	4	3%
			(CF+C) > FC+1	22	17%
Adj D Score > 0	30	23%	(CF+C) > FC+2	8	6%
Adj D Score = 0	82	64%			
Adj D Score < 0	16	13%			
Adj D Score < -1	4	3%	S-Constellation Positive	0	0%
			HVI Positive	10	8%
Zd > +3.0 (Overincorp) 36	28%		OBS Positive	0	0%
Zd < -3.0 (Underincorp) 28	22%				

PTI = 5	10	8%	DEPI = 7	0	0%	CDI = 5	14	11%
PTI = 4	26	20%	DEPI = 6	10	8%	CDI = 4	56	44%
PTI = 3	56	44%	DEPI = 5	18	14%			

MISCELLANEOUS VARIABLES

R < 17	42	33%	(2AB+Art+Ay) > 5	2	2%
R > 27	18	14%	Populars < 4	60	47%
DQv > 2	20	16%	Populars > 7	2	2%
S > 2	50	39%	COP = 0	100	78%
Sum T = 0	120	94%	COP > 2	2	2%
Sum T > 1	0	0%	AG = 0	92	72%
3r+(2)/R < .33	70	55%	AG > 2	6	5%
3r+(2)/R > .44	32	25%	MOR > 2	10	8%
Fr + rF > 0	4	3%	Level 2 Sp.Sc. > 0	88	69%
PureC > 0	24	19%	GHR > PHR	16	13%
PureC > 1	10	8%	Pure H < 2	72	56%
Afr < .40	40	31%	Pure H = 0	38	30%
Afr < .50	68	53%	p > a+1	20	16%
(FM+m) < Sum Shading	48	38%	Mp > Ma	44	34%

PART III

PRACTICE CODING

12 ❖ Practice Coding

This section of the workbook contains 300 responses for practice in learning to apply the variety of codes and scores accurately. It is divided into 8 sections, each of which contains between 25 and 50 answers. Completion of the scoring for these 300 answers will provide experience that is roughly equivalent to having scored approximately 15 protocols, and that is about the number required for the novice to begin to feel comfortable and competent with the process.

The responses in each section have been selected in accordance with four estimated levels of difficulty or complexity. They also provide additional illustrations about when and what types of Inquiry questions are important.

Sections 1 and 2 contain 75 responses that are fairly straightforward. They reflect the sorts of answers that constitute about 50% of all Rorschach responses. They have been selected to provide experience with each of the basic scoring categories, Location, DQ, Determinants, Content, Populars, and Z Scores, and a some contain Special Scores. Practice with responses such as these should facilitate the easy identification of the various determinants, a skill that is crucial to smooth procedures of administration.

Sections 3 and 4 contain 65 answers that are more difficult or complex. Many contain blends and are interspersed with a greater frequency of Special Scores than the first two sections. They also are illustrative of the types of responses that constitute a significant proportion of Rorschach answers.

Sections 5 and 6 contain 90 answers that tend to extend the complexity of coding decisions as contrasted with the answers in Sections 3 and 4. These answers are no more difficult than those in the preceding two sections but they do include a higher frequency of responses for which decisions concerning the assignment of Special Scores is required. Sections 7 and 8 include 70 responses that will challenge any Rorschacher. A scoring key is provided for each section in the *Appendix*.

It is best to code a few responses at a time, and check those codings against those given in the key. Any time a code assigned differs from that in the key, the material in the workbook should be reviewed again, with the objective of resolving the error. If the number of errors in a given section is substantial, it may be wise to begin that section again, after reviewing the appropriate material in the Workbook.

It is important to remember that, occasionally, some legitimate disagreements will exist among scorers for issues such as, CF versus C, FC versus CF, FY versus YF, etc. Some of these are unresolvable, but almost all will be resolved if the criteria involved are studied carefully and thoughtfully, and applied conscientiously.

Errors of omission *are much more important* than disagreements about whether a response should be coded FT or TF. While neither are desirable, omission errors increase the risk that the *Structural Summary* will present a misleading or even distorted picture of the various psychological characteristics of the client.

Whereas the responses in the first six sections may be thought of in the context of *practicing to learn*, the responses in the last two sections may be regarded more as *a test of learning*. Anyone who is able to score the 70 responses in Sections 7 and 8 accurately, or with only a few errors should feel reasonably confident that their scoring of a real protocol truly represents the salient features of the responses given by the client.

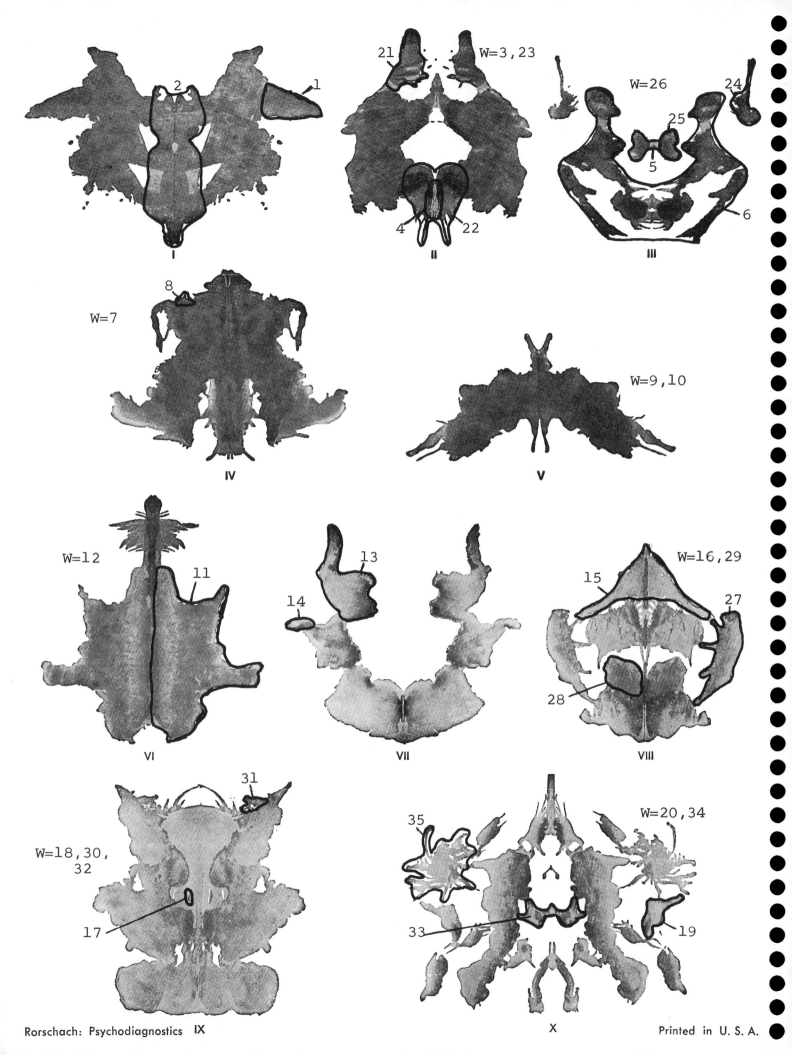

Rorschach: Psychodiagnostics   IX   Printed in U. S. A.

SECTION 1

CARD		RESPONSE	INQUIRY	CODING
I	<	1. If I turn it ths way ths prt ll an evergreen tree	E: (Rpts S's resp) S: Well, it certainly has the shape of an evergreen, u kno sk of an evergreen, like a spruce, very stately looking	
I		2. It could be a person, in the middle, holding her hands up	E: (Rpts S's resp) S: These wld be the hands up here lik she's waving her arms & here's her legs and her body	
II		3. The whole thing ll a face	E: (Rpts S's resp) S: Well, the red wld be the eyes, the cheeks here (black) and the white area wld be the mouth, just the shape of a face	
II		4. This part ll a candle	E: (Rpts S's resp) S: Yes, it's long and slender like one and it ll the wax is dripping down it. This bottom part cld be the holder that the candle is in	
III		5. This ll a butterfly	E: (Rpts S's resp) S: Here, the wings and body. It's flying, c, wings are outstretched	
III		6. 2 ppl picking up s.t.	E: (Rpts S's resp) S: 2 ppl, the head & body, the backs are arched, here r their legs, their arms reaching down and picking up s.t. heavy, c how thyr grimacing and their hands are clutched tightly around it	
IV		7. Maybe a tree	E: (Rpts S's resp) S: It has the general shape of a tree w all the branches hangg dwn sorta droopy, like alot of weight on 'em (outlines), trunk is here	

SECTION 1

CARD		RESPONSE	INQUIRY	CODING
IV		8. This little part cb a hat	E: (Rpts S's resp) U kno, one of those caps with the pointed top, the shape of it	
V		9. It ll a bat, just glidg along	E: (Rpts S's resp) S: Here are the wings spread out and the body is in the middl	
V		10. Well, it cld b an organ of sk	E: (Rpts S's resp) S: Yeah, some kind of organ E: I'm not sure I c it, help me S: It's all of it, I don't know which organ, it just ll some internal part to me, lik an organ of sk, mayb a stomach, it's sorta shaped lik a stomach might b	
VI	<	11. This rem me of a submarine	E: (Rpts S's resp) S: It has the pretty good shape of a sub, the long bow, here's the stern, the conning tower & mayb at the top is the tip of the periscope, it's not moving	
VI	v	12. This way it cld be a sea creature like a fish or stingray	E: (Rpts S's resp) S: It wld have this long tail, a flat body and up here is where the mouth wld be, it's like a stingray swimming along	
VII		13. This top part ll 2 angels talking to e.o.	E: (Rpts S's resp) S: Faces, eyes, nose, mouth just angels talking to each other	
VII		14. Here it's lik 2 A's runng away	E: (Rpts S's resp) S: Just this little part, head is out here and the rest is the body, 2 of 'em, running real fast	

SECTION 1

CARD	RESPONSE	INQUIRY	CODING
VIII	15. This top cld be a man, the upper half, w arms outstrtchd	E: (Rpts S's resp) S: His head wld be at the top and these are his arms stretched out on either side, lik he's reaching out E: I don't thk I c it right, can u help me? S: It just ll a man, the head here & his arms	
VIII	16. It ll 2 A's climbing up the sides of a mtn	E: (Rpts S's resp) S: One on each side, the head, legs, body. The back legs look bigger, more muscular as they push off these lower rocks and strain to climb onto this ledge	
IX	17. This oval area ll a lake	E: (Rpts S's resp) S: Some lakes are long and narrow, this just rem me of a lake lik tht, it's long & narrow	
IX	18. The W thg cb clds floatg ovr a mtn, here at the bttm	E: (Rpts S's resp) S: Thes top prts (D3+D1) just ll clds, kinda shapeless E: U said over a mtn? S: Just above it, floating by, thy cover most of it, u can just c the bottm of it here (D6), the upper prt wb covrd by the clds	
X	19. It ll a person on a bsktball crt jumping up to shoot the ball	E: (Rpts S's resp) S: Right here (D15), the arm's raised, jumping in the air like shootg the ball E: I'm not sur I c it rite S: He's rite here, his body & arm going up, makin a jump shot E: And the ball S: At the end of his arm	

SECTION 1

CARD	RESPONSE	INQUIRY	CODING
X	20. Oh, the W thg re me of 4th of July fireworks	E: (Rpts S's resp) S: Yes, fireworks, thyr all exploding E: I'm not sur wht maks it ll fireworks? S: Well, thyr bursting outward, lik in a very colorful pattern, like fireworks do when thy go off	
II	21. I supp ths red thg cb a lung	E: (Rpts S's resp) S: It just rem me of a lung, it's red with the blood in it and lungs are formed like that I think.	
II	22. This ll blood	E: (Rpts S's resp) S: Yes, this red area, it ll bld to me, c, it's red	
II	23. 2 ppl, faces, hands, thyr wearing hats	E: (Rpts S's resp) S: It ll 2 ppl to me, heads up here, with big red hats on, and the rest is the body. C, arms, back & legs	
III	24. This ll pieces of meat	E: (Rpts S's resp) S: It's like stew meat, one on each side just red like meat before u put it in the pan to cook it	
III <	25. This red prt rem me of a Valentine	E: (Rpts S's resp) S: It just ll a Valentine to me E: I'm not sure wht maks it ll that S: It has a heart shape, valentines r heart shaped, I've sent some tht ll ths one	

SECTION 1

CARD	RESPONSE	INQUIRY	CODING
III	26. Peopl dancg at a party	E: (Rpts S's resp) S: Yes, here's 2 ppl, c, the bodies and heads here, lik thyr doin the boggie, and thes red thgs r lik colorful party decorations	
VIII	27. This cld be a penis	E: (Rpts S's response) S: It has that general shape and as far as I know they are that color	
VIII	28. A flower here	E: (Rpts S's resp) S: The pretty color rem me of a flower, it cld be a flower bud, buds usually hav that round shape	
VIII	29. It cld be a vase, if u thk of the pink as handles, lik an Egyptian vase	E: (Rpts S's resp) S: The handles and the shape, like a vase & all the diff colors r lik designs on it, it's pretty.	
IX	30. Oh, that's pretty. Som pink & green & orange	E: (Rpts S's resp) S: They are pretty colors. Just pink & orange & green	
IX	31. Thes ll guns, the littl orange	E: (Rpts S's resp) S: Here's the long barrel with the small piece on the end for sightg & the curved handle lik an ornate Western gun, the trigger is here, there's one on each side	
IX	32. Tht's like the insides of a fly thts been squashed	E: (Rpts S's resp) S: They are very colorful, the pink wld b an organ and the rest wb the insides, I can't make it out too well, but tht's what it ll if u squash a fly	

SECTION 1

CARD	RESPONSE	INQUIRY	CODING
X	33. Tht cntr part ll a special bra	E: (Rpts S's resp) S: Lik if u hold it up it wld have this form to it, it's blue so it must be special E: Special? S: Sure, blue ones r special, white ones aren't	
X	34. It ll blotches of paint, it's very pretty lik an abstract, lik the artist wanted to repres the beauty of color in the world	E: (Rpts S's resp) S: All of it ll s.o. took a brush and went like this with the blue, green, yellow, pink, it's all very pretty, lik an abstract painting tht represents how colors beautify the world	
X	35. This blue cld be crabs	E: (Rpts S's resp) S: The blue part, it ll a crab with all the legs, crabs usually aren't blue though, I thk thyr brown or green but I guess thy talk about blue crabs in Maryland but I don't thk even thy r blue but I'm not sur, I guess thyr good to eat but I'm not thinkg of blue crabs here, just crabs, forget the blue	

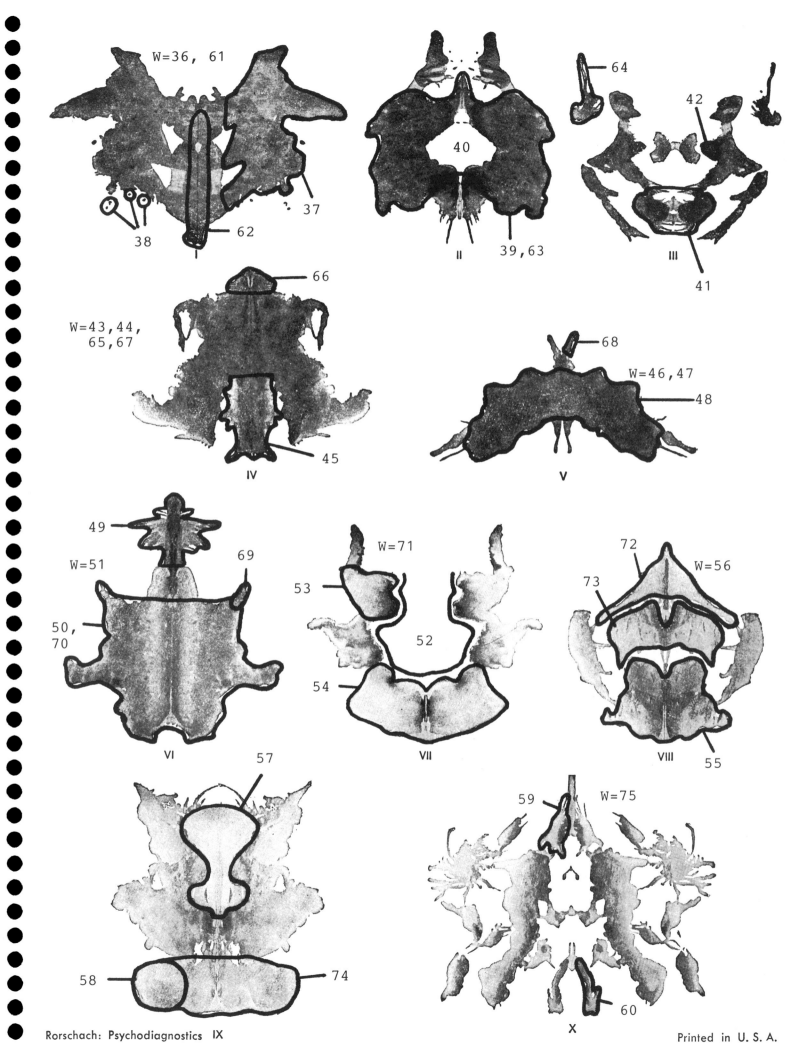

Printed in U.S.A.

SECTION 2

CARD	RESPONSE	INQUIRY	CODING
I	36. It cb a face, it's a dopey face w big white teeth	E: (Rpts S's resp) S: C the big teeth and the eyes, not a real face, lik a mask w the cheeks and big funny ears.	
I	37. Clds on either side	E: (Rpts S's resp) S: The drk blacks & lite blacks re me of how a storm cld looks E: U said on either side? S: Yeah, one here & one here (Points)	
I	38. These ll pieces, or lumps of coal	E: (Rpts S's resp) S: Thyr black lik coal, just littl round lumps of coal	
II	39. Ths black cb 2 littl bears tht r touchg their noses	E: (Rpts S's resp) S: It's the blk area, it cb bears, here r heads, ears, front paws, body & the rear legs E: U said touchg their noses? S: Yes, lik sniffing e.o	
II	40. There's a snowflake there	E: (Rpts S's resp) S: The center part, it's equal on all sides lik a white snowflake, snowflakes hav equality, u kno thgs tht r the same on all of the sides, I thk thy usually hav 4 or 6 sides	
III	41. Might be an X-ray	E: (Rpts S's resp) S: It's all black lik an X-ray, I don't kno of what, mayb the chest mayb not, it just ll an X-ray to me	
III	42. Ths looks sorta like a jellybean	E: (Rpts S's resp) S: Kinda round like a black jellybean, yeah it ll one, lik Reagan used to keep on his desk, he was a jellybean nut but I don't lik thm very much, at least not the black ones	

SECTION 2

CARD	RESPONSE	INQUIRY	CODING
IV	43. It just ll ink to me	E: (Rpts S's resp) S: Just a bunch of ink, some parts r more dry than others, c, its darker here in the middl & liter around the edges	
IV	44. Mayb anothr cld, like at night	E: (Rpts S's resp) S: Thyr just black like this when u look at the sky at night, & thr r clds thy ll ths, just a cloud, all of it, it's lik som I'v seen at night	
IV	45. Ths part cb a fish	E: (Rpts S's resp) S: The fish's head wld be down here & the rest wld be the striped body, the dark lines ll stripes	
V	46. Might be a bat	E: (Rpts S's resp) S: Sure, the wgs and head and it's blk lik a bat	
V	47. It's sort of lik a billow of smoke sorta spreadg out	E: (Rpts S's resp) S: It looks smoky, not all one color, just lik a puff of smoke tht's spreadg out	
V	v 48. This way it cb an x-ray of a chest	E: (Rpts S's resp) S: Just ths part, symmetrical lik a chest bone and it's colord all dark blk & grey lik an X-ray	
VI	49. Cld b a totem pole, I guess	E: (Rpts S's resp) S: The pole and the ground beneath it & it's shaped lik a totem w the wgs & the dark markings painted on it, we saw a lot of em on our trip out west	

SECTION 2

CARD		RESPONSE	INQUIRY	CODING
VI		50. Ths prt ll an old cast iron kettle, my grandmothr used to hav one lik it	E: (Rpts S's resp) S: Just ths lowr area, it's shaped lik one of thos old kettles tht I guess everybody had, it has the handles on it, & it's all black, ths one looks lik it had a lot of use cuz it's got all thos diff shades of black there	
VI	v	51. It re me of a brain thts dead & ths is the stem	E: (Rpts S's resp) S: It's all dark lookg, lik a dead brain, a live brain is all one color but ths has the diff concentrations of grey, I'v seen pictures of one's lik ths, it's sorta round & ths is the stem down here	
VII	v	52. A snow sculpture lik childrn build	E: (Rpts S's resp) S: It's white lik snow, I'm not sure what it is, just smaller at the bottom & rounder at the top	
VII		53. Ths mite be 2 faces	E: (Rpts S's resp) S: Ths grey cb the face of a person, w puffed out bangs, the indentation for the eye, a button nose, & a firm jaw, 2 of them, one on each side	
VII		54. A cpl of baby shoes that r bronzed	E: (Rpts S's resp) S: Thy hav that shape, lik littl baby shoes E: U said thy r bronzed? S: The coloring makes them look shiny, lik they were bronzed	
VIII		55. Somthg burng, a bonfire	E: (Rpts S's resp) S: Well it's lik flames, it's orange lik fire & the way it's shaped ther it rem me of a bonfire	

SECTION 2

CARD	RESPONSE	INQUIRY	CODING
VIII	56. Oh, a dead crab, all opened up	E: (Rpts S's resp) S: Yeah a crab, the whole thing ll a dead crab E: I'm not sur why it ll tht S: It's got the shape of one E: I'm not sur why it looks dead S: It' has the white bones (DS3) & all the colors tht u'd c inside, it's lik the shell has been taken off & all u c r the colored insides	
IX	57. Ths white prt ll a salt shaker	E: (Rpts S's resp) S: It's got the form of a shaker and it's white lik there's salt in it, if it were black it cld be a pepper shaker, anyone can tell the diff betwn them cuz salt is white & pepper is black	
IX	58. It looks round, lik an apple	E: (Rpts S's resp) S: Yeah, it's red & it's round, lik an apple E: Round? S: Like a circle, lik an apple or cherry, I thk an apple	
X	59. These ll 2 rocks, grey rocks	E: (Rpts S's resp) S: The grey, tht made me thk of a rock's color & thyr kinda round, not really round but thy cb rocks	
X	60. Ths ll a hook, a fishg hook	E: (Rpts S's resp) S: Tht's the shape of fishing hook & it's shiny lik metal, too E: Shiny? S: The diff shades of the color make it ll tht	
I	61. It ll a bat, flyg	E: (Rpts S's resp) S: It's all black, the wngs r outstretchd & the body in the middl	

SECTION 2

CARD	RESPONSE	INQUIRY	CODING
I	62. A vagina, too	E: (Rpts S's resp) S: Just the cntr prt w the crack ll a vagina to me E: I don't thk I c it as u do, help me S: C here (runs finger around area) E: And the crack? S: The dark line in the middl, it's the opening	
II	63. It ll 2 teddy bears propped up so tht the noses r togethr	E: (Rpts S's resp) S: Thy ll 2 littl teddy bears, u can c the heads & noses & the fur & it ll sbody sat them in ths position so tht their noses r togethr, touchg E: U said u cld c the fur? S: The way the colors r there, it makes them look furry	
III	64. Thse red thgs ll an artists representatn of musical notes	E: (Rpts S's resp) S: Thy hve tht sort of shape to them, lik you c in a cartoon to represent tht music is playing	
IV	65. It ll a piece of velvet	E: (Rpts S's resp) S: It has a soft look to it, c the diff marks, it just ll a piece, not a coat or hat, just a piece of velvet	
IV	66. A flower up here	E: (Rpts S's resp) S: It ll a flwr, the soft petals comg out fr the cntr E: I'm not sure wht maks them look soft S: The way the colorg is there, it ll thy wld be soft	

SECTION 2

CARD	RESPONSE	INQUIRY	CODING
IV	67. It makes me thnk of a chocolate ice cream cone, I'm a chocaholic	E: (Rpts S's resp) S: The cone at the bottom, I guess som people don't lik choc but if u do u go crazy about it, it's a lot better than vanilla or maple walnut E: I don't thk I'm seeg it yet, help me S: Ths looks all lik choc ice cream, lik piled ovr the sides E: Wht maks it ll choc ice cream? S: It just does, c the diff shades mak it look gooey, lik choc	
V	68. It's lik the head of a caterpillar	E: (Rpts S's resp) S: Just the shape of a fuzzy caterpillar E: Fuzzy? S: Thse markgs in the ink make it look fuzzy lik a caterpillar	
VI	69. Ths littl points cb a dog's paw or rabbits foot	E: (Rpts S's resp) S: Here, it ll dog's paw or a rabbits foot E: I'm not sur wht makes it ll tht S: Well it has tht shape & shading makes it ll fur lik on a rabbits foot	
VI	70. The bttm ll fur, mayb a rug, just pretty furry	E: (Rpts S's resp) S: It sur ll fur, the way the ink is (rubs card), cld be a rug w an interesting shape	
VII	71. It cb 2 Indian kids squatting on a rock	E: (Rpts S's resp) S: It's lik 2 of them, c the forehead & the nose & chin & neck & their bodies r rounded, lik when u squat down, & it ll thy hav their arms out behind them & thyv each got a feather in their hair, lik Indians wore, but their faces look young, lik kids playg a game, or doing sthg special togethr	

SECTION 2

CARD	RESPONSE	INQUIRY	CODING
VIII	72. It cld be ice I guess	E: (Rpts S's resp) S: I guess the way the colors r mixed there makes it look cold, lik ice, lik if u touched it u wld stick to it bec it's so cold	
VIII	73. Thse ll flags in the cntr, hangg dwn on a flagpole	E: (Rpts S's resp) S: The square shape with fringe on the side, lik thyr hangg fr the pole in the middl, thy even hav the texture effect of cloth E: Texture effect? S: The ink makes them look soft lik cloth	
IX	74. Som cotton balls (rubs card)	E: (Rpts S's resp) S: 4 of thm, 2 on each side, & thse markgs on them mak them look soft lik cotton feels	
X	75. All thse thngs mite b islands & the white is water	E: (Rpts S's resp) S: Just the diff land masses, the white wb water, islands & the water wld be between them	

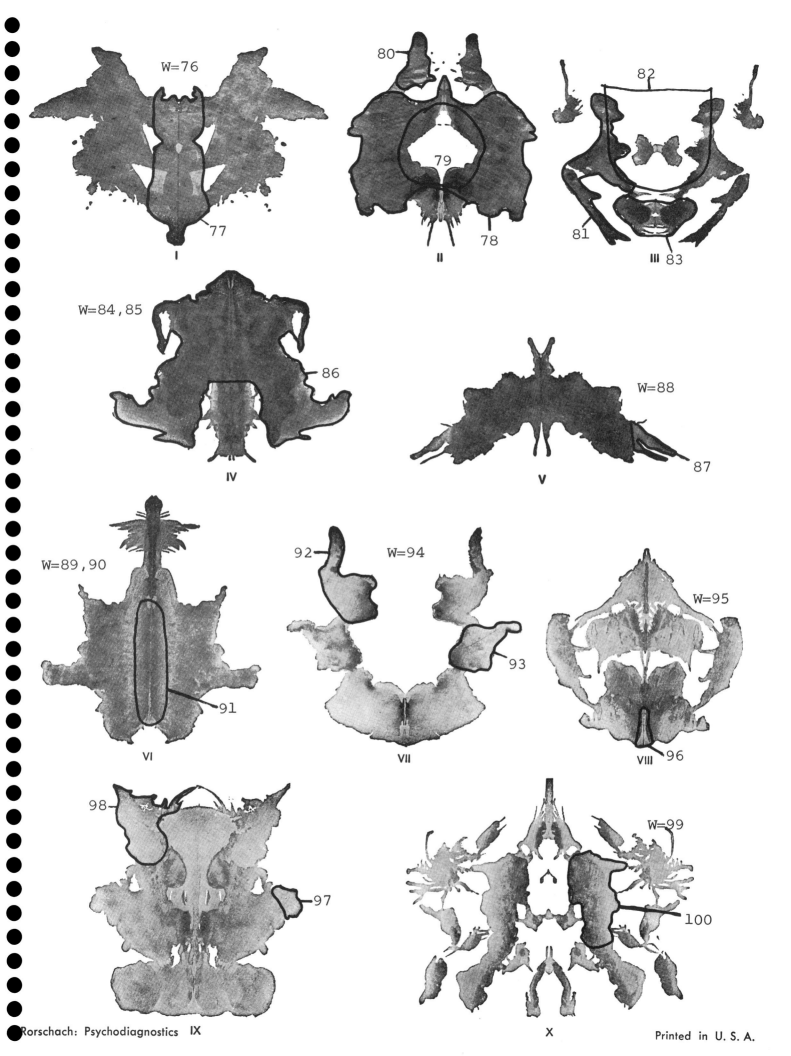

SECTION 3

CARD	RESPONSE	INQUIRY	CODING
I	76. I thnk a crab or lobster prob a crab	E: (Rpts S's resp) S: The cntr is the body & the outsides r the arms & claws, it ll a crab to me	
I	77. Ths part cld be a woman, u can c thru her dress	E: (Rpts S's resp) S: Here's her head and the body, thin waist, u can c right thru the dress, the liter prt, she's got pretty broad hips here where it's darker	
II	78. If u don't use the red it cb pelvic bones	E: (Rpts S's resp) S: It's shaped lik the pelvis with a hollow thru the cntr (points) E: A hollow thur the cntr? S: The white, there's just nothin there, lik the hollow in the pelvis, it goes back in	
II	79. The cntr ll a pit or puddl w water in it	E: (Rpts S's resp) S: The white prt is water and it's down in this pit, the sides arnd it seem to go in E: I'm not sur wht makes it ll that S: The diff colors give it a sense of depth	
II	80. Thes ll 2 wrinkled mittens	E: (Rpts S's resp) S: Thyr shaped lik mittens, round at the top E: U mentioned they're wrinkled S: Thse liter areas ll folds, they sorta go in, like wrinkles	
III	81. Here's a person & here is a mirror image of him	E: (Rpts S's resp) S: The head, arm, body, leg, and a reflection of him over on this side	

SECTION 3

CARD		RESPONSE	INQUIRY	CODING
III	v	82. Ths way it's lik a giant red bf in front of a cave	E: (Rpts S's resp) S: The red is the bf and the white is the cave and the black is the side of it, lik the bf is in front of it, c the wgs E: U said it's a giant bf? S: It must b, it looks big lik a giant one	
III		83. Prt of a man's face, the nose	E: (Rpts S's resp) S: It's the nose, u can c in the nostrils u know? E: The nostrils? S: The blker prts ll the inside part of the nose, u can c back in lik, it's darker, it's just a nose	
IV	v	84. A leaf with all the folds in it	E: (Rpts S's resp) S: The W thing ll a big leaf that has all these folds in it E: Folds? S: C whre it's darker ll folds all over it, lik wrinkles, leaves get tht way after thyv fallen & died	
IV		85. Lik smthg from a sc fict movie lik lookg up at him	E: (Rpts S's resp) S: Here's the legs and weird head, a big, fat bulky thing, like he's standg there & u'r lookg up at him E: Lookg up at him? S: It looks lik in perspective	
IV		86. Boy, that's ugly, it ll a frog w weird arms	E: (Rpts S's resp) S: U can tell it's a frog bec of the small head & big feet & weird arms & it's all bumpy E: Bumpy? S: The colors make it look raised up	

SECTION 3

CARD	RESPONSE	INQUIRY	CODING
V	87. Thse ll 2 crocodiles gettg ready to chomp on sthg	E: (Rpts S's resp) S: Just the ends, top jaw here & the bottom jaw, just the heads, their mouths r open lik their gonna bite smthg	
V	88. It cb a boy inside a tent	E: (Rpts S's resp) S: The W thing is lik a translucent tent and u can c his outline there, head & body, & thse r stakes at the end holding it up E: U said it's transluscent? S: U can c thru it, maybe there's a lite behnd it and that creates diff colors, anyhow u can sorta c thru it	
VI	89. It rem me of smthg deep, I'm not sur what	E: (Rpts S's resp) S: It just ll depth, it gets deeper in the cntr where it gets darker, just a big deep place	
VI	< 90. Sideways it ll a reflection of some trees in the water	E: (Rpts S's resp) S: It's a reflection in the water, c, it's the same here. Thse cb trees, the shapes, some taller thn the others	
VI	91. Mayb a rivr dwn the middl, lik a gorge	E: (Rpts S's resp) S: Ths ll the land arnd it, alot of trees and stuff E: I'm not sur I understnd why it ll tht S: It ll it's down in, all darker there in the cntr	
VII	92. The head of a littl girl w a pony tail, a littl black girl	E: (Rpts S's resp) S: Her nose & forehead & her pony tail E: U said a littl black girl S: She's dark colored	

SECTION 3

CARD	RESPONSE	INQUIRY	CODING
VII	93. It ll 2 heads of a goat	E: (Rpts S's resp) S: Here & here, it ll a goat, the horn & mouth, & nose	
VII	94. Pieces of crackers tht hav been soaked in water	E: (Rpts S's resp) S: They're puffy, parts are raised, the shades give that impression lik thyr a lot thicker	
VIII	< 95. Sideways it ll a wildlife scene relected in the water	E: (Rpts S's resp) S: Here's an animal standg there, the head, 4 legs, & these r shaped lik rocks & bushes & the blue is water E: U said reflected? S: Down here wld be water, & it ll a reflection of the othr prt	
VIII	96. Lik a vagina, it's got all the pink inside flesh exposed	E: (Rpts S's resp) S: Ths is the slit, opening it's deeper cause it's darker here, lik the folds of it. Just looks formed like a vagina to me & it's colored tht way too	
IX	97. Thse might be 2 bushes	E: (Rpts S's resp) S: To me it ll some shrub or bush, sort of round lik a bush	
IX	98. Up here ll 2 witches, thyr leang backward, lik havg a good laugh	E: (Rpts S's resp) S: Thy hav orange suits on, the pointed hat, long pointed fingernails, a funny crooked nose, wide fat body and thy ll thyr leaning backward, sort of rolling in laughter at smthg thy thot of or smthg tht one said to the othr	

SECTION 3

CARD		RESPONSE	INQUIRY	CODING
X	v	99. It ll a beautiful bouquet	E: (Rpts S's resp) S: It has all diff kinds of flowrs, pink & blue & yellow, thyr all tied togethr dwn here (D11), the pink might b gladiolas & the blu cb asters I suppose, it's very pretty	
X		100. It ll the pancreas of an evil person	E: (Rpts S's resp) S: It's shaped lik a pancreas, I kno about them, I've studied the insides of evil people E: How do u kno it's an evil person? S: The pink is not an even color, it has diff shades of pink & when u see diff shades of pink u kno the person is evil	

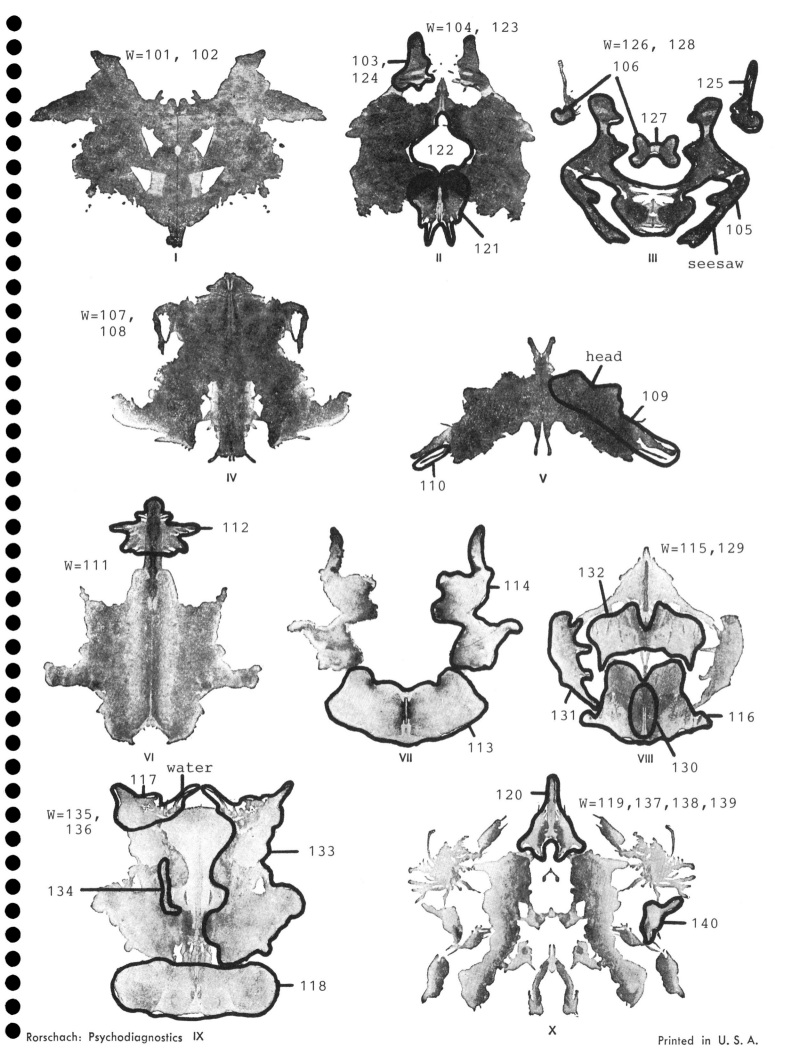

W=101, 102

I

W=104, 123

103, 124

122

121

II

W=126, 128

106

127

125

105

seesaw

III

W=107, 108

IV

head

109

110

V

112

W=111

VI

114

113

VII

W=115, 129

132

131

116

VIII

130

water

117

W=135, 136

133

134

118

IX

120

W=119, 137, 138, 139

140

X

Rorschach: Psychodiagnostics   Printed in U. S. A.

SECTION 4

CARD	RESPONSE	INQUIRY	CODING
I	101. The face of a dog w 4 eyes, he's angry	E: (Rpts S's resp) S: Just the dog's head, ears, eyes, 4 of em, a weird dog, he's got his mouth open lik he's growling, lik a dog does when angry about smthg	
I	102. Lik in mythology, a goddess in the middl & a cpl of wged A's on each side	E: (Rpts S's resp) S: She's stndng here with her hands raised and the 2 wged A's r on their hind legs, kinda raised up arnd her, lik thyr doing wht she wants them to, thyr lik her servants E: I'm not sur about the A's S: On each side of her, c the wgs & the hind legs dwn here & the frnt legs & heads, thyr jumping up bec she has raised her arms up, lik a signal for them to do ths	
II	103. It ll a chicken, it's running	E: (Rpts S's resp) S: The top red cld be a chicken, round body, little legs lik it's running, one over here, too.	
II	104. 2 ppl sittg by a campfire to keep warm	E: (Rpts S's resp) S: 2 ppl sittg hunched over, thyr wearg red hats, c the backs bent, holdg hands over the fire to keep warm E: I'm not sure wht maks that ll a fire S: It's red lik a fire & the shape of it ll flames leapg up	
III	105. It ll 2 ppl on a seesaw tht has a motor on it so all u hav to do is sit there	E: (Rpts S's resp) S: Their heads here and the bodies sittg on this lwr prt which is the seesaw & the engine (D7),& it's going up & down E: I'm not sur I c the peopl correctly S: Their heads, legs sorta on the board, lik squattg	

SECTION 4

CARD	RESPONSE	INQUIRY	CODING
III	106. A lot of animal blood there	E: (Rpts S's resp) S: There's som here & here (D2) & more down here (D3) E: I'm not sur why it ll animal blood S: It's all red but not as red as human blood so it is A bld	
IV	107. This rem me of anger	E: (Rpts S's resp) S: The W thg, I don't kno why, but it rem me of anger E: I'm not sure I c it as u do S: I don't know, nothing in particular, I just thk of anger	
IV	108. A man riding on a motorcycle	E: (Rpts S's resp) S: Here's the man's head and body and legs E: And the motorcycle? S: Down here, u can c the wheel & thes wb the handlebars	
V	109. Ths ll a person lying down	E: (Rpts S's resp) S: It ll the outline of a person lying down, it must be at nite E: I'm not sur I c the person S: Well the head & legs & body E: U said at nite? S: Well, it's lik a silhouette, all black, so I thot prob at nite	
V	110. A worm crawlg along	E: (Rpts S's resp) S: Yes, long & thin lik a worm and it's crawling along there, just ths littl part, it ll tht to me	
VI	111. It ll one of them wealth bombers	E: (Rpts S's resp) S: Yeah, thy cost a lot of money cuz the radar can't pick them out, ths one is flyg along, it's got funny wgs & a pointed nose	

SECTION 4

CARD	RESPONSE	INQUIRY	CODING
VI	112. It som littl animal lik an otter popping up out of the water	E: (Rpts S's resp) S: It ll the water is splashing E: Show it to me lik u c it S: Here's the water splashing lik he's popped right up out of it, here's the head, eye's, whiskers	
VII	113. Ths prt cb a bf floatg w the wind	E: (Rpts S's resp) S: Yes, the cntr is the body, it's wgs spread out just lik he's floatg along, lettg the wind do the work	
VII	114. Two littl girls playg w e.o.	E: (Rpts S's resp) S: Thyr kneelg dwn & thy each hav one arm behind them lik thyr playg some game where u hide smthg fr the other, c the head & nose & arm & their hair is in a pony tail	
VIII	115. An emblem for a wildlife club	E: (Rpts S's resp) S: Here's the bears on the sides and it's lik a mtn, they're standing on & these ll human hands reaching dwn toward them to symbolize harmony btwn man and animals	
VIII	116. The bttm sect ll a person's face, smiling, a clown	E: (Rpts S's resp) S: Just here (points), the eyes on top & dwn here is the smile, it looks lik a happy face E: U said a clown? S: It's all painted orange & pink lik a clowns face	
IX	117. It ll 2 creatures w guns shootg water at e.o	E: (Rpts S's resp) S: Just the top, the upper half of a creature, fr the shoulders up, & in their hands r the guns and ths ll water shootg at e.o.	

SECTION 4

CARD		RESPONSE	INQUIRY	CODING
IX		118. This might be a cloud floatg along	E: (Rpts S's resp) S: Kind of round lik a cloud, just floating in the sky like on a calm day E: U said round lik a cld? S: It looks full, the way it's shaped makes it look thick lik clouds r sometimes thick	
X		119. A whole bunch of insects crawlg arnd thse 2 dead thgs	E: (Rpts S's resp) S: Thy just ll insects to me, all diff one's all crawlg arnd thes 2 big thgs here, crabs & spiders & othr insects E: U said thes r dead thgs? S: Well, thyr all red lik dead parts of dead A's E: Can u show me som of the insects? S: Well the blue ones ll crabs (D1) & othr crabs dwn here & mayb ants & thgs & worms dwn here (D5)	
X		120. 2 coats hangg on a coatrack	E: (Rpts S's resp) S: The grey part, 2 coats, rather shapeless as they hang on ths coatrack in the cnter	
II	v	121. A red-headed man tht looks embarrassed	E: (Rpts S's resp) S: The eyes, nose, very embarrassed, c the red cheeks and he has his hands up on either side of his face	
II		122. A rocketship blastg off	E: (Rpts S's resp) S: The white w b the rocket & here's the exhaust shootg out E: What makes that ll exhaust? S: It's firey, see, red lik fire	

271

SECTION 4

CARD	RESPONSE	INQUIRY	CODING
II	123. 2 bears in a circus balancg smthg on their noses	E: (Rpts S's resp) S: The cntr thg is smthg thyr balancg & thse r the bears, their heads and bodies E: U mentioned a circus? S: Thyr doing an act and the red color is the lites lik thy shine dwn, u kno, it sets thm off as thy do their act	
II	124. Thse cb som flowrs ready to open	E: (Rpts S's resp) S: The top red, 2 flowers, just ll thyr beging to open up, 2 red flowers	
III	125. Mayb 2 sides of beef hung up lik in a freezer	E: (Rpts S's resp) S: Lik sides of beef, lik hung up in a freezer, just hanging E: I'm not sure why they ll tht S: Thyr red lik raw meat & theyr shapes ll beef sides, it ll thyr hanging the way thyr drawn	
III	126. 2 ladies moving furniture, thy must be redecorating	E: (Rpts S's resp) S: Thse r the ladies with high heels & thyr moving a piece of furniture E: U said thy must be redecorating? S: Well, there r som red decorations or paintings in the bkgrd so I assume thy r redoing an apartment or room	
III	127. A red insect flyg in the middl	E: (Rpts S's resp) S: It's red & ll a butterfly, the wgs r out lik its flying	
III	128. The face of a clown, he's smilg	E: (Rpts S's resp) S: His nose is red & so r his ears, & most of his face is painted white. Thse wb eyes & mouth, lik he's smiling	

SECTION 4

273

CARD	RESPONSE	INQUIRY	CODING
VIII	129. 2 animals climbing a mt, pretty	E: (Rpts S's resp) S: Here, 4 legs and the head and the cntr cb rocks or a mtn E: U said it's pretty? S: Yes, the diff colored rocks and bushes on the mtn r pretty	
VIII	130. The bttm cb the inside of a volcano	E: (Rpts S's resp) S: Lik if u were lookg dwn fr a plane into the volcano, it's a round pool of lava boiling away, ths is the color of lava E: Boiling? S: It ll it's all moving around lik lava boiling E: U said lik lookg dwn fr a plane? S: Yes, we did tht once in Hawaii & it ll ths, u can c rite into the volcano lik ths, it just ll a small pool but of course it's not, it just ll tht bec u r hi up	
VIII	131. A pink tiger	E: (Rpts S's resp) S: It just ll a tiger to me, the head & legs & tail, I never saw a pink one tho	
VIII	132. A lrge bird flapg it's wgs, not a real bird, smthg fr mythology	E: (Rpts S's resp) S: The large squarish wings and the blue color made me say a mythological creature, flapping its wings	
IX	< 133. A guy on a motorcycle going up ths hill, u can c his head hunched ovr the handlebars	E: (Rpts S's resp) S: The green part is the guy & here r the wheels of the bike & ths out in frnt is lik sand, all the orange, its the color of the sand lik u have in some hill climbs, lik he's zippg up there w his head hunched down	

SECTION 4

CARD	RESPONSE	INQUIRY	CODING
IX	> 134. A gator, one on each side, lying in the grass	E: (Rpts S's resp) S: Just the head and a bit of the shoulder part lik he's hiding in there, most of his body is covered by the grass so u can only c part of it	
IX	135. It just re me of happiness & contentment	E: (Rpts S's resp) S: All the pretty colors make me thk of contentment & happiness, a peaceful picture tht gives me a good feeling about myself	
IX	< 136. It cb a jungle reflected in the water	E: (Rpts S's resp) S: A multicolor jungle, w trees & bushes & some pink stuf ovr here, all diff colors & the cntr wb the water, the blue, & it's all reflected down here	
X	137. The W thg ll a bunch of insects having a party	E: (Rpts S's resp) S: Thyr all dancing around looking for fun & food, the blue ll spiders, little green worms, crabs, ants and the rest cb leaves	
X	138. A fireworks display	E: (Rpts S's resp) S: The finale, all the individual fireworks explodg at the same time, a beautiful scene E: I'm not sur wht maks it ll tht S: All the diff colors bursting out, in a pattern tht smbody planned pretty well, thts how firewrks look when thyr done by professionals	

SECTION 4

CARD	RESPONSE	INQUIRY	CODING
X v	139. The face of a Chinese whore, she's swinging her blue earrings tryg to attract attent	E: (Rpts S's resp) S: She's got a slanted brow (D10) & slanted eyes (D2) & a littl mouth (D3) & thos blue earrings r lik swinging back & forth lik she's wantg people to look at her, & of course she's got tht beard (D11) E: U say tht she's Chinese? S: Chinese whores hav beards	
X	140. It ll a bird just sittg there feeling kinda sad I guess	E: (Rpts S's resp) S: Just the shape of a bird, yellow, lik a goldfinch, it doesn't ll it's flying, just perched there E: U said feeling kinda sad? S: Yeah, it looks kinda tilted ovr a bit, lik it's feeling sad, lik it hasn't been a very good day	

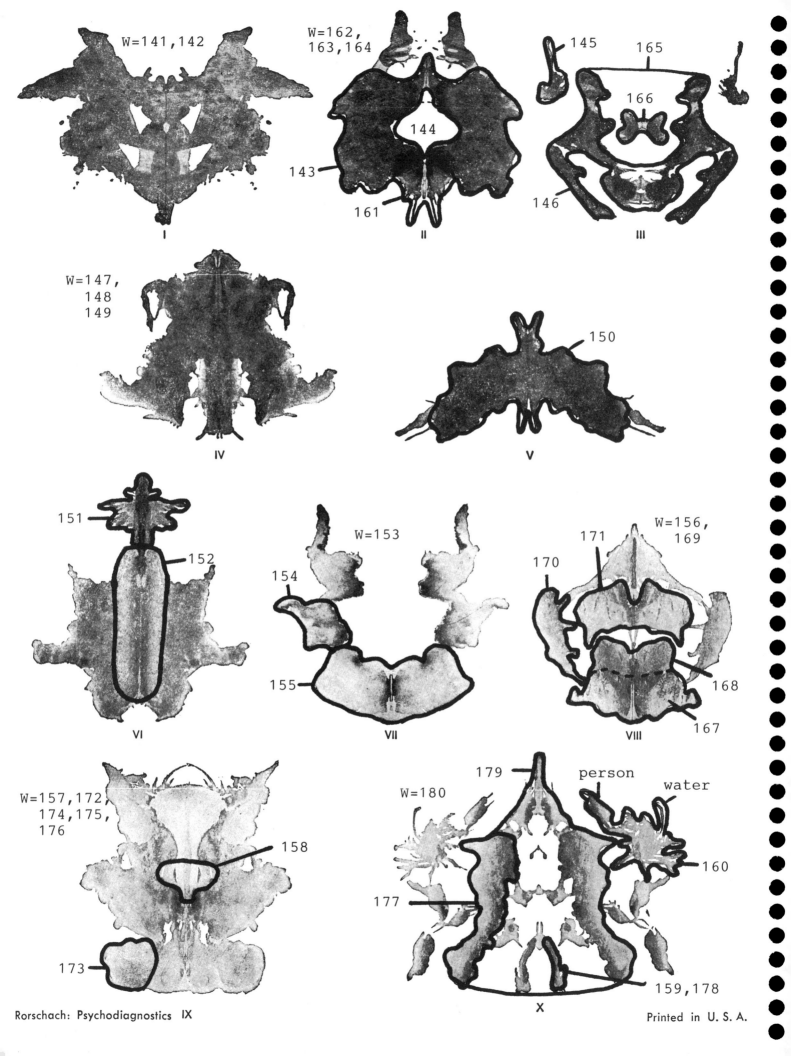

W=141,142

W=162, 163,164

144

143

161

I

145   165

166

146

III

W=147, 148 149

IV

150

V

151

152

VI

W=153

154

155

VII

W=156, 169

171

170

168

167

VIII

W=157,172, 174,175, 176

158

173

IX

179   person   water

W=180

160

177

159,178

X

Rorschach: Psychodiagnostics   Printed in U. S. A.

SECTION 5

CARD	RESPONSE	INQUIRY	CODING
I	141. It ll a bf flyg	E: (Rpts S's resp) S: Here's the body & the hands & out here r its wgs, thy got spots on them, white spots, lik a design	
I	142. Cld be a flying object lik a kite in the air	E: (Rpts S's resp) S: The W thg, the string here, c the dark line is lik hanging down & it's lik a Chinese kite, a bird or dragon E: I'm not sure about the string, u said hanging dwn? S: Just this darker line, thts the string, it's drkr & tht makes it ll it's hangg dwn in frnt of it	
II	143. 2 furry poodles expressg their lov for e.o. w a kiss	E: (Rpts S's resp) S: C all the dark marks there, it has bunches of fur lik poodles have, here's the nose and cute ears, thyr deeply in love, thy prob had a fite & now thyr makg up	
II	144. A pretty person doing a pirouette in the cntr	E: (Rpts S's resp) S: The toes r down here, hands up here with grey gloves on, her arms up & this is the full skirt (traces)	
III	145. A lock of a girl's hair	E: (Rpts S's resp) S: Basically the shading made me think of hair, this (rubs) ll the texture of hair to me, hang-g down, kinda droopy w a curl at the end.	
III	146. 2 ppl digging in a pile of dirt, real black dirt	E: (Rpts S's resp) S: Here and here, arms extended down, necks bent forward, heads, noses, backs arched as thy strain, their feet r firmly plantd dwn here, thyr workg to move the pile use the dirt for smthg	

SECTION 5

CARD	RESPONSE	INQUIRY	CODING
IV	147. A stretched out cowhide, lik for drying	E: (Rpts S's resp) S: It's been trimmed, the forepaws, rear, the place where the backbone was is pretty clear, c where it's darker here, thts where is was E: I'm not sur why it ll a cowhide S: I thk tht's how one wb shaped	
IV	148. A sponge growg in the water	E: (Rpts S's resp) S: Growg in the wtr, c the cntr is the base and it spreads out, sort of floating and the dark spots wb the holes in it E: Holes? S: Yeah the drk spots ll holes	
IV	149. It rem me of evil, u kno bigotry and hatred	E: (Rpts S's resp) S: Well it's all black, to me tht symbolizes all of the evil thgs lik hatred, war, violation of rights, just evil thgs	
V	150. A silhouette of a bf	E: (Rpts S's resp) S: It's the shape of one, lik one flying, not the ends E: U said a silhouette? S: It's all black lik a silhouette, u don't c all the details	
VI	151. It cb lik a fire, lik when u strike a match	E: (Rpts S's resp) S: Ths wb the match & all ths cb the fire shooting out, lik when it lites & it has all the diff orange colors lik this E: Orange colors? S: Yes, it ll diff shades of light orange, almost white but u kno it's orange	

SECTION 5

279

CARD		RESPONSE	INQUIRY	CODING
VI		152. It re me of muscle tissue	E: (Rpts S's resp) S: It has the textural look tht rem me of muscle tension, lik fiber, it rem me of the little things that are encrustd along the spinal cord, c rite along here (outlines) E: U said it ll muscle tension? S: Lik the muscle is taut, lik when it's flexed	
VII		153. Two angels sittg on a cld	E: (Rpts S's resp) S: This cld be a halo, the face, & wgs back here, lookg at e.o., ths bttm is grey lik a cld & tht's what thy'd be sittg on	
VII		154. A cpl of 2 dogs heads	E: (Rpts S's resp) S: Ths part ll a dogs head, lik he's got a horn or smthg stickg out of the frnt E: I'm not sur I c it rite S: Here (D3), the nose & eye & it's got ths horn on it	
VII	v	155. It ll a sheep's rear end	E: (Rpts S's) S: It looks soft lik wool & the way the edges r makes it ll a sheep, u can c the asshole, the dark spot there E: I'm not sur why it looks soft lik wool S: The colorg there, it gives a wooly appearance	
VIII		156. It's lik a big sailing ship coming towrd u	E: (Rpts S's resp) S: It's just a ship w big colorful sails, here's the mast (cntrln) & the hull (D2) E: U said it's coming towrd u? S: Well eithr comg towrd u or going away, it's lik in a distance	

SECTION 5

CARD	RESPONSE	INQUIRY	CODING
IX	157. It's an explosion, smthg is gettin blwn to hell	E: (Rpts S's resp) S: Tht prt in the cntr is gettin blown up, there's fire & smoke goin every which way E: I'm not sur I c it rite, u said fire & smoke? S: Sur the orang is fire & so is the pink, & the greenish prt wb smoke I guess, it's not lik real smoke, it's green & smoke usually ain't green but it's prob tht color bec of the thg thts gettin blown up, ths thing back there in the middl E: U say back in the middl? S: Well, prt of it is covered by the smoke & fire so it's back in, it's lik a round buildg or smthg round	
IX	158. It ll a little face starring out thru a window	E: (Rpts S's resp) S: A little face, the white is the eyes peeking out & this prt looks translucent, lik u can c thru it and he's behind it E: I'm not sur why it looks translucent S: I dkno, I guess the coloring, sorta lite blue, u can't c all of the face, it's a little blurry lik lookg thru some sort of translucent stuff	
X	159. These ll 2 slithering snakes	E: (Rpts S's resp) S: Their bodies r bent lik when thy crawl, I guess theyr just garden snakes E: Garden snakes? S: Yeah, I thk thyr usually green lik ths	

SECTION 5

CARD	RESPONSE	INQUIRY	CODING
X	160. A person diving out of a puddle of water	E: (Rpts S's resp) S: The green is the person & he's diving out of ths big puddl of water, c the blue is water, water is blue E: I'm not sur how u'r seeing the person S: Rite here (D12), his arms r up lik he's diving	
II	161. A spaceship in flyg thru space	E: (Rpts S's resp) S: The white is the ship and ths is the red exhaust & arnd it is the black outer space.	
II	162. Mayb the parts of a dead animal or s.t.	E: (Rpts S's resp) S: Here wb an organ and fur here E: Help me to c it as u do S: The organ is red lik ths and ths is the prt of the animal's fur E: I'm not sur why it ll fur S: The lines in it, thy giv it the appearance of fur	
II	163. It ll 2 ppl, thyr doing a dance of som kind, havg a good time	E: (Rpts S's resp) S: Thy have red hats and shoes & thy hav their hands togthr lik thyr doin the polka or smthg, c the heads & pointed hats E: U said thyr havg a good time? S: Thy just look real happy to me	
II	164. Sk of face, a person w his mouth open	E: (Rpts S's resp) S: The white is the mouth & the tongue is stickg out, ths white up here is eyes E: I don't thk I c the tongue S: Ths red, it's red lik a tongue & it's stickg out, lik u can c it curling ovr the lowr lip, the coloring of it makes it look thicker, lik when s.o. sticks their tongue out	

SECTION 5

CARD		RESPONSE	INQUIRY	CODING
III	v	165. Ths way it ll ss of creature just the uppr prt of him	E: (Rpts S's resp) S: There's the hand and black eyes, ths red cb his lungs, thyr red, but his chest is white, he's weird, lik from outerspace	
III		166. Ths cnter cld be a bf	E: (Rpts S's resp) S: It's shped lik a bf, a pretty one, c the wgs & the body E: U said it's pretty? S: It's a pretty red color	
VIII	v	167. Ths way the top cb lava, very hot	E: (Rpts S's resp) S: It looks firey, the way the colors mix togethr lik it's boiling up the way lava does E: I'm not sur about the boiling up effect S: Well, it's diff colors, pink, orange, diff shadings of them, it just ll it's all boiling togthr	
VIII		168. Ths prt ll sherbet, diff kinds, orange & raspberry	E: (Rpts S's resp) S: It ll sbody mixed orange and raspberry togthr & made one scoop E: One scoop? S: Well, it's only about the size of one but it's got both mixed together	
VIII		169. A leaf, the whole thg, lik after thy fall	E: (Rpts S's resp) S: The point is at the top, round sides lik a birch leaf, lik a fall leaf bec of the colors and the way they merge togethr. It's lik the one's teacher's put on the classroom windows at halloween or Thanksgiving time, pretty	

SECTION 5

CARD	RESPONSE	INQUIRY	CODING
VIII	170. The side re me of lipstick	E: (Rpts S's resp) S: It's just pink lik a blot of lipstick, mine ll tht when I blot it on a kleenex	
VIII	171. There's som blue cloth	E: (Rpts S's resp) S: The middl, it's lik blue cloth, soft lik blue velvet E: soft? S: It looks soft, the way the colors are (rubs), lik a piece of blue velvet	
IX	172. There's a waterfall way bk in a jungle	E: (Rpts S's resp) S: The cntr ll a waterfall back in between a lot of trees & foliage, it's kinda bluish white lik water is spraying as it falls, there r big green trees out in front of it & I guess the orange part up here is a rock formation	
IX	> 173. The face of a baby, lik a newborn, still wrinkly	E: (Rpts S's resp) S: The forehead, the nose, a little chin, it's pink lik a newborn E: U said still wrinkly? S: The littl lines in there mak it ll wrinkles, littl indentations	
IX	174. A modrn art paintg	E: (Rpts S's resp) S: It ll somone just flung the paint on there, the green, white, pink, & orange, just a modern paintg	
IX	175. An excedrin headache	E: All the colors r merging together, the orange is the pain shootg up & the red is the source, the green is what's left, lik it's all a horrible feeling lik if u hav a migraine or lik u'd get from PMS	

SECTION 5

CARD	RESPONSE	INQUIRY	CODING
IX	176. A fancy lamp, lik pottery, all diff colors	E: (Rpts S's resp) S: The pink is the base and the white at the top is the white lite itself & the rest is a fancy design on it	
X	177. The pink is a scab	E: (Rpts S's resp) S: It's lik if u hurt urself & begin to heal, it's usually pink lik ths when it starts to get hard E: Starts to get hard? S: Well the color isn't even, som is lite pink & som is drk pink	
X	178. Mayb green caterpillars	E: (Rpts S's resp) S: 2 of them, littl legs on the sides, thyr curved where the head is	
X	179. Ths ll a face to me	E: (Rpts S's resp) S: Up here is the grey hat, long red hair on the sides, thse cb the eyes, he has blue glasses on, the moustache dwn here	
X	180. Pieces of a jigsaw puzzle	E: (Rpts S's resp) S: Basically bec it's so colorful, c within each color there's many variations, and it rem me of a puzzle, all funny shapes, too	

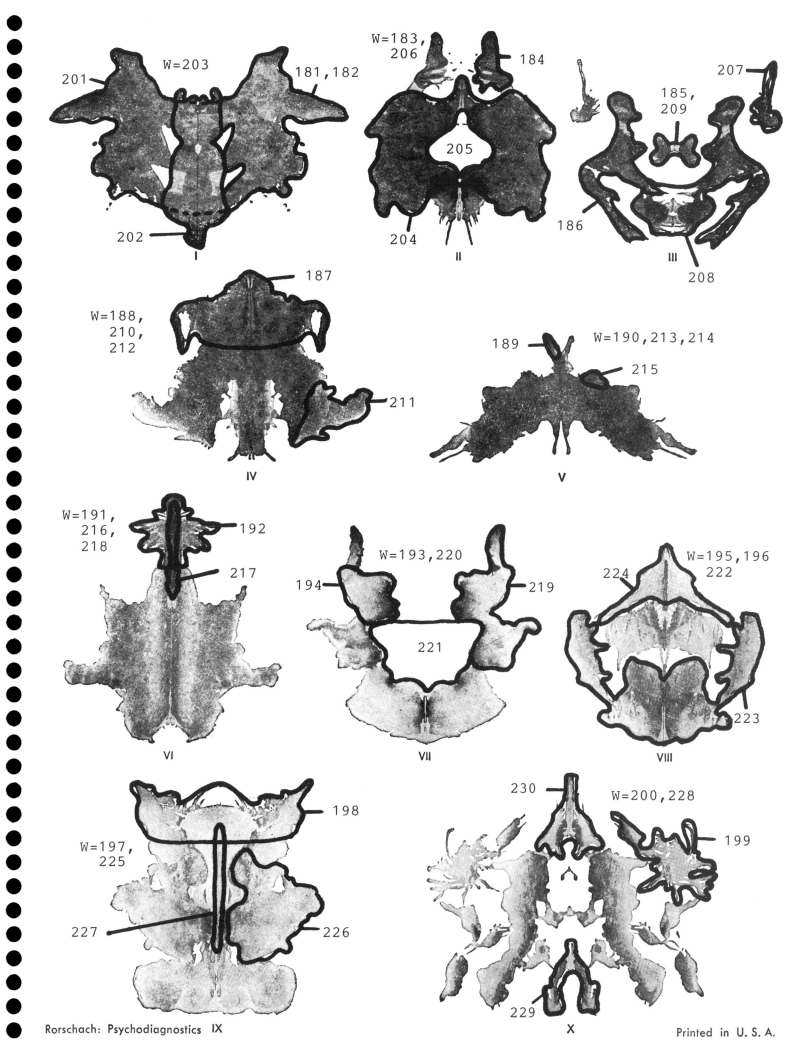

SECTION 6

CARD	RESPONSE	INQUIRY	CODING
I	181. It ll a person lookg at himself in a mirror	E: (Rpts S's resp) S: The nose, funny mouth, tummy, he's standg on one foot, a funny shaped hat & scarf, same on this side here	
I <	182. Tht ll a baby elephant standg thr	E: (Rpts S's resp) S: A pointed snout, head, feet, short tail, hump of the back, great big ear E: U said a baby elephant? S: It just looks littl there so it must be a baby one	
II	183. 2 elephants on their hind legs, thy hav hats on	E: (Rpts S's resp) S: Their feet r on the red barrel here, lik a circus act, trunks togthr, lik leang back, the barrel is in front of them, thy hav their trunks togthr while leang back	
II <	184. Ths ll the heads of 2 birds spitting at e.o.	E: (Rpts S's resp) S: The features ll a bird's face, u kno, mouth, nose, & thyr spitting at e.o., lik thyr mad at e.o. & spitting, u can c spit flyg there	
III	185. A woman ready for a virginal exam	E: (Rpts S's resp) S: Her legs r spread lik in the stirrup thgs, ready to get examind, her thighs r here & back in here is her sex area, c it's smaller back there	
III	186. A waiter who is practicing his bow	E: (Rpts S's resp) S: He's wearing a black suit lik waiters usually wear & he's lookg in the mirror and he's checkg himself out, c his reflection is over here	

SECTION 6

CARD	RESPONSE	INQUIRY	CODING
IV	187. The outline of a very furry dog w big ears, just the head	E: (Rpts S's resp) S: Here's his snout (D3) & big ears, I dk wht kind, it's a top view of him so u don't c the face E: U said it's very furry? S: The colors give a furry appearance, it's almost lik one big ball of fur & u can just c the outline of the snout & ears	
IV	< 188. A puddle of oil or grease	E: (Rpts S's resp) S: Yeah, it's just all black & it looks greasy or sticky E: Greasy or sticky? S: Yeah, u wldn't want to touch it cuz it wld stick to u	
V	189. Ths re me of a man's sex thng	E: (Rpts S's resp) S: Just ths prt (traces), it ll a man's penis, lik he's got an erection, thy ll ths then	
V	190. It a bf, the wgs r out lik it's flyg	E: (Rpts S's resp) S: The wgs r spread lik it's flying, it's lik in perspective lik I'm looking dwn at it so tht it has an angular effect E: Angular effect? S: Well, the legs in back of it look closer, sorta bigger lik I'm lookg at an angle as it flies forward	
VI	191. It's lik being way up in the air lookg dwn at a speedboat	E: (Rpts S's resp) S: The speedboat is this dark part at the top here (D2), c it's makg a big splash as it goes fast thru the water & behind it the trail, the wake tht it left behind, lik a crease in the water (traces midline), c it's darker lik it goes dwn in, lik happens fr a hi speed boat	

SECTION 6

CARD	RESPONSE	INQUIRY	CODING
VI	< 192. It ll a reflection of s.t., it cb a campfire by a lake	E: (Rpts S's resp) S: Thse ll flames of the fire shootg up & it's reflected dwn here in the lake	
VII	v 193. It ll a dance, 2 girls dancg w their backs to e.o. but their heads r touchg	E: (Rpts S's resp) S: It's lik a synchronized dance, thyr dancg on one leg w arms out in frnt of thm & thyv got their heads thrown back so tht thy just barely touch	
VII	194. Sombdy lookg in a mirror & seeing her reflection	E: (Rpts S's resp) S: Thy r the same, ths part here & here, ths is the person & ths (left) is the mirror image of the face, c the nose & chin	
VIII	195. A crystal ball, lik a wizard uses	E: (Rpts S's resp) S: It has roundedness to it (cups hands), it looks rounded at the sides and top, c, the shape gives a round effect E: I'm not quite sur why it ll a crystal ball S: Well thy hav all these weird colors, too, bright orange & blue & pink & there's white in it too, just diff colors	
VIII	< 196. Ths way ll a beaver standg there, being reflectd dwn here	E: (Rpts S's resp) S: It ll the beaver here, c the head & legs, he's just standg there & it's all being reflected dwn here, or mayb he's waitg for s.t., & he's reflected dwn here & so r som of the bushes & rocks & things	

SECTION 6

CARD	RESPONSE	INQUIRY	CODING
IX	197. Som sea plant I guess, yeah	E: (Rpts S's resp) S: It just ll som deep water form of algae or smthg E: Help me to c it lik u r S: Just the W thg gives tht impression E: I kno it does to u but help me c lik u r S: It just has a lot of colors, lik an underwtr plant or ss of underwtr growth, lik seaweed or algae or smthg	
IX	198. A spaceship rising out of a burst of flames	E: (Rpts S's resp) S: The ship is dome-shaped, ths white here (circles) & thse r lik flames coming out here on each side E: I'm not sur why tht ll flames S: Here (points to D3), shootg out the sides & the ship's going thru them, thes big orange flames shootg up on each side, like thyr in frnt of it, & behind it too, it ll it's rising fr in the middl of them	
X	199. This ll a lobster attackg a preying mantis	E: (Rpts S's resp) S: It's a blue lobster w all the claws, the frnt claws are biggr & more powerful than these back ones, & he's reachg out grabbing onto ths preying mantis, c the green here, it's got a small head & pointed antennae, thyr green lik ths	
X	v 200. Inverted it mite b a drawg of a flower, lik in a botany book	E: (Rpts S's resp) S: It's drawn so that each detail can b inspected, som prts closr to othrs to show various relationships, c, thyr largr, lik a sideview, here's the stamen and the stem & whoevr did it used diff colors to set off the diff parts	

SECTION 6

CARD	RESPONSE	INQUIRY	CODING
I	201. It ll a bat	E: (Rpts S's resp) S: In our neighborhood I saw bats flyg & thy ll tht, but not ths prt dwn here (traces), it's a bat E: I'm not sur wht maks it ll a bat S: Ths is the body, the head, wgs & littl hands	
I	202. The cntr prt mite b a snail	E: (Rpts S's resp) S: Well, it's grey lik a snail & here is the body & thse cb the horns	
I	203. A pumpkin w a face lik cut out for Halloween	E: (Rpts S's resp) S: Thse r 2 eyes, the mouth, the teeth are kinda eaten away, it's just tht genral shape, & it's all shadowy E: Shadowy? S: The darkness of it gives a shadowy look	
II	204. 2 puppies w their heads togthr lik thyr kissg	E: (Rpts S's resp) S: Just the heads here, c the ear, the mouths togthr kissing, like 2 furry puppies E: Wht maks thm look furry? S: Thse lines in here mak it look soft like fur	
II	205. A shell fragment lik thy tak out of someone wounded	E: (Rpts S's resp) S: I'v seen alot of thse in the army & tht looks lik the shell fragments that I've seen them tak out of wounds	
II	v 206. A bf maybe	E: (Rpts S's resp) S: It's bicentrical, u know, the same on both sides, head, antennae, the wngs r out lik it's gliding along	

SECTION 6

CARD	RESPONSE	INQUIRY	CODING
III	207. Ths red is the color of blood, almost lik real bld, dried	E: (Rpts S's resp) S: It's wht dried bld ll, it's not bright red, a shade of red but not bright red, it takes no shape, bld don't need to tak no shape, it can tak any shape it wants when it comes out	
III v	208. Lookg dwn at a creepy spider	E: (Rpts S's resp) S: Lik a top view, lookg dwn on it, eyes, 2 big blots, sharp jaws, the body in bk of the head, shoulders, claws w stickery thgs on the end, & it's black and looks creepy to me, I hate spiders	
III	209. Thse ll lungs to me, thyr all red so thy must b lungs	E: (Rpts S's resp) S: The shape is lik lungs, rounded at top and bottom w a small connectg piece bet where the trachea joins, and they hav the diff shades of red also lik u c in lungs	
IV	210. It ll an ape sittg on a tree stump	E: (Rpts S's resp) S: A big furry gorilla, c the head, arms and legs, & big feet, it ll he's leang back bec u c the bottm of his feet, lik his head is way back, the stump is ths middl thng E: U said he's furry? S: Well yes, it all looks furry, c in here (middl) the way it's shaded there, it ll fur	
IV	211. There's a pair of 2 feet w mud on them	E: (Rpts S's resp) S: Rite and here, the toes, heel, just 2 big feet, & prts r drkr lik thy mite hav mud or dirt on them, it's lik ur seeing just the bottom part of a person, just the feet	

SECTION 6

CARD	RESPONSE	INQUIRY	CODING
IV	212. It ll a furry animal	E: (Rpts S's resp) S: It ll som type of hermit crab, the fur & the shape re me of tht E: Fur? S: The liteness and drkness makes it ll it has a furry texture, I thk tht hermit crabs hav fur on them to keep thm safe	
V	213. A mosquito swoopg dwn to bite someone	E: (Rpts S's resp) S: Well, it's blk lik som mosquitos & he's got his wgs out lik he's flyg downward lik he's going to bite someone	
V	214. Thts a rabbit doing exercises	E: (Rpts S's resp) S: Lik he's liftg barbells E: I don't thk I'm seeg it rite, help me S: He's in the middl, c the ears (top) & littl skinny legs & he's tryg to lift up thes weights, one on each side, thy look pretty heavy E: Pretty heavy S: Well thyr bigger thn he is	
V	215. A little pile of brown dirt	E: (Rpts S's resp) S: It's just brown dirt & it's just shaped into a littl pile E: I'm not sur why it ll brown dirt S: It just does, diff shades of brown	
VI	216. Lik a bullet smashg thru s.t. mayb an animal	E: (Rpts S's resp) S: U can c the bullet really blastg thru there & the rest is animal skin, u can c the furriness by all the dots, but it's all deformed by this shell, u can't tell what it is	

SECTION 6

CARD	RESPONSE	INQUIRY	CODING
VI	217. A she-cobra, it ll a cobra but it's a woman too, she has a thin waist	E: (Rpts S's resp) S: The long thin body of the snake, it ll a cobra to me E: U said it's a she-cobra? S: C the woman's head, & thin waist, here r her legs, it's a wm snake, tht's why I said it cb a she-cobra	
VI v	218. I supp ths way it cb a mirror	E: (Rpts S's resp) S: A hand mirror, the handle part & the mirror, but its broken E: Broken? S: All the darker lines in there wld be cracks, lik it's broken	
VII	219. Thos r the sam 2 women u showd me befor but now thyr arguing about smthg	E: (Rpts S's resp) S: Just the upper half of their bodies, the hands r clenched into fists, here's the mouth, it ll thyr yellg & the brow comes out here lik when u r scowlg, it's funny, thy ll thy have rabbit ears, but anywy, thyr fiting about smthg, c the littl nose & the eyebrow here (points)	
VII v	220. It ll 2 elephants dancg w a bf on top of their heads	E: (Rpts S's resp) S: Here's the elephants dancg, c the trunk & the leg & up here this is lik a bf, it's on their heads, c the wings here, I don't kno why it's up there, mayb it's prt of the dance	
VII	221. It cld be a biteplate	E: (Rpts S's resp) S: It ll the biteplate that I'm supposed to wear at night, mine's white lik ths & it's the same shape E: I'm not sur wht a biteplate is S: It's to keep u fr grindg ur' teeth when u sleep, the dentist makes them	

SECTION 6

CARD	RESPONSE	INQUIRY	CODING
VIII	222. Thse r 2 animals climbg up an oriental mtn	E: (Rpts S's resp) S: Here and here (D1), thy ll animals, mayb lions or tigers, c the legs & the head & the rest is the mtn E: U said it's an oriental mtn? S: Sur, it has tht top, it's lik the top that, u know, in China thy hav the top of the houses lik that & hats lik tht & the mtns r lik tht	
VIII	223. It ll 2 men standg on a woman's uterus	E: (Rpts S's resp) S: Here are the 2 men, their legs & their penis E: And u said thyr standg on a woman's uterus? S: Yes, it's a terrible thg to do, c dwn here's the woman's uterus, it's shapd just lik one & thyr pink too, lik ths	
VIII	224. A fir tree, with littl hands on the ends of the branches	E: (Rpts S's resp) S: It's pointd at the top, & its a green fir tree, it has the rite shape for one E: U said there r littl hands on the ends of the branches S: Yes, these ll little hands to me, wait, I don't mean hands, I mean the branches ll hands, thy hav the form lik hands w littl fingers	
IX	225. It's lik a crashing sound, really loud	E: (Rpts S's resp) S: Yes, when I look it brings to mind a terribly loud sound E: I understand tht but I'm not sur wht gives tht impression S: I suppose all the diff colors, great artists often represent sound with color, look at what Disney did in Fantasia, thes colors r presented in a way to make a loud crashing lik sound, prob lik Handel or Rachmaninoff or Bernstein	

SECTION 6

CARD	RESPONSE	INQUIRY	CODING
IX	226. 2 grasshoppers in cocoons, lookg at e.o.	E: (Rpts S's resp) S: It's head is here, c the eye (S), it's wings aren't open yet so it's still form-g in the cocoon, 2 of 'em, thyr green & it's lik thyr lookg at eo, thy can't really move, just look	
IX	227. The cntr is a spine bone	E: (Rpts S's resp) S: Well, it ll a bone & it just goes rite up straight, so it must b a spine, tht's the way thy go	
X	228. A lotta germs lik u c thru a telescope, all diff colors	E: (Rpts S's resp) S: Just a group of little things, u can't c thm w.o. a, a microscope, I've seen them on TV, all kinds of germs, all diff colors lik these, lik in u'r blood.	
X v	229. It ll a person with wings	E: (Rpts S's resp) S: Ths is the person in the cntr, c his legs & head & here wld b the wngs like he's flyg, it just ll that to me but I sur nevr saw anyone lik tht	
X	230. Up here it ll a knife stickg in a skull	E: (Rpts S's resp) S: The skull is all except this which is the knife stickg up, kinda at an angle, leang back, mayb fr the weight of the knife it's lik tipg over a littl or mayb tht's the way it went in, gruesom huh?	

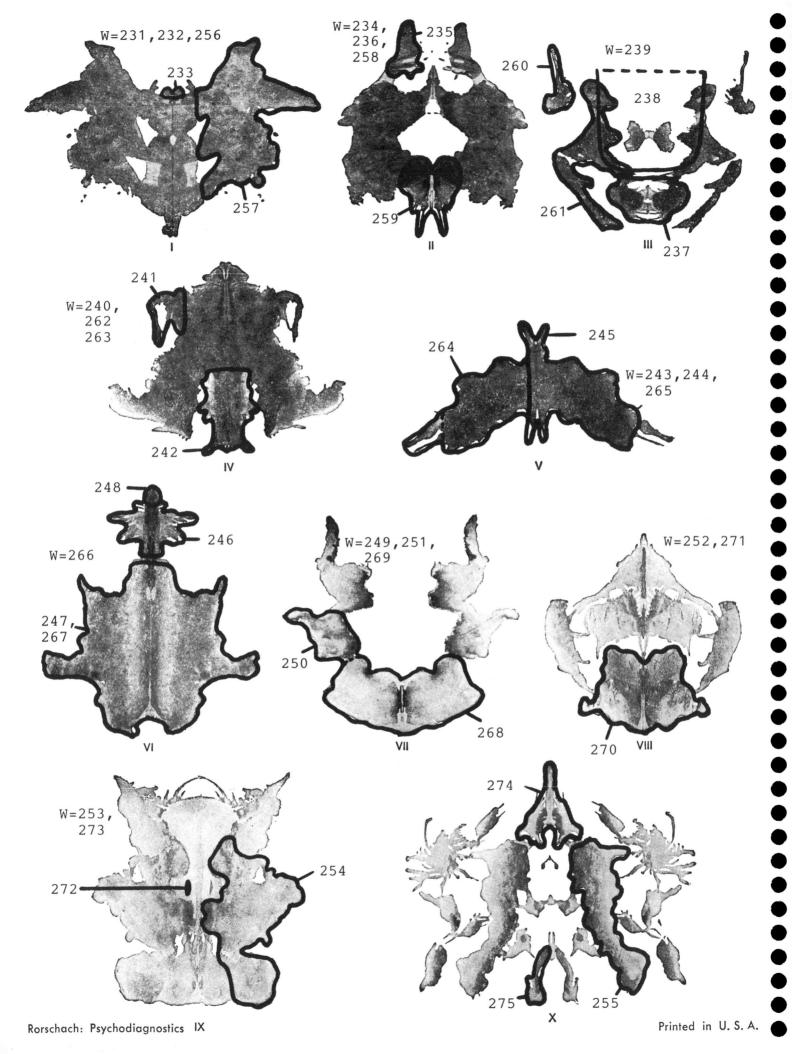

W=231,232,256

233

257

I

W=234,
236,
258

235

259

II

260

W=239

238

261

237

III

241

W=240,
262
263

242

IV

264

245

W=243,244,
265

V

248

246

W=266

247,
267

VI

W=249,251,
269

250

268

VII

W=252,271

270

VIII

W=253,
273

272

254

IX

274

255

275

X

Printed in U.S.A.

SECTION 7

CARD	RESPONSE	INQUIRY	CODING
I	231. That's a bat, zipping along	E: (Rpts S's resp) S: Here r the wngs goin flip, flap, & the body in the cntr & here is the face, the mouth and eyes r thse white spaces, it's a bat	
I	232. It's a magic bird flying	E: (Rpts S's resp) S: The wgs & body, the wgs r out lik it's flyg E: U said it's a magic bird? S: Yeah, it has thes special white designs on the wgs, thyr triangles tht represent white magic which is better than black magic	
I	233. Thse cb the breasts of an African queen	E: (Rpts S's resp) S: Thse r big & black lik that, the way breasts r on a voluptuous woman E: U said thyr of an African queen? S: Thyr at the top, thts where u'd put the queen's breasts	
II	234. A man's face w his mouth open	E: (Rpts S's resp) S: Here are his red eyes, this white wb his mouth & the black w b the rest of the face & u can c his tongue too, the red here, lik it is stickg out of his mouth	
< II	235. It ll a piece of raw liver & it's reflected dwn here	E: (Rpts S's resp) S: It's just all red, lik a piece of raw liver & it's the same dwn here lik a reflection of it, just raw liver, I never liked liver, I'd rather see a piece of steak or a good pork chop but ths is nothin but raw liver	

SECTION 7

CARD	RESPONSE	INQUIRY	CODING
II	236. Bears, snood to snood, thyr fiting, there's blood all ovr	E: (Rpts S's resp) S: Here, their feet, head, body, thyr fiting, red blood comg out of their heads, lik splashg out & more dwn here by their tails, an awful fite, thyr both hurt pretty bad I guess	
III	237. This part cld be a face lik Ghandi	E: (Rpts S's resp) S: The big black eyes & the cheeks, the forhead looks chopped off, but u can still tell it ll Ghandi	
III	v 238. A forest with a bf flyg thru the trees, lik winter, the road's all snowy	E: (Rpts S's resp) S: The white is lik a road going thru the forest & ths red bf is flyg dwn the middl of it, there r trees on the sides E: U said it's lik in wintr, the road's all snowy, help me c tht S: Yes, lik in winter with the white snow and as u look furthur dwn the road gets wider E: Gets wider? S: Yes, it looks bigger there	
III	239. Ths repres the Ides of March	E: (Rpts S's resp) S: The day Ceasar was killed, ths is a portrayal of the murder E: I'm not quite sur I c it correctly S: It's an abstract drawing, it shows two of the killers stabbg the body, c thyr leaning ovr w their knives still imbedded in the dead body & the red parts repres the blood tht was spilled tht day	
IV	240. It's a map of a world tht doesn't exist	E: (Rpts S's resp) S: It's a world of it's own, it has a coastline & the white r lakes & a line runs rite dwn the middl, a super hiway	

SECTION 7

CARD	RESPONSE	INQUIRY	CODING
IV	> 241. It's a lake in the middl of a forest	E: (Rpts s's resp) S: It's lik I'm lookg dwn at it fr a great height, the lake is the white part & it's surrounded by a lot of trees E: A lot of trees? S: The diff colors around it mak it ll the tops of trees, thyr not all the same height	
IV	242. Ths ll a feminine vagina	E: (Rpts S's resp) S: Just ths prt, u can c it goes in lik a vagina E: I'm not sur wht maks it ll that S: It's drker in the middl, it looks deeper there	
V	243. A bunnyfly	E: (Rpts S's resp) S: Here's the bunny in the middl, the body & big ears & thse r the fly wgs stretched out & his body in the cntr & it's dark lik a fly, these wld be antennae	
V	< 244. Oh, sidewards its awful, lik a dead man hangg	E: (Rpts S's resp) S: He has his arms raised above his head, lik thyr tied togthr, his stomach is bloated out & his legs are dangling down, it's a very gross lookg picture, I hope they didn't mean for it to look like this	
V	245. It ll a bird w the head of a moose	E: (Rpts S's resp) S: Just this part, don't count the ends, the wgs r stretchd out lik it's flying E: U said it has the head of a moose S: Yeah, a real weird bird, c the antlers r up here on it's head	

SECTION 7

CARD		RESPONSE	INQUIRY	CODING
VI		246. Tht ll the same bf I saw befor	E: (Rpts S's resp) S: Thse r the wgs and it has littl whiskers here, now it ll it's flyg, the way the wings are, out lik in flt	
VI		247. It re me of an animal skin, I used to hunt when I was a kid	E: (Rpts S's resp) S: Just the shape of it, the paws out here, the head wasn't cut off well, a sloppy job, it's all ragged around the edge, it doesn't look lik it's worth much	
VI		248. Ths is a fist ready to hit smthg or sombody	E: (Rpts S's resp) S: Just that round shape, u know lik when u mak a fist lik to hit smthg	
VII		249. Mite be smoke rising up	E: (Rpts S's resp) S: It just re me of smoke, c all the intensities of color, it just ll it's all rising up	
VII		250. 2 animals w smiles on their faces, thy hav funny noses	E: (Rpts S's resp) S: 2 bulls or cows, c the eye, the funny nose, & the mouth, thyr facing in opposite directions but their bodies r touchg, u can only c part, the legs aren't shown	
VII	v	251. It ll my daughter's brain after a CAT scan	E: (Rpts S's resp) S: It ll her CAT scan w all the dark masses where she was clotting, it has no specific shape, some big areas & some small ones E: I'm not sur wht maks it ll a CAT scan? S: It ll the clots in her brain, big chunks of nothing lik the white & dark masses, some small & some big in her brain	

SECTION 7

CARD	RESPONSE	INQUIRY	CODING
VIII	< 252. The pink panther on a surfboard shootin a wave	E: (Rpts S's resp) S: Here he is, c he's pink, he's got his legs firm on the board lik he's takin ths wave & it's all reflected in the water down here E: U said it's the pink panther? S: Yeah, the cartoon guy E: I'm not sur about the surfboard & the water S: Well u don't c the board too well, I guess ths orange prt cb som it it, the water is all the blue & the wave is ths grey part, lik the crest is just falling off	
IX	253. The face of a cat, she's wearg a pink collar	E: (Rpts S's resp) S: Her ears r the orange & the middl is the nose (D8) & the white spots (DdS29) r her eyes & she's got ths pink ribbon or collar on	
IX	< 254. A woman riding a motorcycle	E: (Rpts S's resp) S: She's hunched over the handlebars, c here's her head & body & ths pink here is lik the exhaust or smthg E: Exhaust or smthg? S: Not exhaust, prob som dirt blowing up behind her, mayb she just dug out & it's a lot of dirt got thown up lik in a littl cloud there behind her	
X	255. Thse r giant pink worms	E: (Rpts S's resp) S: Yeah, here & here theyv got littl legs on em, c rite here, thy ll worms to me E: U said thyr giant worms? S: Thyr awful big there lik they must be giant ones	

SECTION 7

CARD	RESPONSE	INQUIRY	CODING
I	256. It ll a crustacean, not a whole one, just a part of a dead one	E: (Rpts S's resp) S: Lik som sea creatur, prt of the skeleton here, the body, It mite hav been a crab thes cld hav been claws, it just looks dead E: I'm not sur wht makes it look dead S: Well, it's black, & it's got these holes in it	
I	< 257. Ths thg ll a coyote baying at the moon	E: (Rpts S's resp) S: Here's his legs & tail & head & he's got this big ear & his head is tilted up lik he's baying, lik thy do at nite, I saw a special on TV about them	
II	258. Ths ll 2 fat women w chicken heads, clappg hands	E: (Rpts S's resp) S: Thyr talkg to e.o. & clappg hands, c the hands r here & the big buttocks, big & fat women, thin wrists, tho E: U said thy hav heads lik chickens S: Yeah, thy do, c the beak, really weird	
II	259. Well, ths lowr prt is red so it cb a vagina	E: (Rpts S's resp) S: It's red lik that & its basically the shape of one, & it gets liter here lik the opening of the vagina, u know how it goes in	
III	v 260. The red on each side, cb blood lik it's running down	E: (Rpts S's resp) S: Well, it's lik a drop of blood on each side & it just ll it's running down, c the way the line comes down here E: I'm not sur wht maks it ll blood S: Well it's all red lik blood	

SECTION 7

CARD	RESPONSE	INQUIRY	CODING
III	261. It cb a dog, 2 of em, both sides r identical	E: (Rpts S's resp) S: A dog w a pointd snozzle, no tail but he shld hav one, paws here, mayb a poodle w a cut off tail, legs, head comes to a point, I'v seen a type lik tht but I don't kno wht its calld	
IV	262. A pair of trapper's boots hanging on a pole	E: (Rpts S's resp) S: Yeah, lik big furry boots lik the old trappers used to wear, c thyr hangg on ths pole in the middl, c the foot part & the laces r hangg out up here (D4) E: U said thyr furry? S: Yeah, thy just ll fur, kinda ragged at the edges, thy hav a rough outline to them	
IV	263. It ll a bad tooth tht got pulled	E: (Rpts S's resp) S: Well, it just has the shape of a tooth, lik the one's in the back of ur mouth, but ths one's all black lik rotted & u can c the cavities E: I'm not sur about the cavities S: Thes darkr areas, lik it's been eaten away & thes r the pits, cavities	
V	264. Ths side prt ll a turkey leg tht smbody left on the broiler too long	E: (Rpts S's resp) S: I really don't lik turkey, especially the legs, if I eat it at all I only eat the breast, ths one really looks yucky E: I'm not sur wht mks it ll a turkey leg S: It's just shaped lik one E: And u said it was left on the broiler too long? S: Yep, it's all burnt up, blackened, blackened turkey leg, ugh	

SECTION 7

CARD	RESPONSE	INQUIRY	CODING
V	v 265. This way is a bf, a grey bf w its wgs reachg upwrd	E: (Rpts S's resp) S: When the wgs are upward it looks beautiful & flowg, the symmetrical shape, the antennae, the slender body, the tiny feet & the mutliple colors E: Multiple colors? S: The wgs r colored w diff shades of grey	
VI	266. A dead cat, lik it got run ovr by a truck, we used to call em sailcats	E: (Rpts S's resp) S: It's all flattened out here's the whiskers & his arms & its got grease marks on it, when I was a kid in Texas we'd wait until thy were good & flat, u kno after a lot of trucks ran ovr them & we'd peel em off the road & sail em, we used to call em sailcats E: U said it has grease marks? S: Yeah, there's dark spots all ovr it	
VI	v 267. It ll a chunk of animal skin, the hide	E: (Rpts S's resp) S: Just the furry hide of an animal, lik a big buffalo hide or smthg E: I'm not sur wht maks it ll tht S: It's shaped lik a hide, thes r where the legs where, it's just lik one mite b hung up to dry, sorta stretched out E: U said it looks furry? S: Yes, it's just rough around the edges lik a fur hide wld b	
VII	v 268. The top prt ll a big rock thts breaking apart	E: (Rpts S's resp) S: Its grey lik rock, & the drk spot is the crack where it's beginning to split, lik a crevase u can c into, where it's cracked & breakg apart, it's a moment befor it breaks in two	

SECTION 7

CARD		RESPONSE	INQUIRY	CODING
VII		269. Tht's a bf, he's carryg 2 toy bunnies on his wgs	E: (Rpts S's resp) S: Well, the bf has large wings & a narrow body & these 2 bunnies r on his wgs as he flies on his wings, cute bunny noses, long ears & here's a little paw E: U said thyr toy bunnies? S: Thy don't look real to me	
VIII		270. The bttm cb a flower	E: (Rpts S's resp) S: Thse cb petals at the top & the stem in the cntr & thse littl handle shaped petals on the sides, a delicate looking flower E: Delicate looking? S: It just looks very delicate to me, the shape maks it look fragile	
VIII		271. Oh, a beautiful old sailing ship w the sunlight on it	E: (Rpts S's resp) S: It's in the distance, lik sailing away fr me, a stern view, very colorful w the mast in the center & huge pink sails out to each side & a blue mainsail & a grey topsail, the hull looks orange but tht is prob bec the sunlite is exaggerating all the colors	
IX		272. Tht's a sperm, its small & white so it must b, 2 of em	E: (Rpts S's resp) S: It's white lik sperm r white, I've seen thm & tht's how sperm look & thyr small	
IX	v	273. Ths is lik being zonked out, it's lik all the feelg rising	E: (Rpts S's resp) S: Lik whn I'm really stoned on s.t. lik exceedingly, it shows all the experience rising, penetrating the sub-conscious lik the middl & its all comg to the top, to reality, u know all the pretty colors equal the feelings	

SECTION 7

CARD	RESPONSE	INQUIRY	CODING
X	274. Up here it ll 2 grey dinosaurs leang up agnst ths pole	E: (Rpts S's resp) S: They must be very tired, they've got weird antennae & legs & thyr leang on this post here in the middl	
X v	275. 2 seahorses who hav had an argument & thyr turned away fr e.o., lookg very stiff lik angry at e.o.	E: (Rpts S's resp) S: It's tht shape & I thk thyr green too, but thes look stiff, lik thyr angry at e.o., lik thy prob just had an argument & thy don't want to look at e.o.	

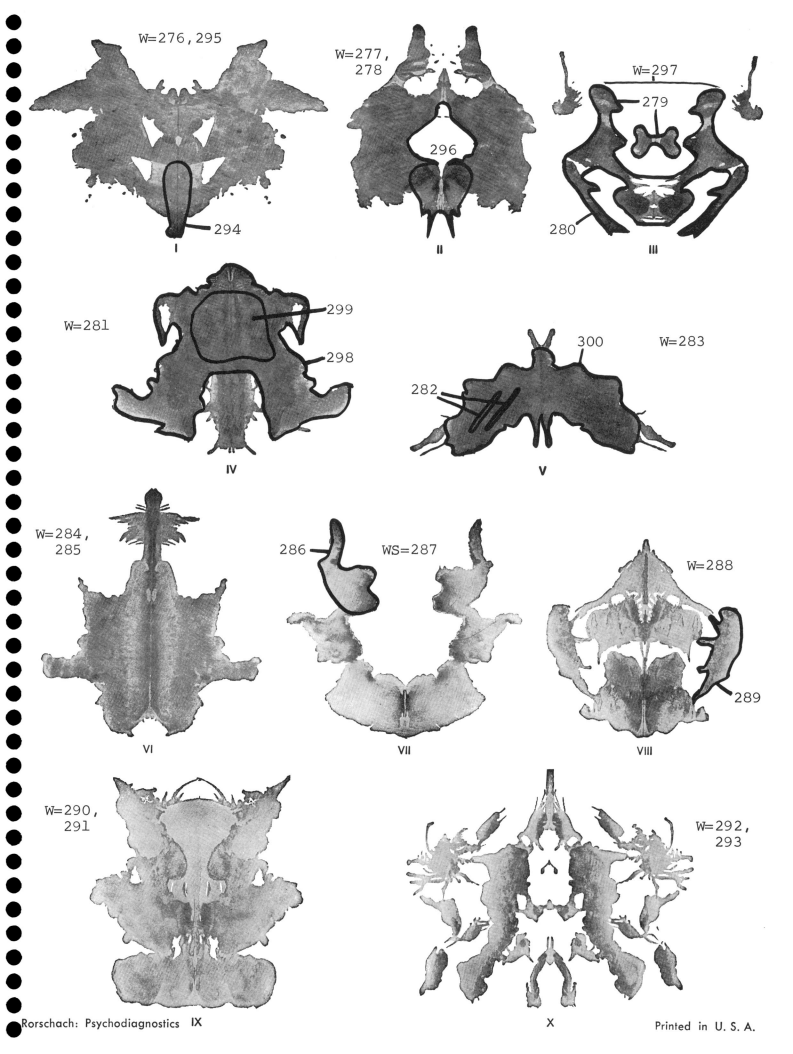

SECTION 8

CARD	RESPONSE	INQUIRY	CODING
I	276. Som one w a cape standg in the wind, w her hands in the air, without her head	E: (Rpts S's resp) S: The body here, stout lookg, not really fat, a small waist & big bust, she has a belt on, the buckl is litr colord in the middl c the litr & drkr, her legs here & a collar but no head E: U said she's standing in the wind? S: All ths is her cape flyg in the wind, it's torn, the edges r all ragged	
II	277. Som poor cat got hit in the mouth, its open lik in pain & he's got blood coming out of his mouth & ears	E: (Rpts S's resp) S: Lik if u fracture s.b.'s skull thy bleed out of the mouth & ears lik ths all red w blood & the white is the mouth, open lik hurtg, ths is more blood gushg out fr the mouth in front of him E: U say it's a cat? S: Yeah, a cat or dog, prob a cat bec it's got the pointd ears but it's kinda hard to tell	
II	278. 2 witches w red shoes on, doing som of their magic	E: (Rpts S's resp) S: Thy hav red hats & shoes & their hands r togethr lik makg a spell, w their black robes pulled arnd thm, hunched ovr w their hands togethr E: U said thyr making a spell? S: Well I just thot of tht, but mayb thyr just whispering to e.o.	
III	279. A couple of peopl tryg to catch ths bf	E: (Rpts S's resp) S: Here is the red bf, it's closr lik its way out in frnt of thm & here r the 2 peopl, c their heads & legs & thy hav nets lik thyr chasg it but it's flyg real fast	

SECTION 8

CARD	RESPONSE	INQUIRY	CODING
III v	280. Lik a dog's face, w a big red nose, his mouth is open	E: (Rpts S's resp) S: Not ths red out here, just the rest, thes r his eyes & ths red (D3) is his big nose & his mouth, it's open, u can c his teeth E: See his teeth? S: Yeah, thyr pointd, lik sharp	
IV	281. Tht ll I feel, depressed	E: (Rpts S's resp) S: It's black lik gloom & it has the mottling E: I'm not sur I'm seeg it rite S: It just ll a feeling, a terrible feeling lik when everythg is bleak & depressing	
V	282. Thes lines here, what a deformed thot, thy ll scars fr an operation	E: (Rpts S's resp) S: Thse drker & liter lines in here, thy just ll scars, my significant othr had an operation and his scars r lik tht, just scars, I don't kno why I thot of tht, I wld hav rather seen smthg else, I supp I'm just preoccupied thes days	
V	283. It cb lik a moth coming out of the chrysalis turng into a bf	E: (Rpts S's resp) S: Well, it's still diff shades of blacks, the shape is not as full blwn as if it was finished w the wings & all E: U say it's comg out of the chrysalis? S: Yes, the middl prt is the chrysalis, u kno the shell c u r just seeing the wgs as it's breakg thru, it still ll a moth but soon it will b a bf & tak on diff coloring, rite now it's just struggling to get out	

SECTION 8

CARD	RESPONSE	INQUIRY	CODING
VI	284. Jesus standg w his shadow, he's casting it out in strange way	E: (Rpts S's resp) S: His arms are out & he's wearing a robe tht spreads out & the way the lite is behnd him its forming this huge shadow in frnt of him, it's all drk grey lik a huge shadow, spreadg out over the plain in frnt of him, it represents a message about his return E: A message? S: Not a specific thot, but just a demonstration, it's so big it represents the fact tht no one escapes judgment	
VI	285. It ll som poor insect is caught in ths peanut butter	E: (Rpts S's resp) S: It's a wged insect, the littl head & the whiskers & he's flappg his wgs fast tryg to get out of ths peanut butter E: Wht maks it ll peanut butter S: The ink maks it look all sticky, gooey lik peanut butter, he was tryg to get som & he got stuck	
VII	286. A wm lookg in a mirror & seeing her reflection	E: (Rpts S's resp) S: Thyr the sam almost, ths one looks a littl blurry, the drkness arnd the edges is mor pronounced & the edges here r mor precise, c this wld b the real one & ths the mirror image	
VII	287. Lik lookg dwn on a jungle, u can c diff levels of trees on an island w a lagoon	E: (Rpts S's resp) S: U can c the diff layers, the diff colors, lik the island is sloped dwn to the lagoon side & its higher on the outr side, it gives an impression lik some trees r higher thn others E: And the lagoon? S: The white part here, lik a lagoon	

SECTION 8

CARD	RESPONSE	INQUIRY	CODING
VIII	v 288. An ugly face of communist w an evil smile & big ears	E: (Rpts S's resp) S: He's got a bumpy forehead & eyes here in the pink & the white is the mouth here curled up in a smile but it looks evil & all the pink hair on the sides too E: U said the forehead looks bumpy? S: Lik its got dents in it, c the way the colors r there, c, it mak it ll it's bumpy, rough lik E: And u said it's the face of a communist? S: Sur thy hav pink hair, tht's why thy call em pinkos	
VIII	289. It rem me of a camelot in the summer	E: (Rpts S's resp) S: Thos thgs tht change colors during the season E: I'm not quite sur wht u mean S: Thyr littl sleezy animals & when thy walk arnd thy change colors dependg on wht season of the year it is, c his legs & his head, he's red now so it must be summer	
IX	290. It ll a fountain lik it was all lit up at nite	E: (Rpts S's resp) S: The thg in the middl wld b the water stream shootg up & all the outside is water & spray as it falls outward & it's all lit up w diff colored lights & the pink is the base of fountain	
IX	291. A paintg of 2 littl birds hiding under a tree	E: (Rpts S's resp) S: There's one here & here (D3), thyr orange birds, mayb orioles & thyr back underneath ths big colorful tree, c the big green foliage & ths huge pink top, the artist really had quite an imagination, thyr back in under it, some of the leaves r concealing part of them	

SECTION 8

CARD	RESPONSE	INQUIRY	CODING
X	292. A wizard castg out spells	E: (Rpts S's resp) S: The top grey area is his face & his robes r the pink part & all thse othr thgs r the spells he's already cast out so thyr in frnt of him & on either side, thyr all diff colors to rep that each has a diff meaning E: A different meaning? S: Each one means s.t. but I don't know what.	
X.	293. It's a burlesque dancer in a bizarre headdress & a robe thts flying outward, she has a littl pendant hangg dwn & a blu bra & a green G-string, she's perfectly anonymous cuz u can't c her body	E: (Rpts S's resp) S: Up here (D11) is the headdress & the pink is the open robe & she's holdg onto thse blue pom pom lik fans w yellow & brown streamers comg fr them as thy flail in the air & here's her pendant & brassiere & the green is her G-string, it's lik she's dancing & evthg is moving but u can't really c her face or body so she's no one	
I	> 294. An alligator floatg along in the water at nite w his reflection down here	E: (Rpts S's resp) S: U just c his head, the long snout with the bump on the end of it by the mouth, here's the reflection in the wter, the same as up here, the shading maks it look all shadowy lik it was at night?	
I	295. The W thg is an abstract drawg of evil	E: (Rpts S's resp) S: It's lik a face tht represents all of man's evil, the vicious lookg mouth, the empty white eyes, the craggy outline of the cheeks & the horns mounted on each side at the top, the artist hoped to repres how evil and rotten the humans r, thy pollute e.o. & everythg tht thy com in contact w but thyr so stupid thy'll never realize how thyv damaged the planet	

SECTION 8

CARD	RESPONSE	INQUIRY	CODING
II	296. A burst of red lite comg fr a white chandelier	E: (Rpts S's resp) S: The chandelier is in the cntr & the red lite is below it, mayb it has a red bulb, but the lite is burstg out the frnt lik it was just turn on	
III	297. 2 clowns who r pretendg to b somthg	E: (Rpts S's resp) S: I said clowns bec of the face, it ll they mite hav masks on & thy hav white collars & thes r red decorations in the bkgrnd E: U said thyr pretending to be somthg? S: The masks r lik chickens, lik thyr pretending to be chickens	
IV	298. A big old gorilla layg flat on his back w his feet out towrd u	E: (Rpts S's resp) S: It sur ll a gorilla, all fur, c the feet out toward u, his arms r here & his head is way back E: U said all fur, wht maks it ll fur S: The shadg I supp, it ll fur E: And u said flat on his back? S: It's got thse big feet comg ths way & the head is way bk so he must be layg dwn	
IV	299. The cntr prt ll a deep ditch in the middl of a muddy field	E: (Rpts S's resp) S: There's a ditch in the middl of ths field or sthg, it looks real drk, deep lik & the field arnd it looks muddy, lik wet, c where it's drkr, lik mud u'd get stuck in if u walkd in it	
V	300. Thts Dracula, stndg there in his black cloak ready to fly	E: (Rpts S's resp) S: His arms r out, but don't count thes ends & don't count ths top thgs, u can't c his face, he's all in blk stretchg his arms out ready to fly & find anothr victim for his masochism	

PART IV

APPENDIX

A ❖ Scoring Keys For Practice Responses

▲ SCORING KEY FOR SECTION 1 – RESPONSES 1–35

1. Ddo34 Fo Bt

2. Do4 M^{a}o H GHR

3. WSo F– Hd 4.5 PHR

4. Dd+24 m^{p}u Hh 3.0

5. Do3 FM^{a}o A

6. D+1 M^{a}o 2 H,Id P 3.0 COP,GHR

7. Wo m^{p}o Bt 2.0

8. Ddo21 Fu Cg

9. Wo FM^{p}o A P 1.0

10. Wo F– An 1.0

11. Do4 Fo Sc

12. Wo FM^{a}u A 2.5

13. D+1 M^{p}o 2 (Hd) P 3.0 GHR

14. Ddo21 FM^a– 2 A

15. Do4 M^p– Hd PHR

16. W+ FM^{a}o 2 A, Ls P 4.5

17. DdSo23 Fu Na

18. Wv/+ m^p.FD– Cl,Ls 5.5

19. D+15 M^a– H,Id 4.0 PHR

20. Wv m^a.CFo Ex

21. Do2 FC– An,Bl

22. Dv3 C Bl

23. W+ FCo 2 H,Cg 4.5 GHR

24. Dv2 C 2 Fd

25. Ddo29 Fu Art PER

26. W+ M^a.Co 2 H,Art P 5.5 COP,GHR

27. Dol FC– Hd,Sx PHR

28. Ddo99 CFu Bt

29. Wo FCu Hh,Ay 4.5

30. Wv Cn Art

31. Ddo26 Fu 2 Sc

32. Wv CF– An MOR

33. Do6 FCu Cg ALOG

34. Wv C Art,AB

35. Dol Fo 2 A P DR

▲ *SCORING KEY FOR SECTION 2 – RESPONSES 36–75*

36. WSo FC'o (Hd) 3.5 GHR

37. Dv2 YFu 2 Cl

38. Ddv23 C'Fu Ls

39. D+1 FM^{P}o 2 A P 3.0

40. DSv5 FC'u Na DV

41. Dv7 C'Fu Xy

42. Ddo27 FC'– Fd DR

43. Wv Y Art

44. Wv C'Fu Cl PER

45. Do1 FY– A

46. Wo FC'o A P 1.0

47. Wv m^P.YFu Fi

48. Ddo99 FC'– Xy

49. D+3 FYo Ay, Ls 2.5 PER

50. Do1 FC'.FYo Hh PER

51. Wo YF– An 2.5 MOR, PER

52. DdSv99 C'Fu Na,Art

53. Do9 F+ 2 Hd P GHR

54. Do4 FY– 2 Cg

55. Dv2 m^a.CFu Fi

56. WSo FC'.CF– Ad,An 4.5 MOR,INC

57. DSo8 FC'o Hh DR

58. Do4 FCo Fd,Bt

59. Dv8 C'Fu 2 Ls

60. Do4 FYu Sc

61. Wo FM^a.FC'o A P 1.0

62. Ddo99 FV– Hd,Sx PHR

63. D+1 m^P.FTo 2 (A) P 3.0

64. Do2 Fu 2 Art AB

65. Wv T Cg

66. Do3 FTo Bt

67. W+ TFu Fd 4.0 DR

68. Ddo31 FTu Ad

69. Ddo25 FTu Ad

70. Dv1 TFo Ad,Hh P

71. W+ M^p+ 2 H,Art,Ls P 2.5 COP,GHR

72. Dv4 T Na

73. D+5 m^P.FTo 2 Art 3.0

74. Do6 TFo 2 Hh

75. WSv/+ Fu Na 6.0

▲ *SCORING KEY FOR SECTION 3 — RESPONSES 76–100*

76. Wo Fu A 1.0 INC

77. D+4 FVo H,Cg 4.0 GHR

78. DSo6 FDo An 4.5 DV

79. DdSv/+99 VFo Na 4.5

80. Do2 FV– 2 Cg

81. D+9 Fro H P 4.0 GHR

82. DdS+99 FC.FDu A,Ls 4.5 ALOG

83. Do7 FV– Hd PHR

84. Wv VFo Bt DV,MOR

85. Wo M^p.FDo (H) P 2.0 GHR

86. Do7 FVu A INC

87. Do10 FM^ao 2 Ad AG,PHR

88. W+ FVu H,Sc 2.5 GHR

89. Wv V Ls

90. Wv/+ rFo Ls 2.5

91. Dv/+12 FVo Ls 2.5

92. Do1 FC'o Hd P GHR

93. Do3 Fo 2 Ad

94. Wv VF– Fd

95. W+ Fr.FM^p.CFo A,Na P 4.5

96. Ddo23 FC.FVu Hd,Sx PHR

97. Ddv24 Fu 2 Bt

98. D+3 M^a.FC+ 2 (H),Cg P 4.5 COP,GHR

99. W+ CFo Bt 5.5

100. Ddo99 CF.YF– An ALOG,PER

▲ *SCORING KEY FOR SECTION 4 — RESPONSES 101–140*

101. WSo FM^{a}u Ad 3.5 AG,INC2,PHR

102. W+ M^p.FM^{a}o 2 (H),(A),Ay 4.0 COP,GHR

103. Do2 FM^{a}u 2 A

104. W+ M^p.CF.mao 2 H,Fi,Cg 4.5 GHR

105. D+1 M^p.m^{a}u 2 H,Sc 3.0 GHR

106. Ddv99 C 2 Bl ALOG

107. Wv M^a Hx AB PHR

108. W+ M^{a}o H,Sc P 4.0 GHR

109. Ddo99 M^p.FC'u H GHR

110. Ddo22 FM^{a}o A

111. Wo m^{a}u Sc 2.5 DV2

112. Dd+22 FM^a.m^{a}u A,Na 2.5

113. Do4 FM^{p}o A

114. D+2 M^{a}o 2 H P 3.0 COP,GHR

115. W+ FM^p.M^{p}o2 Art,A,Hd,Ls P 4.5 AB,PHR

116. Do2 M^p.FC− (Hd) PHR

117. Dd+99 M^a.m^{a}o 2 (Hd),Na,Sc 4.5 GHR

118. Dv6 m^p.FDo Cl

119. W+ FM^a.CFu 2 A,Ad P 5.5 MOR

120. D+11 m^p− 2 Cg,Hh 4.0

121. Do3 FC.M^p− Hd,Hx PHR

122. DS+5 m^a.CFo Sc,Fi 4.5

123. W+ FM^a.CFo 2 A,Id P 4.5 COP,GHR

124. Dv2 m^p.FCu 2 Bt

125. Do2 m^p.CFo 2 Fd

126. W+ M^a.C.FDo2 H,Art,Cg,Hh P 5.5 COP,GHR

127. Do3 FC.FM^{a}o A

128. WSo M^p.FC.FC'− (Hd) 5.5 PHR

129. W+ FM^a.CFo 2 A,Ls P 4.5

130. Ddo99 FD.m^a.CFu Fi PER

131. Do1 FCo A P INC

132. Do5 FM^a.FCo (A)

133. D+12 M^a.CFo H,Sc,Ls 2.5 GHR

134. Dd+33 FM^p.FDo 2 A,Ls 2.5

135. Wv M^p.C Hx AB,PHR

136. Wv/+ rF.CFo Na 5.5

137. W+ M^a.FCo 2 A,Bt P 5.5 FAB,COP,GHR

138. Wv m^a.CFo Ex,Art

139. WS+ M^a.m^p.FC− Hd,Art 5.5 ALOG,PHR

140. Do15 M^p.FCo A,Hx,INC,MOR,PHR

▲ *SCORING KEY FOR SECTION 5 – RESPONSES 141–180*

141. WSo FM^a.FC'o A P 3.5 INC

142. W+ m^p.FVu Art 4.0

143. D+1 M^a.FTo 2 Ad,Hx P 3.0 FAB,COP,GHR

144. DdS+99 M^a.FC'u H,Cg 4.5 GHR

145. Dv2 TF.m^p– Hd PHR

146. D+1 M^a.C'F+ 2 H,Ls P 3.0 COP,GHR

147. Wo m^p.FYo Ad 2.0 DV

148. Wv FM^p.FVu A

149. Wv M^a.C' Hx AB,PHR

150. Ddo99 FC'.FM^{a}o A

151. D+3 m^a.YFo Fi 2.5 CP

152. Ddv99 M^p.TF– An PHR

153. W+ M^p.C'Fo 2 (H),Cl P 2.5 GHR

154. Do3 Fo 2 Ad DV2,INC

155. Do4 FT.FV– Ad

156. Wo m^a.FC.FDo Sc 4.5

157. Wv/+ m^a.CF.FVo Ex,Fi 5.5 MOR,AG

158. DdS+22 M^p.FV.FC– Hd,Sc 5.0 PHR

159. Do4 FM^a.FCo 2 A

160. D+12 M^a.CF– H,Na 4.0 FAB2,PHR

161. DS+5 m^a.CF.C'Fo Sc,Fi,Na 4.5

162. Wv/+ CF.TF– Ad,An 4.5 MOR

163. W+ M^a.FCo 2 H,Hx,Cg 4.5 COP,GHR

164. WSo M^p.FC.FV– Hd 4.5 PHR

165. DdSo99 FC'.FCu (Hd),An 4.5 PHR

166. Do3 FCo A

167. Dv7 C.Y.m^a Fi

168. Dv2 CF.YFo Fd

169. Wo FC.FYu Bt 4.5 MOR

170. Dv1 C Art PER

171. Dv5 C.T Id

172. W+ m^p.FD.CFo Na 5.5

173. Do4 FC.FVo Hd PHR

174. WSv C.C' Art

175. Wv M^a.Y Hx DR,MOR PHR

176. WSo FC.FC'u Hh,Art 5.5

177. Dv9 C.Y Bl

178. Do4 FCo 2 A

179. DdS+22 FC'.FC– Hd,Sc,Cg 4.0 PHR

180. Wv CF.YFu Art

▲ *SCORING KEY FOR SECTION 6 – PRACTICE RESPONSES 181–230*

181. D+2 M^p.Fro H,Cg 6.0 GHR

182. Do2 FM^po A ALOG

183. W+ FM^a.FCo 2 A,Cg,Id 4.5 COP,GHR

184. D+2 M^a.m^pu 2 Ad,Hx 5.5 AG,FAB,PHR

185. Do3 M^p.FD– Hd,Sx DV2,PHR

186. D+9 M^a.FC'.Fro H,Cg P 4.0 GHR

187. Ddo99 FT– Ad

188. Wv C'.T Id

189. Ddo31 M^au Hd,Sx PHR

190. Wo FM^a.FDo A P 1.0

191. W+ m^a.FVo Sc,Na 2.5

192. Dv/+3 rF.m^au Fi 2.5

193. W+ M^ao 2 H 2.5 COP,GHR

194. D+9 M^p.Fro Hd P 3.0 GHR

195. WSo FD.FC.FC'– Art 4.5

196. W+ FM^p.Fro A Ls P 4.5

197. Wv CFo Bt

198. DdS+99 m^a.FD.CFu Sc,Fi 5.0

199. D+1 FM^a.FCu A 4.0 AG,INC,FAB,PHR

200. Wo FCo Art,Bt 5.5

201. Ddo99 Fo A PER,INC

202. Do4 FC'– A INC

203. WSo FYu (Hd) 3.5 MOR,PHR

204. D+1 M^a.FTo 2 Ad P 3.0 FAB,COP,GHR

205. DSv5 Fu Sc PER

206. Wo FM^po A 4.5 DV2

207. Dv2 C Bl DR

208. Dol FC'– A DV

209. Do3 FC.FYo An ALOG

210. W+ FM^p.FT.FDo A,Bt 4.0

211. Do2 FYo Hd,Ls DV2,PHR

212. Wo TF– A 2.0 INC

213. Wo FM^a.FC'u A 1.0 AG,PHR

214. W+ M^ao 2 A,Sc 2.5 FAB,PHR

215. Ddv33 YFu Ls CP

216. W+ m^a.TFo Sc,Ad P 2.5 AG, MOR

217. Do2 Fu (A) CONTAM

218. Wo FYu Hh 2.5 MOR

219. D+2 M^a+ 2 Hd P 3.0 PSV,AG,INC,GHR

220. W+ M^ao 2 A 2.5 FAB2,COP,PHR

221. DSo10 FC'u Sc PER

222. W+ FM^ao 2 A Ls P 4.5 ALOG

223. D+1 M^p.FC– 2 H,Sx,An 3.0 FAB2,PHR

224. Do4 FCu Bt INC

225. Wv M^a.C Hx AB,DR,PHR

226. DS+1 FM^p.FC– 2 (A) 5.0 FAB2

227. Do5 Fo An ALOG

228. Wv CFu A DV,PER

229. Do10 M^ao (H) INC,PHR

230. D+11 m^p.FD– An,Hh 4.0 MOR

▲ *SCORING KEY FOR SECTION 7 — PRACTICE RESPONSES 231–275*

231. WSo FM^{a}o A P 3.5 CONTAM

232. WSo FM^{a}FC'o (A) 3.5 ALOG

233. Ddo22 FC'u Hd,Sx ALOG,PHR

234. WSo M^p.FC.FD– Hd 4.5 INC,PHR

235. Dv/+2 C.rF Fd 5.5 DR2

236. W+ FM^a.m^a.CFo 2 A,Bl 4.5 DV,AG,MOR,PHR

237. Do7 FC'– Hd MOR,PHR

238. DdS+99 FM^a.FC.FC'.FDu A,Na 4.5 FAB

239. W+ M^p.Co 2 Art,H,Bl,Sc P 5.5 MOR,AG,AB,PHR

240. WSo Fu Ge 5.0 DR2

241. DSv/+4 VFu Na 5.0

242. Dol FV– Hd,Sx DV2,PHR

243. Wo FM^p.FC'u (A) 1.0 CONTAM

244. Wo m^p– H 1.0 DR2,MOR,PHR

245. Ddo99 FM^{a}o A INC

246. Do3 FM^{a}u A INC,PSV

247. Do1 Fo Ad P PER,MOR

248. Ddo23 M^{a}u Hd AG,PHR

249. Wv m^p.YFu Fi

250. Dd+99 M^{p}u 2 Ad 2.5 INC,PHR

251. WSo YF.C'F– Xy 4.0 PER,MOR

252. W+ M^a.Fr.CF.m^{p}o (A),Na,Id P 4.5 GHR

253. WS+ FC– Ad,Id 5.5

254. D+1 M^a.m^{p}o H,Sc,Ls 2.5 GHR

255. Do9 FCo 2 A INC,ALOG

SCORING KEY FOR SECTION 7 – PRACTICE RESPONSES 231–275

(Continued)

---

256. WSo FC'o Ad 3.5 MOR

257. Do2 FM^{a}o A PER

258. W+ M^a+ 2 H,Sx 4.5 INC2,PHR

259. Do3 FC.FVo Hd,Sx PHR

260. Dv2 CF.m^{p}o 2 Bl

261. Do9 Fo 2 A DV,PER,MOR

262. W+ m^{p}o (2) Cg,Id 4.0

263. Wo FC'.FV– Hd 2.0 MOR,PHR

264. Do4 FC'u Fd DR,MOR

265. Wo FC'.FM^p.FYo A P 1.0

266. Wo FYo A 2.5 MOR,INC,PER

267. Do1 m^{p}o Ad P

268. Dv4 m^p.C'F.VFo Ls MOR

269. W+ FM^{a}o 2 A,(A) 2.5 FAB2

270. Do2 Fo Bt

271. Wo FC.FD.m^a.FC'o Sc 4.5

272. DdSo23 FC'– 2 Sx ALOG,PER

273. Wv M^p.C Hx DR2,PER,AB,PHR

274. D+11 FC'.FM^{p}u 2 A,Id 4.0 FAB

275. D+4 M^a.FCo 2 A 4.5 AG,FAB,PHR

▲ *SCORING KEY FOR SECTION 8 — RESPONSES 276–300*

276. W+ M^p.FY.m^p+ Hd,Cg 4.0 INC,MOR,PHR

277. WS+ FM^p.m^a.CF.FD– Ad,Bl 4.5 MOR

278. W+ FC.M^a.FC'+ 2 (H),Cg 4.5 COP,GHR

279. D+1 M^a.FC.FD.FM^ao 2 H,A,Id P 4.0 AG,COP,GHR

280. DdSo99 FC.FM^p– Ad

281. Wv M^p.C'.Y Hx AB,MOR,PHR

282. Ddv99 YF– Hd DR2,PER,MOR,PHR

283. W+ FM^a.FYo A,Ad 2.5 INC

284. W+ M^p.C'F.FDu H,Cg,Ls 2.5 AB,GHR

285. W+ FM^a.TFu A,Fd 2.5 INC

286. D+1 M^p.Fr.FYo Hd P 3.0 GHR

287. WSv/+ VFo Na 4.0

288. WSo M^p.FV.FC– Hd 4.5 INC,ALOG,PHR

289. Do1 FCu A DV2,ALOG

290. W+ m^a.CFo Art,Na 5.5

291. W+ FM^p.FV.CFo 2 Art,A,Bt 5.5

292. W+ M^a.FD.CF– (H),Id,Cg 5.5 AB,DR,PHR

293. WS+ M^a.m^p.CF– H,Cg,Art 6.0 ALOG,PHR

294. D+3 FM^p.Fr.FYu Ad 4.0

295. WSo FC'o Art,(Hd) 3.5 AB,DR2,PHR

296. DS+5 m^a.CF.FC'o Art 4.5 DV

297. WS+ M^a.FC'.C.FDo 2 (H),Art,Cg P 5.5 GHR

298. Do7 FM^p.FD.FTo A

299. Ddv99 VF.TF– Ls

300. Ddo99 M^a.FC'u (H),Cg DV,GHR